WORKING WITH NATURE

JOHN W. BRAINERD

Working with Nature

A PRACTICAL GUIDE

NEW YORK/OXFORD UNIVERSITY PRESS/1973

Dedicated to
the authors cited in the bibliography
and to a host of others who have explored
the universe and questioned man's place in it.

May the search go on with a spreading and
deepening natural philosophy, with more
love of life, less fear of death, and
greater understanding of how each of
us must find a responsible niche
with our borrowed time
on earth.

Acknowledgments

Special thanks are due my wife Barbara, who followed me all the way with understanding and a keen camera, and spent long months in the darkroom. My daughter Jill Root for years has served as typist, editorial assistant, researcher, and bibliographer, contributing immensely. Sons Roger and Allen have helped outdoors with many of my conservation experiments. Dr. Joseph Larson of the University of Massachusetts offered suggestions for the chapter on wetlands. Many of my students at Springfield College have been users and kindly critics of early versions. Typing by Florence Metcalf, Beverly Mosley, Susan Stowell, and the Office Services staff at Springfield College has been appreciated as being far more than mechanical. Finally, James Raimes, Joyce Berry, Stephanie Golden, and others at Oxford University Press have formed an editorial team which has been a joy to work with.

Contents

WORKING WITH NATURE

1 Introduction

"Nature" is a big concept, as big as the universe yet involving every minute particle of which we ourselves are made. Man was conceived and raised in nature, and just as it is a part of us so shall we always be part of it. Much of what is wrong with our environment has resulted from our disregard of man's intimate relationship with nature. Do not the more natural environments often seem closer to paradise than the barely livable city-deserts we have created? To be sure, much of what is right with our world is manmade, making our modern modes of existence possible and often enjoyable. But if man is to survive physically and spiritually, we must find a better balance between the artificial and the natural in our surroundings. To do so will require "work."

Sun, air, water, rocks, soil, plants, and animals are our natural heritage. We draw on them daily for our existence. Sometimes we overdraw, and consequently our resources diminish. At other times we do not make enough use of what is naturally available. We can do better—and this book should help us find out how. Even though it may not give easy answers, it should enable us to take a more perceptive look at our natural and partly natural environments. It should aid in figuring out good ways to use their natural components to improve our corner of the world, be it a small yard, schoolground, park, camp, nature center, estate, industrial site, or whatever.

USING THIS BOOK

Note the two main parts of this book; both deal with sites for conservation, places you can actually work with nature. Part I, *Environments*, is the more general, looking at the larger landscape and, very simply at first, helping you recognize *environmental systems* into which you can fit constructively.

First we consider environments as either wet or dry—though of course we recognize that they are often intermediate. *Drylands* are dealt with in Chapters 2–5, which describe areas without standing water. Each of these chapters presents drylands according to the absence or presence of vegetation and the type of vegetation: *Barelands, Herblands, Shrublands,* and *Treelands,* described briefly on its opening page. Each chapter is then subdivided according to recognizable environments within these categories. You can find sections

ENVIRONMENTS

TREELAND
Forest

HERBLAND
Pasture

WATER AREA

many others

TREELANDS
Orchard   Woodlot

SHRUBLAND
Alder Swamp

BARELAND
Field plowed for crop

HERBLAND
Vegetable garden

BARELAND - Paving

SHRUBLAND - Hedge

HERBLANDS - Lawns &
Flowerbeds

WETLAND

appropriate to your conservation site by browsing, using the tables of contents, or looking for clues in the index.

Wetlands, Water Areas, and *Shores,* Chapters 6–8, deal with environments where standing or running water is especially important. If these pertain to your area, search for appropriate sections to give ideas for planning and working with nature.

Trails and Roads, Chapter 9, treats these linear, manmade environments. They may be greatly needed, but sometimes should be avoided as intrusions into the natural scene.

Part I emphasizes planning. Planning is making mistakes on paper rather than on the land. It is keeping out of trouble by thinking ahead, and deciding what should be done first and subsequently by establishing priorities. And planning in a sense lets you enjoy what you have not done yet. Part I will help you talk with professional planners, including city and regional planners, industrial and real estate planners, and landscape architects. We need their aid, espeially when they are well versed in ecology. Also we can consult university extension workers in farming, forestry, wildlife, water management, and allied fields; personnel in state and federal natural resource agencies; and consultants in private conservation organizations. This book can help form a common base for all of us as we try to fit constructively into ecological systems.

Part II, *Environmental Components,* is more specific, with chapters on *Air, Water, Rock, Soil, Vegetation,* and *Wildlife.* As with catching a tiger by the tail, you have to grab onto an environmental system somewhere. One of these components can give you a handle. So here you find more help in carrying out your plans for working with nature by managing its parts.

Hopping around in this book will often give best results. It is not a read-it-through book but a reference book. The numerous cross-references (page numbers in parentheses) suggest related material— to give another grip on the tiger. Nature is not a one-thing-at-a-time business which can be laid out in a straight line starting on page one. Admit its webness and enjoy it; be willing to tangle with it. The index too will help you hop.

The bibliography is worth serious attention. There is always more to learn from others. Parenthetical numbers set in italics *(171)* refer to the excellent books, most of them recent, listed alphabetically and

Nine varieties of herbs, numerous flowers, and a vegetable garden (not shown) add to the livability of the roof of a New York apartment building.

numbered starting on page 474. These will often themselves have bibliographies citing still other books, so your search for knowledge of the environment can go on and on.

CHOOSING A SITE

You will need some piece of land, your own or one you are permitted to use for your conservation work. It may be small or large, wild or tame, like the area between the sidewalk and the front door. Are you a landless apartment-dweller, or an owner of a farm, ranch, or country estate? Do you live in a suburban house, or on a houseboat on a backwater bayou? Wherever, some land near you can profit from your attention to it. So look around.

If you live in a *city*, an alley with cracks in the paving has homes for ants, excellent animals on which to practice wildlife management (Ch. 15); and maybe an ailanthus (also called treeofheaven), an excellent plant to train to cover bare bricks (Ch. 14), sprouts behind some trash cans. Maybe there is a so-called empty lot full of possibilities, or a railroad embankment, or a corner of a schoolground or park that needs loving attention. *(223, 225, 351, 467, 472, 497, 537, 570, 573)*

If you live in a *suburb*, the homes may all be landscaped with uniform lawns and neat shrubbery. But probably you can find a corner where a little less-conventional landscaping could bring intriguing variety to the community (Ch. 3), maybe inviting more kinds of birds to the gardens. Is your suburb already blessed with weedy corners where neglect has brought variety but where you can bring some new feeling of purpose and organization (Ch. 4)? Or possibly yours is a new subdivision where bare soil (Ch. 2) and construction-damaged vegetation are crying out for somebody to bring new life to soften the bleakness of the community (Ch. 3). *(32, 42, 54, 93, 165, 184, 218, 300, 317, 323, 339, 396, 415, 446, 460, 480, 495, 502, 553, 572)*

If you live in the *country,* you are already surrounded by growing things, maybe palms, cacti, corn, or spruces. Whatever your climate and soil produce, some sensitive modification can serve both you and your environment. Perhaps you can increase the shade around a ranch building on the Great Plains (Ch. 5); improve a windbreak in the Palouse wheatlands of eastern Washington (Ch. 10); selectively cut tuliptrees in an Appalachian cove (Ch. 14); or make a screen planting to add beauty to a gasoline station in whatever rural setting. *(14, 17, 33, 40, 78, 83, 96, 111, 137, 156, 166, 185, 208, 224, 226, 239, 261, 293, 305, 322, 327, 373, 403, 439, 453, 470)*

The *size of your conservation area* will determine the intensity of

Pieces of land come in a great variety of sizes and shapes. Here a tile roof supports a little garden of velvet grass and hen-and-chickens. Streatwick, Sussex, England.

your practices. Much can be done in an area measured in feet rather than acres. Witness how much time one can lavish on a small lawn! Indeed, if the only piece of land you can work with is a window box, you can do a lot with it, caring for the soil, planting it, watering it, training the plants as they grow, and watching or manipulating the insect populations which avail themselves of it naturally or which you may introduce. Window box or wildlands, you will spend good hours and energy in planning, watching the ongoing results of your practices, keeping records, and evaluating—all part of your work with nature.

The *diversity of your conservation area* is important too. Start with a relatively uniform environment, perhaps a bit of bareland (Ch. 2), a patch of shrubbery (Ch. 4), or a section of woods (Ch. 5) with just one kind of tree, maybe a pure stand of pines. On close inspection it will prove more complex than you thought. Cutting just one pine out of the canopy of a pine grove will start many happenings as light comes in onto the forest floor, changing microclimates (Ch. 10), soil moisture (Ch. 13), herbaceous growth (Ch. 3), and animal populations (Ch. 15). Even though you think you are simplifying an environment, the chances are you are complicating it—a good reason for starting with one as simple as possible. Later you can add the challenge of managing an ecotone (an area where two environments mingle).

Time will prove to be your most precious resource as you work with nature on your selected site. You have only one lifetime to improve the planet Earth, and perhaps only an hour or two a week on your project, which may be a warming-up exercise for bigger ones later. Plan so that you can learn from doing a good job, not a hasty and poor one. A small uniform area will enable you to use your time most effectively. Also, land close by will be more efficient to work than a more remote tract. Many people waste time going somewhere else to do a job when equally profitable ones sit neglected under their noses. If a nearer area has less charm, maybe that indicates the need for you to spend more time on it.

After choosing an area, near or far as you desire, stick with it, at least for a while. Nature often moves slowly, so results of your efforts may not soon be apparent. You may wish to start a new project elsewhere; if you do, keep in touch with your earlier project, to learn what happens to it and to give it further assistance if needed. Besides, you will find that a site well chosen and conscientiously cared for may be of lasting concern to you.

SITE ANALYSIS

Look closely at your piece of land and keep looking at it. You will need to study your area and learn about it in order to care for it. You will need an *inventory* of its assets and liabilities. Managing land is like managing a store: you need to know what is on the shelves. Too many people have tried to help nature run her storehouse without b'othering to find out in enough detail what is in it.

An earlier volume, *Nature Study For Conservation (67)*, has been devoted to this subject of environmental analysis for beginners, and many other books by different authors deal with special aspects of site analysis beyond the scope of this book. Avail yourself of such books, borrowed at the library or bought at your bookshop. Also ask for help from others, including teachers, professors, researchers at universities and industries, government workers, and well-informed amateurs. Many will be glad to help you work with nature. It is their planet too.

A *notebook* can be profitably filled with observations of the components to be analyzed, including air, water, rock, soil, vegetation, and wildlife (Part II). You will soon recognize their many subcategories, for example warm air and cool air. At first you will be busy

A windbreak planting would improve this shepherd's homestead and help visually to blend the new trailer with the old moor houses. Balnacra, Wester Ross, Scotland.

listing *things*. Then you will become more conscious of *processes*, which make things change, for instance the eating and mating habits of animals, the growth and decay of vegetation, and the erosion and deposition of soil. Complexity becomes increasingly apparent as you analyze nature's store.

Files will be needed for systematic data storage about weather, types of soil, kinds of plants, and so on. At first lists on sheets of 8½-by-11-inch paper are good, filed with copies of plans, agreements with owners, and other business *(67)*; but as lists grow, it is often best to keep data on file cards, especially punch cards for sorting by hand with a knitting needle or by machine. *(99, 543)*

Maps are basic for many inventories. Try to locate any and all existing maps of your area and get or make copies of them. Old maps have special value for studying land-use history *(417)*. Newer maps may have the greatest accuracy and show more present-day features. Get maps at different scales. Sources include owners' deeds, local surveyors, town or city officials such as tax assessors and engineers, and county and state extension services of state universities. The United States Department of Agriculture's Soil Conservation Service is one of many national organizations that help provide maps. See the *Yellow Pages* of your telephone directory. Librarians and historians can aid in finding old-time maps.

This farmyard corner, with a variety of plants and insects and some bare soil for sunning and scratching, is a good place for hens; but its design might be improved by thoughtful planning.

Then make your own *base map*—or skip some of the fun by having another person draft it for you. Perhaps one can be made just by copying an existing map of suitable scale. If none exists, as is likely if you are wise enough to start with a small area such as a corner of the back yard or schoolgrounds, you will need to become surveyor, at least in an amateur way, and go out and map the area. If you need help, call on a member of a youth group trained in mapping, a school mathematics teacher, or an agricultural agent, or borrow a book on surveying or mapping from a library *(67, 220, 367, 489)*.

Your base map should be simple, showing boundaries of your area and such fixed landmarks as roads, buildings, streams, or rock outcrops. It should have a scale, shown graphically in the margin by a line an inch or two centimeters long with a notation of how many feet or meters it represents. Simple arrows marginally or in a corner show magnetic and true north. Always date maps. Leave plenty of empty space for a key to whatever kinds of special data you subsequently record on the base map.

Reproduce your base map in quantity, as by mimeograph or offset printing, to serve as a basis for mapping many particular aspects of your area at various times, such as air, water, rocks, et cetera, and changes in land use. Time and effort in making a good, simple base map will pay well. You will use it not only for recording data but also for working up plans, for fancier maps to solicit help from others, and for reports of your projects. The day may come when your maps will be used for a formal publication describing your piece of land and your efforts in its behalf.

SITE SYNTHESIS

While an analytic approach to your site helps you become aware of components, a synthetic approach helps you recognize *environments as working systems* into which you can sensitively fit, be they back yards or wilderness. You see components working together like intricate clockworks with energy-springs, meshed gears carrying motion, and balance wheels. In your conservation area you see time working in space, beautifully. *(60, 107, 129, 152, 159, 173, 226, 265, 298, 389, 481, 485, 510, 516)*

PERSONAL VALUES

Good and bad can be difficult concepts which each of us must grapple with personally. I wrote this book because I had some developing ideas of right and wrong about man's use of natural resources. If you do not always like what you find in this book, recognize an author's right to be wrong from your point of view. In their "right" place, I like mud and brush and mosquitoes. Bogs often are not bad, and soil need not be dirt. Chemical poisons are wrong only when wrongly used—which unfortunately nowadays is very often. I like people too, in the right place in the right numbers. I believe it is right for man to coinhabit with nature on this planet, accepting the serious responsibilities entailed.

This book hopes to increase your confidence in applying *your* developing values to a piece of land somewhere, to help *you* improve it from your point of view. As you plan and work, think often of Aldo Leopold's "Conservation is a state of harmony between men and land." As you live more intimately with a piece of land and learn much from it that you could never learn from any book, may you and it both prosper.

(See also *81, 149, 164, 172, 181, 182, 210, 240, 283, 326, 334, 339, 374, 418, 435, 459, 518, 545, 557.*)

In England there is a trend toward removing hedgerows to make larger farming units more efficiently managed with machinery. But before eradicating hedgerows, we should analyze their many contributions to the countryside. (For instance, they are Britain's prime wildlife habitat.) Devon, England.

GUIDELINES FOR WORKING WITH NATURE

A simple sermon, easy to give but sometimes hard to follow.

First see what nature offers. Make careful inventories of air, rocks, water, soils, vegetation, and wildlife and of their groupings into various environments and ecosystems. (For techniques, see 67.)

Take time. Do not hasten to make changes. Maybe live with the land a year before making major modifications, observing the site at all seasons.

Consider leaving nature completely alone, to be watched and wondered at, or saved for future purposes still unforeseen. Natural areas are rare and precious, and so are many relatively natural ones.

If and when you decide to modify nature, have your purposes clearly in mind.

Plan procedures carefully. Set down on paper long-term plans to carry out your purposes, and short-term plans for initial steps.

Involve others in your projects, to help both you and them. Do not leave out the very young and the old, who in appropriate ways can often do important jobs to help the environment.

Watch what you are doing. Stand back periodically and evaluate. Be big enough to see your own mistakes as well as those of others, and to modify your plans.

While scientifically dealing with facts and probing unknowns, do not fail to sense the beautiful, by whatever senses felt. Watch too for what others consider beautiful, even though you may not have found it appealing.

Have fun, and be yourself—naturally.

I Environments

2 Drylands: Barelands

Barelands
 Heat
 Stability
 Non-combustibility
 Influences on climate
 Porosity or compactness
 Openness
 Beauty
Occurrence
Duration
Man's Relation to Barelands
Hard-Surfaced Areas
 Uses
 Planning
 Maintenance of hard-surfacing
 Removing paving
 Parking areas
  Single-car parking
  Multiple-car parking
  Parking lot islands
 Planting for cramped parking lots
 Paved recreation areas
 Wildlife
Packed Earth
 Occurrence
 Using packed earth
 Composition
 Preparation

17

Maintenance
  Rolling
  Weeding
Loosening packed earth
Bedrock
  Planning
  Bedrock natural areas
  Small-scale quarrying
  Uses of native stone
  Bedrock for building sites
  Beauty in bedrock
Talus Slopes
Frost-Cracked Stonefields
Boulder Trains and Boulder Nests
Rocky Shores
Gravel
  Uses of gravel
  Gravel deposits and their land use
  Barelands resulting from removal of gravel
    Wildlife and children
    Grading for construction
  Gravel deposits over fertile soil
  Gravelly shores
Sand
  Erodibility of sand
  Revegetation of sand
  Planning
  Uses of sand as a material
  Sandy areas for building
  Sandy areas for recreation
  Erosion control in sandy areas
  Inducing erosion
  Natural areas
  Sandy shores
Silt and Clay
  Loess
  Water-transported silts and silt-loams
    Agriculture
    Forestry

Contents

In this book, drylands are those which lack standing or slow-flowing water most of the year—all land in temperate climates except bog, fen, marsh, or swamp (Ch. 6) and shores (Ch. 8). Drylands may be really wet at times, as with heavy rains or when snows melt. Much of the time drylands may be moist, especially where a cool microclimate results from slopes or vegetative cover. Many areas are intermediate between drylands and wetlands, and these present special conservation problems.

Drylands are divided in this book, first on the basis of whether or not they are bare of vegetation, and second according to whether the vegetated areas have primarily herbs (non-woody plants) or woody plants. Then lands with woody plants are divided into those clothed primarily with shrubs and those with trees predominant. Where transitional types occur, consult two or more sections to work out your conservation plans.

BARELANDS

Barelands are essentially mineral, consisting of bedrock, soil, or some artificial material spread by man. Absence of vegetative covering gives barelands distinctive properties.

Heat.   Bareland heat budgets can mean life or death for plants and animals, of which there are almost always some (80, 163, 301, 395, 461). Lying exposed to the sun, barelands are strongly heated. Light-colored ones reflect much heat; dark ones absorb much, making them hotter. At night under clear skies, unvegetated areas radiate heat and may become markedly cold, sometimes condensing moisture from the air onto their cold surfaces.

Stability.   Great variation occurs, from the maximum stability of bedrock and the relative permanence of man's cement and asphalt to the highly erodible sands and wind-susceptible loams. Resistance to wear can be a great advantage, as on road surfaces. Ever-changing form, as of dune or winding waterway, can be very beautiful.

Non-combustibility. The lack of organic matter, often thought of as the major drawback of a bare area, can help prevent or control wildfire.

Influences on Climate. Factors to consider include rapid heating and cooling, unhampered wind, and fast drying (see Chapter 10).

Porosity or compactness. Effects on water (Ch. 11) vary from maximum runoff from impervious rock and strongly compacted soil to maximum insoak on sands and porous loams. Control of water often depends on amount and type of barelands maintained.

Openness. Lack of vegetation makes clear areas for human activity: active games in recreation areas; grading soil; quarrying sand, gravel, or rock; making roads and trails; and erecting buildings. Existing bare areas can decrease expense in developing areas for these purposes. Openness contributes to landscape esthetics, permitting narrow vistas or broad views, allowing cool breeze to penetrate warm forest, or letting warm sun into cool shade.

Beauty. Many people judge bare areas only by what they lack, such as lush green vegetation and flowers. Barren areas have their own beauties: the color of rock and soil, strong shadows, angular or subtly rounded contours where nature's primal forces are at work. *(1)*

OCCURRENCE

Barelands may be of primarily *geologic origin.* Cataclysmic forces have created great lava flows and deposits of volcanic ash or the exposed rock summits of geologically young mountain ranges. On a much smaller scale, geologic processes often create barelands in regions which as a whole are geologically old, usually where water and wind can work, as along streams and shores of ponds, lakes, and seas. Or erosion and sedimentation may maintain barren soil after wildfire has laid an area bare. Barelands have *climatological origin* where precipitation is too slight to support vegetation, creating deserts *(279, 337).* Barelands may be of *biological origin* where animals (including the human animal) have removed the vegetation, overly compacted the soil, or even poisoned it.

DURATION

Some barelands may remain bare for centuries, for instance sand-blasted mountain rocks, rock-paved basins, alkali flats, and dune areas in arid regions. But where there is moisture, vegetation tends to clothe the bareness. Where environments are harsh, it may be only a creeping of lichens, taking centuries to prepare the stark surface so that other plants can grow. But where mellow soil is turned by plow or where wildfire removes a forest but leaves soil enriched by minerals from burned vegetation, then only a few weeks may dress the bareness in green. Wise use of barelands depends largely upon how long they might stay bare naturally; so their duration is worth more than passing thought, especially in relation to moisture.

MAN'S RELATION TO BARELANDS

Some of the great deserts were probably created by man's mistakes centuries ago as he destroyed the vegetative cover without understanding its relation to soil, water, and the living things they support. Today man, with greater understanding and newfound technical abilities, may well tame the deserts which he himself unleashed. Irrigation by piping water from distant mountains or deep wells, supplying domestic water by desalting seawater or alkali water, enlightened methods of farming desert soils, and reforestation of denuded areas all may help man gain back what he has lost. (349, 395, 463)

But barelands are not limited to distant deserts; they may be conspicuous in the front lawn. And barelands are not always a bad thing to be conquered by revegetation; sometimes they are both useful and beautiful for all their bareness, as the following paragraphs indicate.

HARD-SURFACED AREAS

These are artificial areas where man has spread concrete, asphalt, tar, oiled gravel, rubber compound, or other material. The substance either joins particles of mineral soils so they maintain their position and do not let water penetrate or it covers the ground with some foreign material, achieving the same stability and lack of porosity *(201)*.

Uses. Today's thousands of miles of hard-surfacing are primarily a result of the automobile, although ancient Romans built many miles of stone-surfaced roads for their chariots. Our wheeled culture finds it comfortable to roll on smooth surfaces. Now cars have been designed so completely for hard-surfaced roads, except for off-the-road vehicles, that paved roads and parking spaces are the rule. But in remote areas innumerable farm families still have to worry about spring mud when thawing ground makes dirt roads almost impass-able, and summer dust when acrid dust clouds penetrate closed windows. Hard-surfaced sidewalks follow the roads in all urban and most suburban areas, giving pedestrians the convenience of freedom from mud and dust, but jarring their spines and unspringing their arches. Thus while there is gain in speed and convenience, there are losses too. The greatest sacrifice is of soil porosity and insoak of water, causing urban deserts and downstream flooding. Whenever hard-surfacing is planned, its rapid runoff of water must be considered.

Planning. Don't pave until long-term land use has been worked out. Consider handling of water runoff; preservation of desirable trees which might be killed by depriving their roots of water and air by hard-surfacing over them; microclimatic effects of large areas of paving, especially strong heat in summer and cold wind in winter; comparative appearance of light-colored concrete and dark-colored asphalt; and whether turf or other groundcover might be better.

Maintenance of hard-surfacing. Keep running water from under-cutting the edge of paving. Ditch water away, or run a gutter of hard-surfacing or cobblestones or other unerodible material along the edge, or keep the adjacent area higher than the paving and any bordering soil well covered by grass or other vegetation. A curbing or berm keeps water from running off the edge of the paving except at designated spots where it can be controlled. A catchbasin helps by permitting water to flow down into an underground drain, preventing erosion of the paving.

Prevent cracks. These result from frost action because of inadequate drainage beneath the paving, too little compaction of the bed before paving, too thin a paving, too heavy a load on the paving, growth of tree roots, or expansion and contraction with heat and cold. Inevitable normal wear also makes cracks appear. When they do form, sweep cracks clean, break off or fill compactly under any unsupported edges, and patch with material appropriate to the original paving. The sooner this is done, the less needs to be done. Sometimes, rather than patch many little cracks and holes, it is best to resurface the entire area. Special coatings are available.

Removing paving. When a new plan recommends removal of existing paving, small amounts may be broken up with sledgehammer and pickaxe; larger amounts require a pneumatic or electric hammer, bulldozer with blade or special teeth, or other heavy equipment. Don't waste broken paving by burying it if it can be used for flagstone walk, outdoor fireplace or incinerator, sides for a compost pile, riprapping on a bank to prevent erosion (p. 313), groin to reduce shore erosion (p. 350), or offshore deposit on smooth bottom to make cover for fish.

Parking areas. Adequate parking places help smooth operation of an area, increasing safety and convenience. They should be level except for a slight uniform slope (about one foot rise per one hundred feet) to provide drainage to speed drying and prevent puddles. Provide catchbasins or gutters at the foot of the slope if necessary. Topography, esthetics, and budget will determine the layout for the required capacity. *(408, 535, 552, 567)*

Single-car parking—One-car parking spurs here and there along roads permit a small number of cars to be tucked into the countryside. A large American car parked at right angles to a road needs a sitting area 10 feet wide and 20 feet long. An additional 10 by 20 feet of space parallel to the road on the approach side is usually needed for backing out (because it is not wise to use the main road for such low-speed maneuvers). A second such 20-foot turning area on the far side accommodates those who wisely prefer to back into a parking area, to facilitate loading and unloading the trunk (boot). Single-car parking for several cars tends to keep the area's natural look by leaving vegetated zones between vehicles, providing shade, beauty, absorption of water, and wildlife habitat, and is therefore well suited to picnic groves, campgrounds, and nature trails. However, single-car parking means greater walking distances to places of assembly, which therefore usually have multiple-car parking.

Multiple-car parking—Cars parked beside each other consume less room but create a larger area of artificiality. Each large car needs a space 10 by 20 feet for diagonal parking along a 20-foot strip from which cars turn in. When this strip is doubly flanked by diagonal parking, space is saved because both rows share it. More can be saved by having smaller spaces designated for smaller cars, motorcycles, and snowmobiles. For safety and convenience, sidewalks, not necessarily paved, should parallel each row of parking spaces.

A two-ranked parking unit with sidewalks is about 75 feet wide, difficult to keep shaded or natural-looking without special efforts. If oriented east—west or southeast—northwest (in the northern hemisphere), with large deciduous trees saved or grown on the south or southwest side, it can be shaded in summer. A thick planting of evergreen trees to the north and northwest, especially if kept sheared, gives protection from cold winds and provides a warmer microclimate in winter. Where more than one such two-ranked parking unit is necessary, allow sizable islands between to permit such protecting and beautifying growth.

Parking lot islands—An island with low, dense evergreens on the north of one unit should be wide enough also to support tall deciduous trees if it lies on the south side of another unit. Ornamental and wildlife-attracting shrubbery can be used along with trees but should not encroach on sidewalks, forcing people to walk in the parking zones, and should not obscure vision at turns in the road. Consider carefully the relative value of native shrubbery before spending money on nursery stock. Efforts to save existing plants during construction can save both time and money; then selective planticiding with chemicals (p. 400) and pruning (p. 439) can favor desired native species. Such parking lot islands can also be furnished with benches. These should be well back from the edge of the car zone and face away from the cars so that the view is along and partly into the island. A small wildlife feeding station, perhaps only a suet stick, makes waiting more pleasant. Litter containers are needed if the area is for the public, and will of course need regular emptying.

A small circular island may support one large tree, which can add beauty and comfort to a parking area. The island should also have a sapling that will be maturing when the old tree dies. Contractors may complain bitterly and say that such islands are stupid, but when parking in a hot parking lot they may be among the first to pick a shady corner.

Planting for cramped parking lots.   Because plants tend to offset the barren effects of parking lots, make special efforts to supply greenery. Where a small lot between buildings has been completely paved there is often an unused triangular space by the first diagonally parked car. Here the pavement can be broken and removed and a shade tree planted, with protective stakes, bumper log, or fence giving it a minute triangular sanctuary. There should be a gate or space under the fence for removal of any litter. Avoid weak trees like silver maple and willow. Basswood (linden or lime) and ginkgo are favorites for such situations. Another trick is to break and remove paving from a semicircle or elongated strip here and there along the side of a building for espaliered plants (ones trained flat against the wall) or vines (p. 437).

Paved recreation areas.   Small all-weather play areas help keep one's children around one's own home and also attract playmates. Along an unwindowed garage wall a paved area can serve for handball, paddleball, basketball, tennis practice, and other wall-ball games, and provide spare parking space. A windowed or irregular wall of a wooden building can be covered with exterior plywood. A full-sized paved tennis court (roughly 60 by 120 feet) brings joy to a neighborhood and if suitably designed can in the colder climates be flooded for a skating rink in winter. Tennis courts should usually have their long axis running north–south. It is dangerous to locate swings, slides, and jungle-gyms on hard-surfaced areas. Where schools and parks need extensive hard-surfaced play areas, separate them with absorptive vegetated areas, much as described above for multiple-unit parking lots. At schools particularly, paved areas should not run right up to windowed walls, because growing space should be left for gardens and foundation plantings (284) of educational and esthetic value (42, 238, 245, 257, 313, 549, 550).

Wildlife.   Hard-surfaced areas and wildlife may at first seem incompatible, and usually they are. But just as desert animals burrow and escape heat and desiccation, so some insects, notably ants, make homes under our paving, finding protection and food under our feet. Ants may colonize so happily that they must be discouraged (by poison or flooding with water) from making miniature volcanoes in the cracks we have not mended. At a city school, crack faunas should not be discouraged too much. They have their educational potential. A crumb of hard-boiled egg placed near an anthill creates interesting problems in time, rate, and distance, as well as lessons in conservation.

Litter dropped by untidy humans and seeds brought by beneficent winds supply food sought by other wildlife, notably pigeons, starlings, and sparrows in the daytime and rats and mice after dark. In too-great numbers these are undesirable, but a few add life and beauty to the barrenness of city pavement. One common conservation problem relates to the quantity of city animals. Amateurs can make contributions censusing their numbers and helping work out methods both for control of over-population and for attracting desirable numbers where they are lacking. More planting and well-maintained birdbaths can help introduce a greater variety of wildlife to our paved cities. Do not forget the alley cats who may yowl at night and carry fleas but who also help curb the rodent population (which also carries fleas) *(102, 479)*.

PACKED EARTH

Earth with a large proportion of fine particles of mineral soil compacts readily, smaller particles fitting in between larger ones (if any), leaving very little pore space (see also pp. 335 and 336). Most plants have difficulty growing in packed earth for lack of voids to supply air and nutrient soil solution for the roots, so packed soil stays bare longer than looser soil and retains the characteristics of bare soil described above (p. 20).

Occurrence. Natural compaction results from sedimentation of fine particles in suspension in water, as where silts and clays deposit along streams and in lakebeds, or where fine windblown particles settle to form soil called *loess,* as in regions downwind from arid areas which are a source of windblown soil—for instance in the prairie states east of the Great Plains, and along beds of former lakes or wide rivers which dried up or drained out. Compaction may also

COMPACTED EARTH often causes erosion because of rapid runoff

be caused by the feet of animals, but in nature this is apt to be highly localized, as at points where big game trails converge on waterholes. Where man confines too many hoofed animals in a pasture, the soil may suffer severe compaction, especially on forested soil in a grazed woodlot. Making compacted soil absorptive and/or productive can be a major challenge. A common cause of packed earth is human foot traffic, especially at corners of walks where people take thoughtless shortcuts and in playgrounds and picnic groves where scampering children give the ground a heavy beating. Compaction of trails makes flush-cut stumps protrude after a while and tends to gully the trails.

Using packed earth. Packed earth is used for roads, trails, parking areas, areas for active group games, and occasionally for fuelbreaks, particularly around incinerators, woodsheds, petroleum supplies, or other small areas of high fire danger. These uses are very similar to those of hard-surfacing, described above, but packed earth is less expensive initially though it requires more frequent maintenance. Clay can be thought of as poor man's cement. Esthetically, it looks more natural, but this joy may be lost at certain seasons because of distasteful dust or mud. As with hard-surfaced areas, give thought to careful handling of runoff (see p. 22).

Composition. Soil will pack only when it contains fine mineral particles in the size ranges of silt and clay. If only coarser materials, sands or gravels, are present, bring in finer particles to obtain packed earth. If only the finer materials are present, spring thaws and extended rains will make the soil soft; therefore all-weather roads, parking lots, and play areas need the addition of coarser materials, especially gravel, and for roads even some small cobble-sized stones to help "put bone in it." Sometimes cinders from furnaces are used for road and trail building, but under heavy wear these break down into a dirty powder.

Preparation.   Remove as much vegetable matter as possible (except for corduroy roads (p. 256). Careful removal of roots pays because dead-looking roots often have amazing vitality and may sprout over a period of months if left buried. Where it can be controlled, deep burning can help remove organic matter in the soil (p. 431). Treatment with planticides helps make the soil sterile, slowing revegetation; but chemicals must be used with great caution (p. 400).

Careful grading insures that water runs off slowly enough to avoid erosion of the bare soil or adjacent areas downhill. The slope should be adequate to avoid puddling and insoak, which cause a colloidal ooze of clay particles swelling when wet and making shrinkage cracks on drying; seeds blowing or washing into these cracks speed revegetation which will require weeding. A grade of one to three per cent is good for large areas such as play areas and parking lots; steeper grades can be used on properly constructed roads and trails (p. 257).

Subgrade construction to give good drainage will improve wearability and decrease maintenance. This may mean excavating peat, muck, or loamy soil and filling with coarse stones, then finer, with the top layer of fine particles having some coarser ones admixed. Good surface and subsurface drainage helps prevent frost action (in cold climates) and muddying, and promotes rapid drying. The final surface before compaction should be carefully scraped. For a hand job, an iron garden rake should be used first teeth down, then back down for a final smoothing. Where a sooth surface is essential, as on a tennis court, a finishing drag with a fiber doormat or the like helps give a good surface before rolling.

Compaction can be achieved through use, as on a trail by normal wear or by stimulating extra-heavy traffic at first; or by use of machinery. In the absence of power machinery, a hollow iron lawn roller filled with water or a stone roller can be used. For a very small area, as around an incinerator, a tamper can be made from a section of eight-inch log on the end of a four- or five-foot pole.

Maintenance.   Fill in eroded spots caused by runoff or wheel action; and where sheet erosion has taken place, add a thin resurfacing layer. For roads and trails, it is often necessary to reshape the crown of the road, fill ruts, and clean the gutters (pp. 269, 270).

Rolling—Rolling helps maintain compaction in spite of the forces of wetting and drying, freezing and thawing, and penetration of roots; so rolling increases the stability of the ground and helps keep it bare of vegetation and smooth. Roll when the soil is moist but not so wet that clay particles stick to the roller; rolling does little good when the soil is dry. Calcium chloride spread uniformly and sparingly with a shovel helps keep the soil moist and curbs weeds. Too much on a tennis court will prevent soil from drying adequately. (Too much calcium chloride will kill nearby vegetation!) Where smoothness is important, as for court games like tennis, do not count on the roller to do the smoothing; drag or rake the surface smooth prior to rolling.

Weeding—Unless soil is continuously dry or poisoned, weeding is necessary to keep bare soil bare, because nature has great powers of revegetation. For small areas, as around an incinerator, hand weeding or hoeing suffices. For long areas such as fuel breaks and shoulders of roads, various types of cultivators, harrows, and scrapers can be used to dig up the weeds; scrapers have the advantage of not loosening up such a good seedbed for the next crop of weeds. Chemical weeding (p. 400) can save work but must be used with caution because of the danger of poisoning desired plants and animals in neighboring areas or poisoning soil so that plants would not grow if wanted with changed land use. Mulching with wood chips, shavings, or other materials can discourage weeds.

Loosening packed earth.   Packed earth can be a headache rather than an asset. Where lawns or playing fields get heavy wear, overcompaction harms the grass so that unwanted bare areas develop. This happens frequently along the sides of narrow sidewalks and at corners where people carelessly cut across without feelings for growing grass. With playfields, tractor equipment punches aeration holes to offset compaction. For spots in lawns, the soil should be dug up to loosen it. If compaction is not serious, superficial scratching with a sharp iron rake, prongs of a spading fork, edge of a lawn-edging or ice-removing tool, or special hand tool for aerating may suffice. Then the area can be reseeded to grass. Or let frost action do the loosening over winter; then in early spring rake and reseed.

In a picnic grove or around camp buildings, soil compaction by many feet prevents insoak. Tree roots struggle to live in an underground desert and excess runoff causes erosion, especially on trails leading away downhill (p. 253). Channel traffic so that growing zones remain untrodden (p. 158), but leave bare or turfed spaces for unrestricted running around (p. 157). With trampling ended, loosen the soil and replant it, mulching it well. Growing plants and animals will fluff it up.

BEDROCK

Bedrock is the underlying rock of a region. It may be a geologically youthful deposit, such as some kinds of lava, which have not had time to develop a covering of soil. It may be rock that has lain on the surface for a million or more years with soil being removed by wind, ice, or water about as fast as it was formed, as on mountaintops in humid regions and on mountains and in some basins in arid regions. Bedrock often shows only as cliffs or ledges along the sides of valleys, as in plateaus and other uplands through which streams have cut. In other areas, bedrock has been exposed by continental glaciation whose bulldozing action has left smoothed rock, often scratched with parallel grooves, sometimes with more jagged pieces plucked off at one end of the exposed rock. Bedrock that shows at the surface is called an outcrop. Occasionally a large boulder rolled down from a mountain or deposited by a glacier may be mostly buried and have the appearance of an outcrop.

Planning. Today man has the energy and tools literally to move mountains, and their rock is often important in his economy, as building materials and raw materials for chemistry and metallurgy. Quarrying and mining are expensive propositions; you may never be directly involved in these industries extracting non-renewable resources, but you may have opportunities to see to it that those resources are not wasted and that operations do not unnecessarily destroy other values of the land. In some cases you may help plan positive uses for quarried or mined areas (see small-scale quarrying, below). For small areas of bedrock not being harvested, several uses mentioned below may seem minor compared to great extractive industries, but they can be of major conservational value to a community.

Bedrock natural areas. How strange that dure rock which for many centuries seemed indestructible and forbidding to man now sometimes needs his protection. His haste to be building and leveling has obliterated many fine outcrops of rock formerly used by geologists for research and education, sometimes also destroying paleontological evidence in the form of fossils, and sacrificing archeological sites to the God of Progress (so called). Be alert to the great rate of change of the landscape. Make sure that your community does not suddenly discover that it has lost the last good sample of some geological feature always considered common. Even in stony New England there are communities which no longer have a single good example of a great grooved rock to remind them of the Ice Age which accounted for so much New England history, much present activity, and much New England future. Get the advice of geologists on the distribution of different types of geologic formations in your area and help preserve the best samples of each.

Small-scale quarrying. Soft rocks, rocks that fracture easily, and some others which are partially decomposed by weathering can sometimes be obtained and shaped with hand tools such as crowbar, pickaxe, cold chisels, and sledge hammer, used with a mason's patience (p. 324). (*Always* protect the eyes with glasses, goggles, or plastic visor when hammering stone.) To speed operations, a contractor or farmer licensed to use dynamite can loosen bedrock for subsequent working with hand tools.

Uses of native stone. Structures of native rock tend to blend pleasantly with the landscape. Rock available may be only enough to keep the corners of a shed off the moist ground, but that may look better than four cinder blocks. Stone can be used for walls, terraces, riprapping of banks, and for seawalls, jetties, and groins. Small stones are good for dry wells and ditches to promote drainage. Various sizes can be used as fill for low spots in building roads, trails, parking areas, and play areas. (A large stone broken up fills more of a hole than will the solid stone.) Flat rocks can be used for flagging for paths in turf and for terraces.

Outdoor furniture such as fireplaces, tables, and benches can be made beautiful and durable from native rock. Some stone can be hollowed by chiseling to form a birdbath; if the rock is porous, it will need to be painted inside with a sealer to retain water. Sundials and telescope mounts can be fashioned from stone. Stone is useful above timberline and in other treeless areas for building cairns for trail markers; in recreation areas, use large stones for markers to delimit parking areas and roads so as to keep autos from encroaching on vegetation and soil which should not be compacted (p. 25; 358).

Bedrock for building sites. Rock outcrops sometimes have advantages as locations for buildings. Foundation problems are minimal, with no frost action or erosion. For wooden or metal buildings, holes are drilled in the rock with pneumatic or electric drill, or more laboriously with sledgehammer and star drill rotated slightly after each blow. Straight bolts or eye-bolts driven in the holes secure the foundation timbers. Masonry of stone buildings can be built directly on the rock. In vegetated regions, building on outcrops minimizes clearing of plants, saving labor and preventing disruption of landscape.

Beauty in bedrock. Sometimes bedrock stands out as bold cliffs catching morning sun or casting shadows which bring early evening to the valley; or it may form pink pinnacles with blue-shadowed snow wisped with white snow plumes against noon's dark blue sky. Sometimes bedrock is a tongue of rugged land tasting the sea. But perhaps it is only a little gray bump in the lawn or a ridge of crumbly shale which never does look neat. Accept these bits of bedrock for what they are. See their innate beauty and use them to best advantage in the landscape. Try pruning away some shrubbery to reveal the solidity of the rock, or plant alpine flowers in the cracks, or chip a hollow for a birdbath. A stone bench may help relate this natural feature to the architecture of a nearby building and provide an appropriate seat for contemplation of the attached planet.

TALUS SLOPES

A talus slope, also called scree, is a pile of rocks which have rolled or landslid to the foot of a steep slope. Its base is on the valley floor and a second side leans against the mountain; the third side slopes at an angle determined by the "angle of repose" of the particular type of rock fragments. Talus piles sometimes have determined trees whose lower trunks are bent nearly horizontal as a result of land-slide but which have then grown straight. Specialized plants grow in the crannies and ground squirrels, pikas, and marmots may make homes in the labyrinthine passageways among the boulders.

What use is a rockpile? The rocks can be removed for any of the uses listed above, but care must be taken not to start a landslide, sprain an ankle, or break a leg while moving around on the some-times precariously perched rocks. Talus slopes with igneous or meta-morphic rock yield good mineral specimens to the cautious rock-hound (586). The rockpile as a whole has its value, illustrating as it does the relentless forces of nature whittling down a mountain, and there is beauty of form and color for all the seeming chaos. So talus slopes often are best set aside as natural areas.

In spite of their dangers, talus slopes are sometimes used for trails, because they may prove safer than adjacent precipices for those who must climb. By carefully rearranging stones, a traverse trail (ascend-ing on a diagonal across the slope) can be built with tread notched into the hill. Such dry-masonry (fitting rocks without help of mortar) is time-consuming, but rewarding when one takes a rest to see what his developing skill has built. Take advantage of large, firmly sit-uated boulders on the uphill side of the trail; these give some pro-tection from falling stones. Placing medium-sized stones on the outer edge of the trail, especially at corners of zigzags, marks the trail should it have to be used after dark or in bad weather. Interpretive signs add interest. A talus trail is like the busy road in front of the house, fraught with dangers but useful and enjoyable so long as one is alert and sensible (355).

FROST-CRACKED STONEFIELDS

In relatively level spots at high altitudes and high latitudes unprotected by trees, temperature changes are severe, with numerous fluctuations across the freezing point. Water freezing and expanding in cracks widens them; then when the ice melts the water sinks a little deeper, prepared to exert a new sidewards push when next it freezes. Thus great boulders are riven, and as fine particles split off they tend to work under the larger stones when they are frost-heaved. A major portion of the soil may thus be covered with large rocks. Lichens, mosses, rosette plants, cushion plants, grasses, sedges, and dwarf woody plants adapted to arctic-alpine conditions grow on and between the boulders wherever moisture and the beginnings of soil permit, but still the tops of the boulders give a barren look.

In Alaska caribou may be grazed for a brief season on such terrain. In high mountains farther south, stonefields may be used as summer pasture for cattle; in winter they hold drifted snows which in spring and summer will help water the land farther down the watershed. But for increasing thousands of people these exalted lands swept by free winds are useful primarily for recreation. With extended views and petite wildflowers, these homes of pippits and rock chucks should be left as they are for their natural beauty. They should not be asked to produce more than healthy appetites and rested nerves, and of course clear streams flowing from innumerable unpolluted alpine springs.

BOULDER TRAINS AND BOULDER NESTS

These are stony areas left behind by glaciers. Boulder trains have boulders large and small strewn in somewhat linear fashion for varying distances. Boulder nests lack the linear arrangement. The stones have been rounded by abrasion against other stones in running water or sometimes by scraping against other rock while embedded in the glacial ice. While these stones are usually scattered enough so that considerable vegetation grows between them, sometimes the areas are so rocky that it seems fit to call them bareland.

Many a New England and Canadian farmer has scratched his head over what to do with these stony areas after the virgin timber was cut off with difficulty. Mostly they have been used for pasture, the cows playing hide-and-seek with the grass among the boulders. A few of the boulders found their way into barn foundations and stone walls, laboriously pulled by teams of oxen. Today it is sometimes feasible to clear the boulders from a small area of strategic land with a bulldozer, say for a parking lot or small garden in mountainous topography where level land is at a premium and boulders can serve as retaining walls. Occasionally it is easier to bury boulders than to push them a considerable distance.

Often the best use of such stony areas is to let them grow wild as natural areas or to manage them for forestry and wildlife (Chs. 14 and 15). Sometimes they can be developed for recreation. Intricate trails can wind between the boulders; stone benches can be set at choice spots; and sections can be made into wildflower gardens.

ROCKY SHORES

See *Bedrock*, above, and *Rocky Shores* in Chapter 8.

GRAVEL

Gravel deposits have a preponderance of stones coarser than sand and finer than cobblestones. When a current of water slows down in a stream, lake, or sea, it first drops the coarser particles; then with further slowing, the finer ones settle out. Pure gravel deposits are rare because currents usually vary, so that sand, silt, or clay is deposited on top of the gravel and works down into it, or may even be deposited at the same time if there is a sudden slowing of the current.

Areas of bare gravel are usually found naturally along streams, especially youthful ones (p. 211) where they have been recently deposited during periods of high water, as well as at certain places along coastlines or in deserts. Specialized plants such as willows soon colonize the gravel in spite of its infertility, tapping the water table, which is near the surface along the stream. Artificially bare gravel results from man's quarrying geologically old deposits, in some old river channel long abandoned by the stream or some delta in a glacial lake of the Pleistocene Period, the lake having disappeared some ten thousand years ago. Where these gravel beds now lie high above water table in dry seasons, they may remain bare a long time.

Uses of gravel.   Gravel is a much-sought building material. In the United States the supply is diminishing fast. For mixing with cement to form concrete pure gravel is best, or gravel with some sand. In commercial gravel quarries the gravel is sorted by sifting through screens of different meshes, or occasionally by using running water. Washing gravel removes fine particles of silt and clay that stick to the coarse particles after screening; dusty gravel gives poor adhesion with the cement.

For road building and fill for low places, gravel mixed with coarser and finer particles has the advantage of more solid packing; sands and clays fill in the pores between the particles of gravel. Gravel used without sorting is termed run-of-the-bank, and costs less. Sorted gravel is also used for tar roofs; it reduces their flammability. Coarse gravel without finer particles is good for promoting drainage in filled-over ditches, septic tank drainage fields, and dry wells, and under foundation footings, walls, walks, and tennis courts to provide drainage and discourage frost action.

Carefully selected pebbles are sometimes used in crafts. After being polished with special abrasives on a gem-polishing machine (sold by scientific supply houses), the pebbles often have great beauty. They can also be of geological interest, revealing many kinds of rock brought by geologic agents from different areas in a wide region.

Gravel deposits and their land use.   Before quarrying, the value of the gravel must be mentally weighed against the value of the surface if left undisturbed by digging. A gravelly knoll sometimes makes an ideal house site with good view and good drainage for a dry basement, and sometimes a gravelly hill is the best place in the neighborhood for a picnic ground. Unfortunately recreational, educational, and scientific values are not easily reckoned in dollars and so are often discounted in evaluations. Sometimes you can sell some gravel yet keep enough gravel bank for such surface uses.

Barelands resulting from removal of gravel.   This denuded land is hot in summer and cold in winter, and in some ways unsightly.

Have you ever noticed that gravel bars are always the right shape to fit the landscape? Streams make and remake them to conform to nature's changing designs. Clark Fork, Montana.

Its bleakness is often turned to ugliness by thoughtless parkers who jettison litter from car windows. Conservationists should exert themselves to make positive use of abandoned gravel diggings rather than let them deteriorate as unloved landscapes. Best uses are usually wildlife management and recreation. (40, 281, 360, 538)

Wildlife and children—When, as often happens, gravel is removed down to water table or close to it, only a little bulldozing is needed to excavate permanent or semi-permanent ponds attractive to swallows, herons, shorebirds, and sometimes waterfowl (p. 209). Leaving well-planned ridges and knolls provides interesting walks and observation lookouts between the ponds, with sites for benches and picnic tables. Such recreation areas are good for fireplaces because of minimum fire hazards. Planting willows and cottonwoods adds shade and beauty. Buttonbush planted at spots in the ponds and shrubs like silky dogwood in moist areas create diversity of habitat and increased edge for wildlife. Bird boxes on poles may attract tree swallows.

As a playground, an old gravel quarry is safe if banks are cut back to angles which will not slump, with humps and ridges left to challenge the imagination. Too often adults grade all play areas on the assumption that red-blooded boys must play baseball or soccer, even though they would rather be playing king-of-the-castle. Such a playground will need some supervision, interpretation, and maintenance. It should have a well-kept fence and welcoming gate; but it can be an inexpensive park to create and maintain. Given adult support, the children can do most of the planning and work.

Grading for construction—Where gravel-pit ponds are not feasible, there are other possibilities. Perhaps, graded nearly flat, the area can supply parking for adjacent areas, or building sites; or it has another highly artificial use that will remove civilization's pressure from somewhere else.

Gravel deposits over fertile soil.   Fertile farmland along a stream may unfortunately have gravel deposited on it in a flood. Although it is expensive, the best measure if possible is to bulldoze the gravel off. (In China, the stones are picked up by hand and carried off in baskets.) Such gravel can usually be used for improving farm roads or dikes.

Gravelly shores.   See *Gravel*, above, and *Gravelly Shores* in Chapter 8.

SAND

Sand deposits are made by the sorting action of water or wind or both. When its velocity becomes great enough, a current of either water or wind can pick up particles of mineral soil. A forty-mile-an-hour gale can even pick up wet sand from a beach and cake it on an observer's face and clothing. But when a current slows down, it must deposit some of its load, the heavier particles first, then the lighter ones. So sand deposits occur where streams, lakes, or seas have dumped mineral particles between 2.0 and 0.05 millimeters in diameter, and these may have been shuffled and reshuffled by water and wind. The bodies of water which laid down the sands may have vanished geologic ages ago. Inland dunes may now occur on long-dry lake beds, and ancient sea beaches lie many miles from any modern sea *(30)*.

Erodibility of sand. Sand is highly erodible. Its particles are easily picked up by wind or water. Gravel pebbles, which are larger and heavier than sand, require greater forces to move them. Clay particles, which are smaller, require less force but tend to get wedged together, achieving cooperative resistance to passing wind and water. But sand particles form a soil of single-grain structure; each particle has maximum independence from those around it but is at the mercy of passing currents.

Revegetation of sand. Bare sand areas are only slowly healed by vegetation. Except for limey sands of shells in warm seas, most sands are predominantly of highly insoluble silica which the waters toss around long after they have dissolved out more soluble materials. This glassy and quartzy residue is infertile because its nutritious companions have gone. Seashore sands, and sands in arid regions rich in alkalies, may have large quantities of such salts as sodium and calcium carbonates and chlorides coating their grains; these salts are very soluble and have been concentrated in the water. Highly specialized plants, such as members of the goosefoot family, can tolerate them, but most cannot; they find sands infertile—lacking in soluble elements for their roots to imbibe, or else with toxic salts. Furthermore, to colonize bare sands a plant must withstand a micro-climate of intense sunlight, rapid evaporation, and strong wind, which may use the sand as a tool of destruction, sand-blasting to bits anything in the way of its flying abrasive particles. No wonder sandy areas are healed only slowly, if at all, by vegetation! Some highly specialized plants like American beachgrass, woolly hudsonia, and European beachgrass do withstand this exacting environment, beginning to stabilize the shifting sands and to create a more favor-able microclimate for less hardy plants (p. 349).

Planning. The basic choice with a sandy area is whether to tie it down with vegetation or to enjoy its shifty nature when left bare. A sandy shore (see p. 240) can be very beautiful and can also provide an amazingly effective buffer against shore erosion by waves. So can bare sands inland, their subtle windblown curves casting deep shadows when the sun gets low. Art, science, education, and recreation can all benefit from bare sand. Any community is the loser when all its sand is captive behind drift fence and under turf and blacktop. But sand on the loose can be a headache, etching window glass so that it is no longer transparent, cutting down telephone poles with its incisive blast, burying forests and cottages on the lee side of active dunes, and drifting across roads which must then be plowed. The more arid the climate, the more sand is to be feared. Even in humid climates it can cause trouble, as in housing developments on old lakebeds when too much vegetation has been removed; even a few lots not quickly replanted can cause a nuisance.

Uses of sand as a material. Sand is useful to mix with cement for masonry. In climates with freezing weather sand is spread on roads to make them less slippery, the sand being stored dry, as in sheds or under tarpaulins, or, most regrettably from an ecological viewpoint, premixed with salt to keep it from being frozen when needed. For flowerpots, flowerbeds, small vegetable garden plots, and greenhouses, sand is sometimes mixed with clay soils to improve their texture. A backyard sandbox or even just a sandpile is a wonderful little world for a child to influence as the child sees fit, a source of highly educational recreation, a place to learn about soil texture, highway-building, and much more. Where oil fires are likely, as in remote homes still lighted by kerosene lamps, buckets of sand ready at hand make good fire extinguishers; and institutions use sand buckets for cigarette disposal, the janitor sifting out the butts with a scoop of hardware cloth. In cranberry country, sand is used in the maintenance of the bogs. And sand is used by various industries, notably glass manufacture. Possibly a property will have a sand deposit of commercial value. But even a little sand bank can be of help for a home, school, camp, park, or nature center.

Sandy areas for building. Sandy areas are readily cleared for housing developments and industry. Barren sandplains near cities or rural industrial developments are burned, bulldozed, and built upon with great speed these days. Often these are the best uses, though sometimes such areas are used for buildings when they might better be reserved for future airports.

Sandy areas for recreation. Frequently sandy areas have been used for recreation largely because they were no good for farming or forestry and hence were available at low cost. But aside from cost, sandy areas have real advantages for recreation. Sand is more comfortable to sit or sprawl on than gravel, and is relatively clean compared to silt and clay, whose fine particles do not brush off readily. Open spots in sandy areas permit pleasant breezes and vistas, because they are usually sparsely vegetated. The relatively simple landscape may be easier for many of us to enjoy than are more complicated scenes such as dense woodland.

Erosion control in sandy areas. (See Chapter 12 for methods of soil erosion control.) For sandy areas, special attention must be given to revegetating with plants adapted to the sterile and often mobile soil. It is best to study natural development of vegetation on sands in the area and try to duplicate it but speed it up with special devices such as drift fences (made of snow fence, brush fence, or rows of discarded Christmas trees) to help ameliorate the environment (p. 277). Bringing in loam for topsoil will speed stabilization but is expensive and destroys the natural advantages of sand.

Inducing erosion. Erosion is not necessarily evil. In some ways an active dune is more beautiful than one stabilized by vegetation, and a gully with its angular edges and dark shadows can be a pleasure if it is not where it can cause harm. Also it is good to have some erosion, especially at schools and camps, so that people can learn about it and how to cope with it. If a sandy area is totally vegetated, it can be beneficial to remove enough plants to let the elements of the atmosphere work directly on the bare soil. But don't start more erosion than you will be able to control!

Natural areas. Serious consideration should be given to keeping samples of sandy areas without further disturbance by man, so that they may serve for research and education and special forms of quiet recreation *(279, 395)*.

Sandy shores. See Chapter 8.

SILT AND CLAY

These soils are composed of mineral particles smaller than sand, less than 0.05 millimeter in diameter. These fine particles make for a fertile soil, because the tremendous surface area of the myriad par-

For crop production, these barelands are badlands; but for shadow-watching they are beautiful. Wind River Valley, Wyoming.

ticles lets minerals dissolve into the enveloping soil solution. Fine soils, especially the finer clays, tend to be too compacted for good plant growth, unless the soil is kept porous. Where the soil includes coarser particles (sand), or where careful plowing, cultivating, and cropping form the fine particles into crumbs with spaces between, or where organic matter makes the soil porous, the soil is termed a *loam*.

These soils are very widespread and of a multitude of varieties. They may be *transported soils* carried by wind, water, or ice; or they may be *residual soils*, residing where they have been formed by the breaking up of the bedrock beneath.

Loess. Fine-textured soils transported by currents of wind are called *loess*. They are found in regions downwind from arid areas or formerly arid areas whence the soil has blown. They make rich agricultural soils but must be protected from wind and water erosion.

Because of their remarkable compaction when wind-deposited, they have a vertical angle of repose, which in central Europe and Asia has led to some remarkable forms of land use and architecture. There houses and roads have been sculptured from deep deposits of loess.

Water-transported silts and silt-loams. These soils are well sorted by particle size according to the rate of flow of the water from which they settled out (p. 214). They occur along valleys of former streams or ancient lake beds, or they lie along existing streams as floodplain deposits during periods of high water.

Agriculture—The levelness, fertility, and boulder-free character of these soils suit them ideally to agriculture; and thus they have been used since man first became a farmer. Until recently farming has been accorded top priority for these soils, because the battle for food through almost all of human history has been foremost in survival. Today, however, there is a great disparity between the so-called underdeveloped nations, where there are scarcely enough fertile soils to keep growing populations from starvation, and some of the so-called advanced nations, where technology enables populations to produce more than their own needs without having to use every available inch of fertile soil.

Today in the United States, and to some extent in northwestern Europe and elsewhere, tremendous urban growth has often short-sightedly used fertile soils for non-agricultural purposes. Homes and industries have been built on floodplain soils; shopping centers and drive-in theaters have polluted the soils with paving. Remaining pockets of fertile soil in urban and suburban areas should be kept as farmland, for three major reasons. (1) The day may soon come when these agrarian soils will be needed for producing food, fiber, and/or medicinal plants. (2) These farmed areas contribute to the environmental esthetics of the cityscape, making for open space, greenery, and air conditioning amid the hard, rectangular restrictions of the city. (3) Farming areas are increasingly important for education and recreation of urbanites. A short turn of planting, weeding, or harvesting may be a delightful special experience for one whose daily life is running a machine or standing behind a counter. Many city officials and businessmen may not agree yet, but we should conserve the farm scene even in the midst of the city, just as some European cities have a mini-vineyard as part of a city park between tall buildings.

Forestry—Today forests are fortunately being handled as a long-term crop, the trees harvested on a sustained-yield basis by selective cutting or else replaced by seeding or transplanting after clear-cutting. But most forestry in the United States has not been the far-sighted operation that it should have been. The more fertile soils, instead of being allowed to grow generation after slow generation of trees as a long-term investment, have been converted from forest into farmland in the hope that a short-term investment could soon show a profit. While much clearing of forests in colonial and westward pioneering times was necessary then, today, with so much farming intensely machine- and chemical-supported, we do not need to put every inch of fertile soil into farm crops. We should use more of our silt-loams for trees again, partly because in urban areas forests affect the local climate and esthetics; partly for educational and recreational reasons alluded to repeatedly in this book; and partly because we do not know just what will be wisest land-use in the years ahead. We need to maintain diversity of landscape, particularly where plants and their related animals need a long time to develop. Pines cannot be produced like radishes in one growing season. It would be too bad if man in the future found himself surrounded by only short-lived creatures in here-today-and-gone-tomorrow biotic communities (see also p. 135).

Wildlife—Animal production is high on silts and silt-loams because of their fertility. But like forestry, wildlife has been given no priority on these rich soils. Wildlife, however, can be helped by appropriate farming methods. Strip cropping creates edges for wildlife; farm ponds attract waterfowl and support fish; hedges for fencing give cover for rabbits, quail, and many others; and times of harvesting and types of cover crops can help some species (see also Chapter 15).

Recreation—Rarely does a small city park survive on rich soil in the middle of a floodplain city, though it may be the only part of the city which really should be on a floodplain! Conservationists will do well to help establish farm-parks on these rich soils. Not only should there be agricultural scenes for city people to look at, there should be many opportunities to participate through recreational animal husbandry and gardening and other phases of horticulture.

Education—Cities may have a park zoo with exotic animals from foreign habitats and yet fail to show farm animals and plants, which are quite as strange to most city people. Respect for the land and what it produces for our civilization comes only through knowledge. Thus good agricultural soils must be available to our parks and schools for education. Preferably they should be on or adjacent to sites of school buildings, but often it will be necessary to have them on school-controlled tracts some distance away *(67)*.

Natural areas—Some of the most impressive educational and recreational areas are where nature has managed itself on rich soil undirected by man. Where areas of silt and silt-loam can be set aside for education and recreation, parts of the tracts should be zoned as natural areas.

Water-transported clays.   Clays are the finest particles of mineral matter, less than 0.02 millimeter in diameter, the last to settle out from lake or stream. Because of their small size, they have special physical properties. The particles pack tightly together, shrinking closer when dry and expanding considerably when wet, actually grabbing onto water by chemical bondage. Despite their high fertility, clays by themselves are not generally good for plant growth because they do not afford adequate pores for penetration by and aeration of roots; and when clays dry they tend to contract, leaving shrinkage cracks which tear roots or expose them to the air. Therefore clays make good growing soils only when mixed with coarser particles of silt and/or sand. But clays may help plant growth by underlying better-textured soils; they form a waterproof layer keeping moisture in the overlying topsoil.

Clays are the basis of ceramic industries. When baked into brick and tile, they are important construction materials. In semi-arid and arid regions, they can be used as *adobe* for sun-baked bricks and plaster for surfacing. They are also used in other industries and have applications in art, science, and medicine. Clay mixed with enough sand and gravel is used as a binder for fill and in road construction. Certain grades of clay can be used for surfacing tennis courts.

In humid regions, clays may lie bare on steep slopes where streams or machines have exposed them, or on fields where topsoil has been removed by erosion, fire, or bulldozing. Good clay banks can be an asset, but large exposures of clay soil are signs of a sick landscape needing aid from the conservationist (p. 338, *462, 576*).

Claybank—A large clay deposit of high quality may have commercial possibilities. A small supply can be used around the home, school, or camp for ceramics and science. The finest particles should be procured by shaking the clay into suspension in water and then using only the last-deposited sediment. This can be stored moist in a crock, large jar, or plastic wrapping. And clay makes the best mud-pies, non-nutritious but educational. Some claybanks show seasonal layers (varves) of coarse and fine particles, worth preserving intact in the bank for their geological interest.

For horticulture, clay mixed with sandy soil increases its water-holding capacity, in flowerpots, flowerbeds, or when planting trees and shrubs. When building a lawn on sandy soil, a layer of clay brought in to form a subsoil will keep more water up near the grass roots, especially if the lawn is nearly level; and clay mixed with the sand will have a permanent effect on the soil's water retention, compared to the temporary effect of the often-recommended peat moss.

Large exposures of clay soil—Unlike bare sand, clays are too dirty for relaxing on them to be much fun—dusty in dry weather and muddy in wet. New vegetation can recolonize them only with difficulty. They constitute very poor watershed, with high rate of eroding runoff and very little insoak. Most wildlife, except for specialized insects, shuns them. Their beauty is the fascinating beauty of badlands, bizarre, repulsive to many—though sometimes with alluring colors and forms.

The big challenge here is to reproduce an absorptive watershed through revegetation (p. 304). Plants can be so chosen and planted as to achieve further use of the land, for instance for forestry and wildlife management. With vegetation somewhat established, recreational use can be developed with trails and picnic groves; but the type of use should not jeopardize the healing vegetation, nor should trails be carelessly laid out so that they accelerate erosion. When erosion control measures are being established on most of the area (see Chapter 13), one or more small parts can be left natural; their slow healing by natural plant succession will make an instructive comparison with the managed parts.

Ponds for claylands. Because clays permit so little insoak they are well adapted for grading to form ponds collecting runoff, and the water thus caught adds beauty and variety, attracts wildlife, and conserves moisture to stimulate revegetation. The ponds may be seasonal in climates with high evaporation and low precipitation, and they may silt in rapidly until their watershed is revegetated; but even so they can be a great addition (p. 205).

Wet claylands.   See Chapter 6.

Muddy shores.   See Chapter 8.

(See also *9, 80, 169, 274, 409, 424, 431, 463, 474.*)

3 Drylands: Herblands

Kinds of Herbs
Animal Components of Herblands
Inorganic Components
Occurrence of Natural Herblands
Occurrence of Artificial Herblands
Man's Place in Herblands
Natural and Relatively Natural Herblands
Arctic-Alpine and Subalpine Herblands
    Planning
    Natural areas
    Reforestation
    Wildlife management
    Water development
    Grazing
    Gardening
    Wildflower gardening
    Recreation
Dune Grasslands
    Planning
    Natural areas
    Recreation
    Planting
    Wildlife management
Tall-Grass Prairies
    Planning
    Natural areas
    Controlled burning
    Recreation

Contents

Herblands are vegetated areas where the predominant plants are non-woody. (An herb, technically, is a plant lacking an appreciable amount of woody tissue.) Wood is usually a structurally strong material enabling plants to stand up in the air as trees or shrubs. Herbs are softer, less rigid, and must stay close to the ground (or, in humid areas, they grow as epiphytes on woody plants). The lowly stature of herbs, however, should not lead us to underestimate them; for while lack of wood makes for lack of strength in one sense, in another way it enables them to survive in a sort of judo game with the elements. Bending with the wind, many herbs can survive a hurricane which will tumble trees and tear out shrubs. And over the centuries, low-lying herbs have survived the drying winds and prairie fires which keep woody plants from colonizing plains. Herblands will include some woody plants here and there, as noted below; also, herbs are often numerous and important in the woody environments that are described later in the chapters *Shrublands* and *Treelands.*

KINDS OF HERBS

Herbs are of countless kinds, including the grasses of lawns, vegetables in gardens, "flowers" of flowerbeds, and so-called wildflowers of fields and woods. (The term "flowers" is loosely used by most people to designate herbs with conspicuous flowers; preferably, it should be used only to refer to the reproductive structures botanists call flowers, which may be on herbs, shrubs, or trees.) The great variety of herbs creates problems in identification, an important consideration in conservation practices; therefore close attention to the *taxonomy* (naming and classification) of plants is recommended. However, lack of botanical knowledge at the start should not be a deterrent. Recognizing large groups of plants can suffice at first.

The *grass* family is by far the most important group of herbs in most herblands, in both drylands and wetlands. Their general pattern of narrow leaves growing from opposite sides of the stem is familiar to most, as are the dainty flower clusters whose individual greenish flowers, drying out to straw color, seldom get their deserved attention. Greater appreciation comes with use of a hand lens and study of books and leaflets describing them *(255, 422)*.

Related to the grasses is the *sedge* family, many with stems triangular in cross section and leaves projecting in three directions instead of just two as in the grasses. Sedges are relatively unimportant in dry herbland conservation, although they can be valuable for wildlife in wetlands and are of considerable esthetic worth.

Herbs which are not grasses, sedges, or other somewhat grasslike plants are often conveniently lumped together under the term *forbs*, a word met particularly in range management where most grasses are desired and forbs are often (not always) weeds. For instance, daisies and buttercups, weeds in a farmer's pasture, are forbs, while timothy and redtop are grasses *(214, 426)*.

ANIMAL COMPONENTS OF HERBLANDS

As in most biotic communities, the vegetation of herblands comprises the matrix nourishing and protecting the animals scattered through it. To fail to notice the soil fauna such as earthworms and nematode worms, the myriad chewing grasshoppers and sucking spittlebugs, the meadow mice making mazes of tunnels as they hunt for food and store seeds, and the larger mammals and birds which make a livelihood amongst the herbs is to miss nine-tenths of the herbland drama. The conservationist becomes increasingly aware of such life even though its complexity will always leave him wondering. As he wonders, he realizes that the human animal is one of the most significant in supporting or destroying the herbland community. He therefore treads gently among the herbs. *(8, 139, 400, 439)*

INORGANIC COMPONENTS

Herblands typically are areas where sun and wind are strong, sometimes relentless, as in the great sweeps of grasslands bordering arid areas, whether the tundras of the water-frozen north or the short-grass plains in mid-continent. Climatic factors, along with vegetation and animals, work on the mineral components of the underlying earth, creating in natural herblands a delicately balanced ecosystem.

OCCURRENCE OF NATURAL HERBLANDS

Natural herblands, (other than those discussed in Chapter 6, *Wetlands*) are most extensive in subhumid regions with insufficient water for shrublands and treelands. (Woody plants pay a price for standing tall: their height above the ground increases the rate of evaporation from them, requiring greater water intake through their roots.) It pays to consider the possible climatic causes of any extensive herbland, although wildfire or grazing animals may also have had a role in determining its presence. In some cases, as with the grassy balds of the southern Appalachians, the precise reasons for occurrence are somewhat obscure. Less extensive herblands occur as patches in transition areas (savannahs) between wooded regions and wide-spreading grasslands.

Small areas of natural herbland often represent a temporary condition where vegetation (Ch. 14) is beginning to colonize bare soil, as on freshly deposited river silt, or in a woodland opening where a great tree has blown over, or where lightning-caused fire has exposed mineral soil.

OCCURRENCE OF ARTIFICIAL HERBLANDS

Artificial herblands may exist as (1) minor modifications of a naturally occurring grassland, for instance a fenced tract of plains with controlled grazing and perhaps grasshopper control; as (2) major modification of natural grassland, for example tall-grass prairie plowed up and planted to corn and other crops; or as (3) forests or shrublands which man has cleared, planted to herbaceous crops, and maintained so that woody plants do not recolonize, such as farms, gardens, and lawns in humid regions and irrigated tracts in arid areas.

MAN'S PLACE IN HERBLANDS

Human history has noteworthy milestones at the edges between tree-lands and herblands. For example, man's first farming was presumably in woodland clearings where he planted his primitive herbs, forerunners of our modern wheat, corn, beans, and squash. These first steps in agriculture made possible the beginning of permanent villages, which set him on the road toward the urban cultures of today. And consider the early colonists of the humid Northeast of the United States. Coming as they did from the humid Northwest of Europe, they felt relatively at home in the forests of the New World. But then they pushed west to the edge of the grasslands and encountered the formidable tasks of plowing the turf and building sod houses in the prairie, struggling steps toward colonizing the less humid reaches of the continent. Today as our densening population pushes into the still drier Southwest deserts, there is a great challenge to get herbaceous cover onto the arid soil, not just to paint the ground green as is sometimes done. Similarly, as our urban population pushes out to make new suburbs, the success of the real estate developer and new homeowner in creating a satisfying environment depends largely upon promoting a vigorous and beautiful herbaceous cover, usually lawn, where the land has been scraped and re-graded.

Because the literature of gardening and agriculture is already voluminous and very helpful, this book gives only very brief treatment to the subject of intensely managed herblands. Users of this book are urged to study the references in order to become better managers of farms and gardens. *(19, 407, 458, 460, 494)*

NATURAL AND RELATIVELY NATURAL HERBLANDS

The following pages describe some of the herblands less disturbed by man. There is always the challenge to use restraint in dealing with them, to leave them as natural as possible. In many cases it is wisest to leave them untouched. Working with nature sometimes means letting it do everything its own way. Sometimes, however, subtle modifications by man are in order. A subsequent section (p. 75) deals with artificial herblands such as lawns and athletic fields.

ARCTIC-ALPINE AND SUBALPINE HERBLANDS

It will be a rare user of this book who has a chance actually to practice conservation on land with vegetation of this type. But many can help see to it that such areas are not despoiled by others, practicing conservation by contributing ideas to public opinion and legislation and by donating money to government and private agencies interested in conservation.

Wind and cold seem to have fashioned these lands, where abundant moisture typical of the short growing season is followed by a long winter drought in which the water is unavailable because it is frozen.

Frost action is significant in affecting the soil. Grasses, sedges, mosses, and lichens are prevalent, together with flowering forbs such as the lupines and avens which brighten lush mountain meadows. Some shrubbery is intermixed with the herbs (see p. 109). In addition to invertebrates and such small mammals as mice, voles, hares, and marmots, these areas help support large grazing animals such as elk, caribou, reindeer, bighorn sheep, and mountain goats. Bears may also loom large in the landscape.

Great sweeps of arctic tundra belong in this category, although much tundra is better classified as shrubland because of the preponderance of alders, willows, dwarf birches, dryas, and other northern shrubs. Farther south, exposed coastal headlands and islands may persist in herbaceous cover; and even farther south, alpine meadows may be found near the summits of mountain peaks and high ridges, sometimes with the same species as those in the far north. The farther south such areas occur, the more important it is to conserve them for their scientific and recreational uses, because of their increased rarity and their nearness to greater populations of people who may visit them.

Planning.   The day will come when vast areas of the arctic wastes will no longer be considered wastes; they will be needed. Minerals, petroleum, space, and shoreline will become increasingly precious as we become more crowded. The arctic tundra will need the co-operative protection of people who have never seen it. The caribou should be able to carry on their ancient migrations, feeding on the lush herbs of the arctic summer and eking out winter sustenance from the frozen lichens. The wolf and bear should be spared the fate of the bison, crowded to the verge of extinction by the reproductive rate and avarice of aggressive humanity. The bleak coastal headlands farther south should be spared the usually ill-fitting architecture of shore real-estate development. Their natural esthetic and scientific values should be preserved, even if at great cost. The watershed and wildlife values of our alpine meadows should be considered along with the growing pressures for recreation. Summer recreation must be considered along with the planning of winter sports areas.

Natural areas. Areas selected for their beauty and/or scientific worth need to be clearly delineated and administered for their long-term protection. Fortunately, because of its location and climate, most arctic-alpine vegetation is not prone to wildfire damage; but in mountain valleys, keep some springs cleaned out for pumping water for fire suppression. Beaver may flood a subalpine meadow without permission, but that is in the natural scheme of things, many meadows having been formed where silt washed in behind a beaver dam. Highways, off-road vehicles, resort buildings, lifts and tows, and communications towers pose great threats to natural areas of alpine herblands, but even hikers are creating serious stress in these fragile environments. In any one location, weigh the value of "improvements" against the natural values which they inevitably destroy. Litter and other forms of thoughtless vandalism, including removal of plants for rock gardens and painting names on smooth-faced boulders, must be prevented, not to mention the destruction underfoot of delicate plants when people leave established trails.

Reforestation. Sometimes because of fire, grazing, or even tillage, arctic-alpine herblands occur where there was formerly forest but vegetation development is moving only very slowly, if at all, toward forest conditions. In some few instances it may be wise to convert the herbland to forest, for instance to try to reduce avalanche danger in steep mountains, to create a windbreak for a building, garden, or corral in an exposed location, or to provide wood for fuel and building material for a home on some remote moor. Black spruce and larch will probably do best on poorly drained soils; other spruces, firs, aspens, birches, and in some cases sugar maple or sycamore maple may survive on drier soils when protected from wind, as by rocks, shrubbery, and/or fencing. They may also need protection from browsing by rodents, hares, and deer (p. 462).

Wildlife management. Greater diversity of wildlife can be achieved by planting shrubs and trees in herblands in sites where they can grow. Tip-pruning can keep them low and dense, creating thick cover for animals (pp. 439, 461). Irregular groups of lines and patches give more edges (p. 458) than do more uniform plantings of extensive areas. Trees and shrubs native to surrounding areas will usually survive best, at least if they have comparable soils. Those with profusion of fruit have added attraction.

In some arctic-alpine herblands, fresh water may not be readily available; in such cases cleaning out springs and building catchment basins may draw wildlife (p. 206).

Control of wildlife numbers may be necessary when one attempts to have a garden. If fencing, electric fencing, and chemical deterrents do not suffice, it may be necessary to shoot, trap, or poison competing animals as humanely as possible (see Chapter 15).

Water development. Water in arctic-alpine herblands may be a feast or a famine. Mountain meadows may be moist throughout the warm season, yet because of their nearness to the top of the watershed there may be almost no surface water. Search may reveal small springs which can be deepened, walled with rock, and covered to provide small amounts of high-quality water, which can be important for daily living and fire suppression. Dug, driven, or drilled wells may yield ample water in some areas.

Where ground and surface water are inadequate, as in some high mountain meadows or coastal moors, devices for gathering precipitation can help (p. 206). On a building, gutters can lead to a rainbarrel or cistern. (Sidetrack the first rain after a dry spell to wash off dust and other debris.) Similarly a paved area, preferably a concrete catchment apron designed for the purpose, can prevent precipitation from soaking into the ground and run it into a cistern or pool which will minimize evaporation and keep the water clean and cool. In certain climates with considerable atmospheric humidity but deficient rain, dew ponds can be made from stoned or paved areas which cool sufficiently at night to condense enough dew to run off into a collecting pool or tank.

Excess water can sometimes be removed by careful ditching or laying of drain tile (p. 355). The inconvenience of too much water can be minimized by laying corduroy road (p. 256) and by building structures on piles of larch or other rot-resistant wood, or on high stone foundations.

Grazing. Man has traditionally used arctic-alpine herblands for grazing, whether by seasonally climbing and descending mountains with cattle, horses, sheep, and goats or by nomadic following of the caribou on the tundra. Where grazing can be conducted profitably on a sustained-yield basis, it should be considered wise use of the land. However, infringement on natural areas, curtailment of recreational opportunities, or damage to watersheds by grazing must be prevented at all costs. Grazing methods are beyond the scope of this book; consult government bulletins, extension agents, and private conservation organizations.

Gardening. Vegetable and flower gardens may grow luxuriantly in arctic-alpine herblands during the short growing season. Hotbeds and coldframes (cloches) can lengthen the season by starting seedlings under glass or plastic when it is still cold outside and can ward off early autumn frosts. Avoid frost pockets where cool air settles (p. 281); seek the warmer south-facing slopes which are not too steep; and favor the lighter-textured (sandier) soils because, with their better drainage, they warm up sooner in the spring than do more clayey soils. Windbreaks of stone walls, board fences, or spruce hedges can help create a good microclimate.

Wildflower gardening. Arctic-alpine flowering herbs and dwarf shrubs are much loved for their beauty. Many a rock garden in other zones is indebted to artic-alpine herblands; but probably the loveliest are those in their natural setting. Gather considerately samples of the many scattered wildflowers and grow them in niches suited to their special needs, arranged naturally along narrow paths which enable those interested to admire and study them without trampling on them. Maintain records, a little map, and perhaps inconspicuous labels to help the student. Here and there a bench of native stone or weathered wood invites one to rest and enjoy the broader view of the vegetation. A beehive nearby makes alpine honey. *(75, 138)*

Recreation.   Few of us visit the tundra for recreation—the wild-fowler, the botanist, the artist. The shortness of the warm season, the mosquitos, the distance, all keep most of us from knowing first-hand the beauty of the far north. But the alpine and subalpine meadows are now being sought both winter and summer by a host of nature-hungry people. The more that seek refreshment, the more important are the conservationists' efforts.

Most people who read this book will in a sense be part owners of federal parkland in the mountains of the western United States or of Nature Conservancy land in Wales or Scotland. We have the duty to be watchdogs and supporters for these parks even when we ourselves cannot carry on firsthand management. Those who plan public recreation or who have private mountain meadows usable for recreation must realize that only the greatest care can preserve the natural beauty and wild things at the same time that development invites people to enjoy them. Buildings, roads, chair lifts, and railways should be laid out where they will least obstruct natural beauty. Any signs should be in harmony with nature's patterns. *(410, 466, 577)*

DUNE GRASSLANDS

In few other environments can the struggle of vegetation with its physical environment be more readily seen than in dune grasslands. Here man can often, with just a little effort, swing the balance toward actively blowing sand or toward more stable greenery, whichever seems wiser.

Dunes form where water or wind has sorted out sand-sized grains of resistant rock, usually quartz and occasionally gypsum or other material. Particles of this size form pores which hold almost no water and are chemically quite infertile. Vegetation grows very slowly, leaving the sands uncovered, susceptible to wind, which shapes dunes according to its direction and velocity. The windward side slopes more gradually than the leeward side. Moderate winds create *trans-*

verse dunes, at right angles to the prevailing direction of blow; strong winds make *longitudinal dunes*, lined up with the winds' direction. Variable winds make cusped, complex dunes. *(341)*

A few plants are adapted to live in this droughty, strongly heated, highly mobile, and sand-blasted environment. American beachgrass and European beachgrass (Marram grass), for instance, have leaves which bend along with the wind rather than opposing it, and roll up longitudinally when the humidity is low, reducing evaporation and conserving their moisture. When buried by blowing sand, these beachgrasses are usually able to grow up through the deposit, their long stems extending from moist lower levels up to the dune top. Beachgrasses thus have an advantage over plants which try to grow on the dune by starting at the top and attempting to reach down with young roots through layers of dry and infertile sand. A few other herbs, such as the forb called dustymiller, a gray, woolly-leaved relative of sagebrush, can sometimes grow on moderately active dunes. Some viney plants, such as maritime peavine and poisonivy, can creep onto active sand from its edges, helping stabilize it. Once these pioneers slow the wind and anchor the sand, other plants adapted to sandy soil can succeed them, until finally the dune may be completely stabilized, perhaps even wearing a dense oak forest in humid regions. However, a slight weakening of the vegetation in some spot or a local concentration of wind may cause a blowout, undercutting the pioneering vegetation; the area will revert to actively blowing sand. Where a blow-out forms a dune hollow down to water table, as in some coastal dunes, the depression, (called a *pan)* may be colonized by moisture-loving sedges, grasses, and forbs. *(453)*

Planning.   An actively moving dune can be a menace or an asset. See p. 42.

Natural areas.   While most dune visitors will be interested in swimming, sunbathing, beach-buggy riding, fishing, and picnicking, some like to leave the bare sand and explore the grassy flanks and summits of the dunes, to see the curved sand-doodles scribed by the tips of the American beachgrass leaves and to watch the solitary wasps provisioning their nests with parasitized spiders. Some will wish to paint, photograph, and write creatively, others to observe and record more scientifically. Certain sections of dunelands should be set aside for these activities and be off limits for beach-buggies and picnics. Signs and sometimes fences will be needed, and in some cases patrolling.

Recreation. In addition to recreation of the types mentioned above, dune grasslands provide sites for semi-formal development of dunetop patios for deck-chair relaxation, especially for older people and invalids, and for observation towers to give a broader view of the landscape and to facilitate bird-watching. Such structures should be designed to blend as well as possible with the dune topography and colors. Also, remember that a structure on a dune top in dune grassland may soon find that its dune has moved away from it, if the dune grass no longer restricts the blowing of the sand. A dune building stilted on tall piers sunk deep in the sand can let the dunes come and go beneath it.

The wind currents over dune grasslands make them fine sites for flying kites and model gliders. More extensive dune areas are used also for sail-planing, an etherial sport close to nature.

Planting. Too-active sand can in many cases be slowed by planting dune grasses judiciously dug from an area which can spare them. In recent years, American beachgrass has been on the market on the eastern seaboard at commercial nurseries. Buying it is better than digging wild stock. Three to five deep-stemmed sprigs are set in "hills" (clusters) from one and a half to two feet apart, depending upon the windiness of the site, during fall or winter when the plants are relatively dormant. Fertilizing helps them keep ahead of sand erosion. Put controlled-release fertilizer in the bottom of each hole at planting; or, just as the plants start growing in the spring, ammonium sulfate applied at the rate of forty to sixty pounds per acre will strengthen growth. Do not use lime or mulch. Forbs such as seaside goldenrod and bindweed added here and there will give touches of color for those who wish to use the grasses as a matrix for a duneland wildflower garden.

Shrubs will increase the stability of the dunes but can destroy the grassland effect if too thickly set out. Woody vines such as bearberry, crowberry, and hudsonia form soil-anchoring mats close to the ground. Taller shrubs such as rugosa rose, used as marginal hedges, help keep most people off the grassland, protecting it from overuse. Small, scattered plantings of shrubs in dune hollows will add beauty without spoiling the sweep of the view; they also afford food and cover for wildlife (pp. 461, 465).

Wildlife management. Birds and mammals are scarce in dune grasslands, except for those which come in from adjacent shores, marshes, or woodlands. Nesting boxes on tall poles may attract some swallows; and a sturdy pole with platform may invite an osprey to nest. Where natural perches are few, a dead tree trunk with two or three branches still on it can be set in the sand, enabling one to get better views and photographs of hawks and other perching birds. Swallows will enjoy a wire strung between two such trees if there are no utility lines for them to assemble on during migration. Brush piles and fences, such as those made from discarded Christmas trees for wind erosion control, provide cover for sparrows and occasionally other small songbirds during migration.

Because fresh water is often in short supply on coastal dunes and interior sandy lands, wells or catchment basins that can provide drinking water will be much used by wildlife (p. 466).

Insects, the most prevalent animals of dune grasslands, are worthy of close study. Water and various baits (such as a jam sandwich which has fallen in the sand!) can attract them, as will an old board or burlap placed for them to crawl under. Too-numerous mosquitoes and flies from adjacent marshes are best dealt with by using insect repellents, plus netting when sleeping out at night. *(136)*

TALL-GRASS PRAIRIES

Once the prevalent landscape in the midwestern United States along the western edge of the broadleaf forest, this grassland type has almost entirely given way to the cultivated farmlands and industrial cities of Ohio, Indiana, Illinois, and parts of neighboring states. Today the few remaining stands of true prairie are of great scientific and historic interest. Along with grasses two to six feet or more tall, including such kinds as grama grass and beardgrass, were many beautiful prairie forbs such as blazing star and sunflower. The tall-grass prairies are partially the result of a climate intermediate in moisture between the humid eastern forests and the drier short-grass plains to the west. However, the relative amounts of influence of the great herds of bison and of numerous wildfires remain to be understood; both these factors favored the prairie species of plants and tended to exclude others. Today, small atypical prairies can be found eastward all the way to the Atlantic, some kinds of land use having created fields of little bluestem grass, notably where areas have been perennially burned over, as along railroad right-of-ways; but these are most often on sandy soil and are relatively sterile compared to the lush prairies formerly so extensive west of the Allegheny Plateau.

Planning.   The basic choices for the conservationist are (1) to try to perpetuate the grassland as nearly like true prairie as possible; (2) to let vegetation development without wildfire and grazing gradually change the grassland into some other vegetation type; (3) to manage the grassland for hay and/or pasture; or (4) to convert the land to some new and different use, for instance a cultivated field, a forest plantation, or a real estate development.

Natural areas.   Great need exists for tracts of prairie for scientific research, large enough so that some can be used for experimentation while others are left strictly alone to see what natural changes will

Remnants of *original prairie* like this are rare and precious. We also need *reconstituted prairie* of native grasses and forbs planted on land given up from other uses. Sheeder Prairie Reserve, Guthrie Center, Iowa.

occur when fire and grazing are excluded. Also, setting aside a prairie natural area can help the historians who try to make the past come alive for ensuing generations, grasslands being an important setting for the study of frontier days. Even very small tracts of tall-grass prairie, preferably on or near a school or college, are valuable assets for any community, a fit setting for a school-shop-built "prairie schooner" as a facility for an outdoor classroom.

Controlled burning. Burning is prescribed to maintain the fire-dependent grasses and forbs while weeding out competing species which might change the nature of the grassland. Kept in grass, the area can be maintained as an open space to afford vistas or broad views, air circulation, traffic safety along roads and airports, fuel-breaks, and for the beauty and interest of the grasses themselves and their associated wildflowers; also, the grass provides a protective cover for the soil, preserving watershed. Controlled burning is also valuable to reduce the hazards of wildfire (p. 431).

Recreation. When burned over annually or biennially, level fields of beardgrass and other prairie genera make inexpensively maintained fields for playing ball, flying kites, holding fairs, and other events. Since some of the common grasses are bunch grasses, however, the turf will be uneven. Flat or rolling stretches of prairie grasses form esthetically pleasing open spaces in the forested and built-up sections of the East. The inexpensiveness of maintenance by controlled burning should make such fields much more prevalent than they are, providing distant vistas and broad views where otherwise the humid climate would cause woodlands to close in. The fields may in themselves be beautiful; beardgrass turns a delicate salmon pink to red in the autumn but looks silvery when back-lighted, the sun shining on its fuzzy fruits.

Wildlife management. On fertile soils, wild animals usually have to take a back seat while cattle or crops determine the course of events, except where there are designated natural areas. However, some regard can be given wildlife in croplands by delaying mowing until field-nesting birds have raised a brood and by using flushing bars in front of mower blades to warn quail and other game. Leaving strips of native prairie plants along roads and fences between fields, around ponds and streams, and along gullies will help wildlife maintain their populations in the face of modern agriculture. To balance the trend toward fewer, larger, and more mechanized farms, more small pieces of farmland should be turned over to wildlife management as public or private hunting preserves or as sanctuaries and study areas. Such areas should be financially self-supporting, for instance by selling hunting privileges, or admission privileges for people with non-capture recreational interests in wildlife. Communities should purchase easements for building and other development rights and modify tax assessments on areas to be kept partly natural for esthetic and educational reasons, particularly in urbanizing areas.

On more sterile soils, wildlife management has less competition economically and may be a primary land use. Then plantings to encourage wildlife can disregard farming patterns. Shrubbery and trees dispersed irregularly through the grassland can greatly increase its capacity for wildlife (p. 457). Fire-resistant plants like blackberries and pitch pine fit in well with controlled burning to arrest vegetational development and keep the land partially open. Sterile-soil shrubs like bayberry and sweetfern provide good food and cover. Eastern redcedar and ground juniper are typical evergreens of unburned prairie-like fields in the eastern broadleaf forest region of the United States; both provide valuable berries and shelter for birds. However, an ambitious planting program plus natural succession can make the tall grasses disappear unless mowing, chemical planticides, and/or controlled burning maintain open areas important in maintaining high levels of wildlife.

Grazing.   The rich and level prairie soils of the Midwest are among the world's best for livestock. Many detailed conservation practices have been worked out for modern farming in this region. Consult agricultural extension workers and published material beyond the scope of this book *(465)*. But before committing every square foot to regular farming, consider alotting land to natural areas, recreation, and wildlife management as outlined above. The patches of tall-grass prairie eastward on sterile or burned-over soils are often poor grazing lands and should be used with care, especially where slopes make them susceptible to erosion if there is over-grazing.

Grazing in Great Britain has been one of the mainstays of the economy and a major contributor to pastoral beauty. It will be unfortunate if population pressures and short-term economics progressively do away with the grassy moors. In order to stay solvent, sheep farmers have tended to put more sheep on the land than it could stand, with consequent erosion. Somehow more recreation money from those who appreciate pastoral beauty should go to grazers, so they can operate within the carrying capacity of their land and not have to sell out on a massive scale to higher-paying forestry programs. In the past in Scotland, financing of grouse moors perpetuated by burning has helped maintain herblands, but now these lands must be supported by a broader, more popular base if they are to compete in the landscape with the pressures of modern forestry.

In the south of England, the fertile downs are under duress from urbanization and machine-style farming, which tends to eliminate hedgerows to create larger fields. While the hedgerows may be considered primarily shrublands, they host great quantities of herbs which must disappear as the hedges are converted to arable land or pasture. England cannot afford to lose too many of her famous wildflowers. And who is to say how many is too many?

Building with sod. On fertile Midwest prairie soils which have been in fibrous-rooted grass for a long time, the thick turf can be carefully dug with a straight spade and used to reconstruct the primitive sod houses of frontiersmen. These will be primarily of academic interest in this age when building materials are so readily shipped around the country. Conservationists, however, recognize the academic importance of getting people to think about the close relation of their forebears to local natural resources.

Cultivation. The above practices leave intact the tall-grass turf whereas cultivation breaks the sod. On much of the tall-grass prairie, man now raises tall grasses of his own choosing, notably corn. Where hybrid corn and corn-fed livestock mean money in the bank, it is tempting to put as much land as possible into this amazing scientific production. However, the first paragraph under *Grazing* above applies equally here. The tall-grass areas on less fertile soil eastward are sometimes suitable for cultivation when level, the light soils being good for crops such as strawberries. The slopes should almost always be kept in grass rather than open-tilled crops.

Planting trees and shrubs. Farther west toward the drier edge of the prairies there is ever more reason to plant trees, for they are naturally fewer (mostly occurring along water courses), and they are more needed for shade, windbreaks, and fruit. Eastward where trees are plentiful, there is more reason to preserve the openness and turf of prairie and to resist the urge to set out woody plants.

Windbreaks—In the more windswept, drier prairies, rows with progressively taller shrubs and then trees on the windward side of buildings and croplands make for warmer microclimates and help conserve moisture by creating shade and encouraging snow to accumulate in drifts deeper than those in exposed places (pp. 121, 276, 300).

Orchards—Fruit trees add beauty and utility to any home in herblands. The more western prairies do not have a good climate for commercial orchards, but near Lake Erie and eastward, rolling lands give good air drainage for orchards and vineyards. In the more southern part of the tall-grass region, hickories, walnuts, and pecans are productive.

Groves—In the westward part of the tall-grass region, groves (locally called "openings") for shade and visual beauty can be composed of fruit and nut trees but include also burr oak and other oaks, basswood, buckeye, sycamore, tuliptree, and other beautiful trees of the region, though westward they may need protection from the wind when they are young. Sugar maple and beech thrive only with shade, soil moisture, and protection from wind. Cottonwoods will develop fast on stream banks and river flats; there sycamores and pin oaks will also be most at home. Eastern redcedar, the only evergreen tree of the western part of the region, provides beautiful groves, but its conical shape affords little overhead shade; its dark color makes a fine background for blooming redbud trees. Scots pine is an attractive introduced evergreen for groves.

In burned-over tall-grass fields eastward, the native, bird-planted black cherry and pin cherry can be thinned, pruned, and protected from fire to make attractive groves in the sunny expanses kept open by controlled burning. Planted black locusts also make excellent groves; a thick green grass develops beneath, even on sterile soil.

In pruning groves, low branches should usually be left on the windward side to keep out desiccating winds. Shrub borders to wind-

Broomsedge is not a true sedge but a bunchgrass which, like other species in the same genus, can be maintained by occasional controlled burning. Charlottesville, Virginia.

ward will also help. On the leeward side, branches may be pruned high to give a sense of lofty airiness (p. 440).

Christmas-tree plantations—Scots pine and red pine are frequently used for plantations in the Midwest. Eastward, red pine, Austrian pine, and white pine have been much used to reforest fields of little bluestem. For any commercial venture in Christmas-tree growing, consult local private or extension foresters. Regular shearing of pines improves their Christmas-tree shape and texture and increases their market value (p. 439).

Blueberry lands—On the acid, burned-over fields eastward, low-bush blueberry can be substituted for little bluestem grass. If areas of grass are left and mowed at the end of the summer, the hay (of little value for most purposes) can be spread on top of the blueberry bushes for late winter or early spring burning to prune their tips (p. 439). The little bluestem grass can be burned over at the same time to maintain it as tall-grass prairie (p. 431). These lands can also be used for highbush blueberry plantations. Blueberries are not adapted to the limy soils of the Midwest (p. 126).

Protection from wildfire. Tall prairie grasses are highly combustible when dry. When not burned, the dry leaves and stems accumulate, adding to the fire hazard. This is true of other vegetation to a degree, but a forest tends to build up humidity inside it; and the interior is not so exposed to dry wind as a field of grass. Controlled burning of grasses in late winter or early spring while the soil is wet reduces the severity of any subsequent wildfire. Fuelbreaks along roads and around buildings where fire might start are made by plowing the sod under and maintaining bare mineral soil by cultivating (p. 396). Fuelbreaks, as well as affording valuable protection during dry seasons, will simplify the work of controlled burning. Farm ponds or other pumping stations give added protection.

SHORT-GRASS PLAINS

Short grasses have developed in the interior expanses of North America over thousands of years, largely as a result of the dry climate in the rain shadow of the Rocky Mountains and the coastal ranges, which shut off much of the moisture brought from the Pacific by prevailing westerly winds. The 100th meridian of longitude coincides closely with the boundary between the humid East, with more than twenty inches of average annual rainfall, and the subhumid West. But such generalizations tell only a superficial part of the climatic truth. For instance, the rainfall for any one year or even a group of several years may not be average; it may be considerably more or less. Also factors not so directly climatic, like wildfire and the grazing of herbivores, first bison and then cattle, have undoubtedly contributed to the natural growth of short grasses in these plains.

Soils of the short-grass plains, while varying greatly, tend to have an upward movement of capillary moisture which concentrates soluble salts near the surface, helping make the topsoil more alkaline than in the humid East, where greater precipitation tends rather to leach the soluble salts downward to the subsoil. Over great areas, the soils are dark prairie-earths (chernozems), rich in bacteria and nutrients which are highly fertile for grasses whenever and wherever there is adequate moisture. More locally, there are alkaline flats more or less covered by vegetation specially adapted to their conditions, often relatives of coastal plants adapted to saline soils. Toward the more arid edges of the short-grass plains, the grasses are shorter still and more sparse, with scattered shrubbery such as sagebrush, black-brush, and mesquite. Toward the more humid edges, the short grasses merge gradually with the tall-grass prairies.

Planning.   Careful use of the plains grasses has produced some of the best wheat, beef, and wool in the world. Poor use has created some of the world's worst problems in soil erosion and human misery. Dustbowls and badlands have resulted from cropping the grasses too closely, preventing them from giving adequate ground cover in dry years; and breaking the native sod by plowing has made millions of tons of fertile topsoil into dark, choking clouds. Until the golden year when we can predict moisture conditions with certainty, management of short-grass plains must be based on how much use can be made of the land in the driest years. Those who gamble on moisture may profit heavily, but they may also ruin themselves and the land for generations. Farmers and ranchers and their economic dependents in this region must see themselves as a delicate gear in nature's watchworks of climate, soil, vegetation, and animals. If their spindle of operations is out of line, the spring may snap. They *must* plan carefully. *(267)*

Natural areas.   With grass from horizon to horizon, the need of natural areas is not so obvious as it may be in a city; but need there is. Those who know the most about scientific range management admit readily to ignorance of the subtleties of nature's processes and urge setting aside study areas to compare with experiments in managing the land. Cattle may appear as dots under the immensity of the plains sky, but in numbers their influence is great; how great can be determined only when there are areas from which they are excluded. A jeep running up a grassy hill may look insignificant, but gullies resulting from its tire tracks might start a badlands formation and sediment a precious watering pond lower down in the watershed. Airplanes that hunt coyotes keep them from preying on lambs; but how many coyotes is too many when one considers the rodent problems of range management? Planticidal chemicals remove sagebrush from hundreds of acres; does this have an appreciable effect on the water-table, on wildlife, on grass production? Numerous natural areas are needed for comparative studies of these problems under various local conditions. And in a vast region where a house lot is apt to be 640 acres rather than 60 by 40 feet, natural areas must be extensive so the effects of wide-ranging animals can be studied.

In addition to the needs of science are the requirements of the types of recreation that are incompatible with speedy travel on billboarded highways: a chance to stop your horse on the brow of a hill where you can look down at bison and indulge in don't-fence-me-in feelings; an opportunity to lie on your back amid the prairie wildflowers and watch the afternoon gathering of fluffy clouds without vapor trails scratched on the blue slate. Are these luxuries which mundane man cannot afford?

Recreation.   Horses! Six legs are better than two in the great stretches of plains. A pickup truck or motorcycle may get you there faster, but some of the joys of the saddle will be missing. More urban families are wheel-camping and need farms and ranches with camping facilities where one or two families can informally join in the ranch life as paying guests for a couple of weeks. Something should slow down American tourists so that they actually see the country. Two to five well-trained riding horses can remake life for a high-octane family—if anything can.

Improved water management in plains country has provided multiple-use reservoirs admirable for flat-water fishing, boating, and swimming. While many are large federal public works, each community and homeowner should see what can be done locally to catch the precious water for recreation as well as for domestic use and fire protection. Where surface water is inadequate, a deep well and wind-driven pump may supply enough water for a recreational pool or puddle, the water being released for farm purposes as it is replenished for cleanliness. Consult county, state, or federal technicians skilled in soil and water resources. Over-pumping groundwater and inexperienced efforts at irrigation create major problems in water and soil management (p. 448).

Wildlife management.   Water in this region is often a limiting factor for wildlife; so anything from a birdbath on up will be appreciated. Once started, the supply should be maintained throughout the summer. In some areas, "gallinaceous guzzlers" condensing dew into evaporation-protected drinking fountains will be used by small animals (p. 466). On a larger scale, the wildlife-conscious land manager will prevent unnecessary drainage of sloughs and potholes where waterfowl breed and many other forms of wildlife make their homes.

Woody plants are conspicuously absent in this region. Wherever shelterbelts and groves are planted to slow the wind and give shade and moisture, they will be used by wildlife, especially if wildlife preferences are considered when selecting the plants (see *Planting Trees and Shrubs*, below).

Control of predators, rodents, and grasshoppers should itself be controlled. Research should guide all shooting, poisoning, trapping, and biological control. Many ecological sins have been committed in the name of predator control (see also Chapter 14).

Grazing. This is primary use of the short-grass plains in terms of economic production, but the grasses are also essential for watershed protection. Grazing practices must be carried on with understanding of the intimate relations of animals, grass, soil, water, and wind.

Cultivating. Breaking the sod by plowing and leaving the soil exposed by cultivating (p. 396) must be done only with the greatest care because of danger of wind erosion, and of water erosion caused especially by cloudbursts associated with summer thunderstorms. Plowing, strip-cropping, and other farm operations should be on the contour (p. 338), except in cases where they should be at right angles to the wind (to slow it down and to catch snow in the furrows). Shelterbelts and fences will help lessen wind erosion and conserve water by accumulating snowdrifts. Mulching can help stabilize the soil, store moisture in the ground, and lessen evaporation into the air. Cover crops should be employed whenever possible. The less extensive the bare area the better; what may be safe in a moist year may contribute to disaster in a dry one. When one plows, one cannot foretell what the weather may be.

Planting trees and shrubs. Shelterbelts and shade trees make a great deal of difference in the comfort of living on the short-grass plains, but they are hard to come by! Few conservation practices are so altruistic as setting out and tending small trees in the grassy ex-

panses where woody plants make struggling growth because of wind
and drought. The harvest of shade and stilled air may be long in
coming (p. 276). Experimentation has researched the species of trees
and shrubs most likely to succeed, so consult the references indicated
in Chapter 14, and check with local extension agents. But all the
answers are not yet found, so try some experimental plantings of
your own.

Protection from wildfire. While the grasses are shorter than in
the tall-grass prairies, creating less combustible material, conditions
are usually drier and hence can be very dangerous in terms of wildfire. Fire safeguards are similar to those described above for tall-grass
prairie, p. 69.

Brush control. In many areas shrubs compete with grasses for
space and moisture. Sometimes the shrubs move in when over-grazing or other poor grassland management weakens the sod-forming
grasses. Shrubs in small areas can be cut by hand with loppers.
Stumps can be sprayed with planticides or dug out with a mattock.
For range reclamation of large areas, great mechanical brush-cutters
are employed to break down and chop up the bushes, working the
pieces into the soil. Also, large areas are sprayed with chemical
planticides (p. 400).

Today man has the technical knowledge and power to make tremendous changes in the vegetation of the short-grass plains. He
should consider humbly his role in the landscape. Certain shrubs
compete with him for water; these are *phreatophytes,* "well plants"
whose roots reach down into the soil and deplete the groundwater.
But these same shrubs slow the wind, create food and cover for wildlife, bring tints and shades to the landscape which can please the
eyes of those who see more than production dollars in the grassland
view. It will be tragic if hasty management of vast areas of grasslands
is as ill-conceived as the complete cutting-over of the forests of the
eastern states by the impetuous white man. The term "brush" should
not be used synonymously with "dirt," in the sense of something bad
to be avoided or removed as soon as possible. Rather it should be a
term similar to "soil," denoting something to be investigated, appreciated, and carefully used. (see also *342, 368, 452, 512, 529, 562,
563, 564.*)

OTHER GRASSLANDS OF THE DRYLANDS

In the southwestern United States, in the great Basin between the Rockies and the Sierra, northward to the plateaus of Oregon, Washington, and Canada, and in southern California, one finds assorted grassland types merging with desert scrub (scattered bushes with relatively bare soil in between), with more northern shrub types, and with chaparral (dense shrubbery of the warm-wintered, Mediterranean-type climate). Conservation practices for these areas should be worked out by studying the above sections on herblands together with Chapter 2, *Barelands*, and Chapter 3, *Shrublands*, as well as books, pamphlets, and journal articles dealing with the specific locale.

ARTIFICIAL HERBLANDS

The following pages are concerned with when and how to use artificial herblands. Chapter 14, *Vegetation Management*, describes basic methods of planting, propagating, weeding, and so on. Consult the voluminous literature available in libraries and government publications for details.

Often artificial herblands merge with natural ones; in such cases reference to the preceding pages will help. At certain stages of development or use, these herblands may be bare, as when a new lawn is being seeded, so reference should then be made to Chapter 2.

LAWNS

Lawns are familiar to almost everybody, except in the driest parts of the country. Traditional in humid northwestern Europe, they have been the subject of much experimentation, so that there are species and varieties of lawn grasses and methods of lawn maintenance adapted to nearly every local condition. Government and private research has been published in leaflets which enable almost anybody to have a lawn. Now millions of dollars and millions of hours are spent in trying to develop turfs which are at least as good as the neighbors'. Why all these lawns? *(460)*

Characteristics and general uses.   Lawn turf is made from grasses
which *tiller*, that is grow sideways by stems along the ground. Some
species make a very fine mat, like the creeping bent grasses used on
golf course greens. Others are coarser. Poorer lawns sometimes have
grasses verging on the bunchgrass manner of growth, like sheep
fescue used in shady areas of soil incapable of supporting more uniformly textured grasses. All grasses typically have fine, fibrous roots.
Stems, leaves, and roots together give the soil excellent protection,
keeping it from blowing when dry and washing away when wet.
Grasses keep the soil porous, promoting insoak and thereby lessening runoff; thus they stabilize the water table in the ground and keep
surface waters filtered and clean. These are good reasons for lawns;
but other types of vegetation will also protect soil and maintain a
good watershed.

Most grasses have stems which grow upward as well as ones which
tiller. Unlike the stems of most plants, which grow at the tip, grass
stems have growing regions lower down, so that cutting the tops of
the grass keeps it short without stopping its upward growth. Thus by
repeated mowing or grazing, grass can be held nearly stable at a desired height.

Lawns have a soft texture which feels good to walk, sit, and lie on.
A well-cared-for, uniform, level lawn allows balls to roll in a con-
sistent direction and at a regularly diminishing speed. Much of the
year lawns have a green color which is easy on the eyes and pleasing
to most of us.

Lawns provide a feeling of open space. Their simplicity of pattern
sets off other designs in the landscape, for example trees standing in
their middle. They allow the eye to travel away, past local detail to
some more distant view. In landscape design, they function like the
rest in a bar of music or like the plain mat around a watercolor or
etching. Where there are tall buildings or trees, this open space also
lets in sunshine and gives a view of clouds, blue sky, and stars. And
it permits motion of the air which would be impeded by taller vegetation or structures.

But lawns have disadvantages, such as relative expense of upkeep
for a fancy lawn, and need for repeated mowing. In many situations
people use lawn when they might better use other types of vegeta-

tion, such as so-called rough grasses, ground-covering vines, or shrubbery. Before committing an area to a large lawn and committing yourself to its upkeep, consider carefully other types of land use discussed in this book *(165).*

Specific uses of lawn.

Edges of roads—Lawn is nearly ideal for the verge along driveways and roads. For safety, it provides a color distinctive from the road surface, stabilizes the soil, prevents a dangerously ragged edge, gives a safe surface for emergency runoff and parking, and provides maximum visibility. (Taller, rough grasses mowed once or twice a year are almost as good but tend to hide small animals which may suddenly emerge onto the road.) Grass does not suffer from having snow from the road piled onto it. To keep vigorous grass from growing out onto the road, have a berm of board on edge, of slabs of stone (standing on edge and slanting downward and inward to the road), or of cement or asphalt. Chemical planticides *carefully applied* (p. 400) can keep a gravel road weed-free when that is desirable (not always the case). The width of the lawn depends upon such factors as the rate at which cars travel along the road and the amount of space available for grass compared to other landscaping desired, for instance flowerbeds, flowering shrubs, or evergreen shrubs (safer than trees close to a road). A short length of pipe set into the ground with its top flush with the lawn surface makes it possible to insert road-marking stakes for snowy seasons or for making corners visible at night; they can be easily removed for mowing.

Along sidewalks and other paths (including bicycle paths)—Most of what applies to roads applies also to sidewalks. In addition, there is a real safety factor in having sidewalks separated from roads by a strip of lawn, to keep pedestrians farther from moving vehicles. A major problem with grass along walks occurs at corners where people tend to cut across, compacting the soil and killing the grass. When designing walks, study the traffic needs of pedestrians. Too often walks are laid out to be a symmetrical pattern when seen from the air, rather than a pattern attractive from the point of view of the pedestrian. Part of the problem stems from the lesser expense of laying pavement in straight lines, though a curve would be more acceptable in terms of flow of foot traffic. The curved sidewalk, however, will result in lower maintenance costs for the bordering lawn for years to come, because pedestrians are more apt to stay on the path; uniformly vigorous, attractive turf will grow along the path. On straight walks, low fences at right-angle corners are a nuisance to mow around. They can be light and rigid enough to pick up and move when mowing. Or they can be of heavy pipe just high enough above the ground for the lawn mower to pass under, and with as few upright T's as possible (though still strong enough for children safely to practice balance-walking on, which they surely will). But if possible avoid such fences by good design! A poor solution is to plant large, dense, prickly bushes to discourage corner-cutters (p. 374).

Another turf problem occurs where sidewalks are too narrow for two-way foot traffic. Laying a wider walk is easier than restricting the path to thinner or more thoughful pedestrians. Social approaches to the problem include suggestion and remonstrance, educating people about the purpose of sidewalks and the problems of lawn maintenance, perhaps letting them have a hand at repair.

Front lawns—The "entrance area," "approach area," or "public area" of a home, school, or other building set back from the road has often in Anglo-American tradition a front lawn which permits a view of the building as one comes towards it. A large lawn can make a superb setting for a mansion; a little lawn can add delight to the prospect of a cottage. However, because of the volume of modern traffic with its noise and odor, it is sometimes well to use some of the front space for dense evergreen shrubbery or trees. If the front of the building faces cold prevailing winds, there is added reason to have less lawn and more shrubbery between the building and the road. Also, at many schools far too much educationally useless front lawn could be better employed for a variety of other types of vegetation to increase the diversity of instructionally useful environments. Likewise at hospitals for chronic cases, a variety of environments in place of vast expanses of lawn would diversify the view and bring birds and other interesting animals into the patients' drab world.

Side and back lawns—These turf areas have many uses for family recreation. The type of grass used may be less fancy-looking but better able to withstand wear. A modern tendency to build homes and their garages closer to the road in front is good in that it leaves more back yard for outdoor family living. Sometimes with an older home it is possible to move the garage to the front of the property to provide more lawn in the rear. If possible, have a small part of the lawn partially set aside by shrubbery or wall as a quiet place with nice lawn for older people; also have a larger part of the turf area for active children's play, with tough turf; the inevitable bare spots will look not out-of-place.

Lawn design—The area of a lawn is determined by its edges. So is its effect on the landscape design. Straight edges give lines which may relate well to the architectural lines of buildings. Curved ones often relate better to natural features such as slopes of hills and crowns of trees. Rectangular edges following property lines or straight walks may make a space look smaller than the longer lines of diagonal edges within the same space. Therefore, in laying out lawn, give careful attention to the position of surrounding landscape items such as buildings, clumps of shrubbery, hedges, isolated specimen trees, and the like. One big old oak or paper birch against pines looks its best with a lawn in front; and the effect is reciprocal. In constructing lawns, take care not to cause unnecessary damage to plants to be conserved around the edges.

ATHLETIC FIELDS

The more we use wheels, the more we need athletic fields, open areas where young people can have unobstructed room for running and playing ball. Middle-aged people can stay younger and more fit by maintaining their capacity for play. Many of us today cannot chop kindling and walk a mile to the store, so our health suffers.

Construction and maintenance of first-rate fields are beyond the scope of this book, but frequently the hard work of making and maintaining a field will do more for people than simply being given one ready to play on, charged to their taxes or their club dues. A real problem of young people today is finding useful employment in their own communities. Given leadership (not dictatorship) they can accomplish an amazing amount, including construction of their own recreational areas *(515)*.

Characteristics.   Most athletic fields should be nearly level, with about a three per cent slope to provide surface drainage. The surface should be covered with a strong, uniform turf, except when certain games have special areas like the mound and base lines for baseball. Subsoil should be sufficiently porous to provide subsurface drainage of water beyond that held by the topsoil for the needs of the grass (p. 334).

Planning. The number and variety of athletic fields should be worked out with reference to the present and projected needs of the population. With decreasing space available for almost everything in many communities, the amount of land to be dedicated to athletics is a serious problem. People do not like to wait a turn for a tennis court or a softball diamond, but neither camp nor municipality should overextend itself on such facilities, causing destruction of sites which as picnic or natural areas might serve a larger portion of the population over more hours of the day and more days of the year. Many a school recently has filled in a marsh or buried a brook in a culvert to make relatively unneeded areas for active play. And the tragedy is permanent. *(96, 137, 480)*

Location. Land already flat is least expensive to develop for athletic fields. Dry beds of ancient lakes are therefore excellent. Terraces along streams are good where normal stream level is low enough to provide good subsoil drainage. Bottomlands on flood-plains of streams may be excellent but may stay moist longer than desirable because of the high water-holding capacity of river silt and the high water table at certain times of year. Laying drain tile can expedite drying in such locations (p. 355). Since these sites are susceptible to flooding, any associated buildings should be built on higher ground. Streambank plantings should be kept thick to minimize wash and catch debris. The rich soil of floodplains promotes good turf which withstands erosion; but deposition of sediment on the grass can be a problem unless thick plantings are maintained upstream and along the sides. Avoid thick plantings on the downstream side, because once flood waters have reached the field they should be encouraged to keep in motion and carry their load of sediment well beyond.

On filled land. Hilly land requires considerable cutting and filling to provide level terrain, involving sacrifice of both hill and hollow and causing major alteration of the watershed. If the hollow is a stream valley, provision must be made for the stream which owns it. There are several possibilities. *If the fill must extend all the way across the valley,* the stream must be given a culvert or culverts large enough to carry flood waters from the entire watershed above, or a dam must be built on the upstream side of the fill adequate to store all flood waters which the culvert(s) cannot handle (p. 305). And the dam must be sufficiently empty before the flood to hold these waters. Otherwise, expect trouble. *If the fill need extend only part way across the valley,* the remaining stream space must be wide and deep enough to carry flood waters from the entire upstream watershed, or a dam similar to the above must be constructed. Also, since the stream has been squeezed into a narrower valley, special efforts will be required to prevent bank erosion caused by its concentrated flow (p. 219). An impounded pond on the upstream side of the fill may be desirable for recreational purposes and watershed management, but less so than a wildlife marsh. In some cases such a pond should be kept drawn down enough for flood control. Try to work out a multiple-use reservoir, taking into account recreation, wildlife, and watershed (see Chapters 7 and 11).

The cut hill—Where the hill is cut to provide fill and extend the athletic field, there should be careful consideration of the remaining excavated slope (unless the whole hill is removed). To insure stability it should not be left steeper than the normal angle of slope (p. 000) for the material of which it is composed. And unless it is of blasted rock, it will usually need artificial revegetation to prevent erosion, although mulching and natural seeding may be adequate. Such a hill makes a fine backstop for balls if steep enough to stop and roll them back; and the field may be laid out to take advantage of this slope unless factors such as orientation of the field in relation to the sun are more important. If the soil is particularly liable to erode, this slope should be protected by backstop or other fence to keep people from running on it to retrieve balls. In some cases, careful terracing of this cut slope can provide a fine gallery for spectators (p. 343).

Separation of fields—While topography is usually a controlling factor in location of athletic fields, consideration should also be given to nearness of drinking water and toilets, and in some cases field houses with lockers and showers. Separation of fields from other fields and other activities prevents distraction, particularly important at schools and camps. When possible, strips of relatively natural areas should be left between fields. The beauty, educational variety, improved microclimate, watershed protection, and habitat for wildlife are worth any extra work retrieving balls.

Orientation.   Orient a field to minimize sun in players' eyes; for instance a tennis court should run north–south and a baseball field should have the line from the pitcher's box to home plate running north–south. Where fields are used for more than one sport with some overlap, as when a field primarily for soccer (usually an autumn sport) overlaps the outfield of a baseball diamond (usually a spring sport) to save space, the ideal orientation may not be obtainable for each sport. In such cases screen plantings of tall trees can minimize sun in players' eyes. Quick-growing trees like lombardy poplar give a rapid screening; but when they are set out there should be one or two rows of longer-lived trees planted along them to take over when the poplars get scraggly. Evergreens can in addition sometimes make a windbreak, improving the microclimate and extending the season of comfortable play in cooler climates. Shearing (p. 439) improves their effectiveness.

Landscaping.   Strips of relatively natural areas between and around fields are usually desirable. Take care during construction to minimize damage to tall trees which can shade the area in hot weather. Also protect small trees which can supply shade years hence. Selective thinning and pruning bring along the most promising saplings (pp. 151, 410). Inexpensive snow fence or chicken wire is often adequate to keep balls within bounds if neatly installed and properly maintained. Screen plantings improve the microclimate, shut out distractions, and give a good background against which to see balls. For informal fields, homemade benches of local stone and/or logs improve the utility and beauty of the area.

Construction.   Since drainage and uniformity of turf are important factors in an athletic field, a good one should be built from the bottom up, not just made from the top down by tearing into overgrown pasture with a power mower. First the topsoil should be bulldozed aside (p. 337). Then subgrade soil should be uniformly leveled.

If the subsoil lacks uniformly good drainage provided by sands or gravels, install drainage tile or porous pipe or lay stone drains (p. 355). Then the topsoil is returned uniformly, allowed to settle, fertilized, and seeded to a grass mixture which promises turf which resists wear. Keep off the grass, except when caring for it, until a strong turf has developed, at least a year, and, in the north, preferably two growing seasons. *(96, 137, 480)*

If funds and power equipment are not available to make an athletic field from the bottom up, work from the top down a little at a time with hand tools and enjoy each little enlargement as it is won. Planticides help eradicate woody plants a year or more before you dig them, making digging easier and reducing sprouting (p. 400). When cutting trees to make a field, salvage any that are suitable for fence posts, backstop logs, and benches (p. 417). Stockpile stones of a size suitable for benches or riprapping of banks (p. 313).

GOLF COURSES

A golf course can be one of the most beautiful herblands, even to the non-golfer. Golf permits a flexibility of open-area design unknown to other fields for recreation. The varying lengths and widths of the fairways and the variety of ground conditions, including traps, hazards, and turf, lend excitement. Make maximum use of natural features of the terrain, permitting at least narrow strips of relatively natural areas bordering the fairways. Brooks should mostly keep their natural courses, but small impoundments are better than marshes when it comes to locating stray balls. Small marshes, however, should be welcomed near tees and other areas of minimum ball loss because of their beauty, wildlife, and water-storing capacity. *(379)*

Artificial topography. Where natural topography fails to supply sufficient variety, modern earth-moving machinery guided by the plans of an imaginative and sensitive designer can create ridges and other land forms. Remember, though, that most big machines and their operators like to move in straight lines, including flat planes; where these do not blend with the natural topography, or for other reasons do not create the desired beauty in our urbanizing culture often unconsciously surfeited with rectangularity, clearly drawn plans and close supervision during grading will be needed to achieve the subtler results of curving contours.

Trees. Set out trees where natural vegetation is inadequate to provide visual beauty, shade, wind protection, dark background for golf ball visibility, and screening for privacy. Evergreens have the advantage of longer season of usefulness; but except for the smallest sizes, which can be planted bare-root, they are more expensive to buy or more laborious to transplant from the wild. (See ball-and-burlap method, p. 382). Young maples, basswood, and other deciduous trees, on the other hand, can be transplanted bare-rooted when dormant. Needle-leaved trees on windward sides of fairway, green, or tee help keep deciduous leaves from blowing onto the grass, thus reducing the leaf-removal problem. Needles, offering little wind resistance, tend to fall to the ground under the trees; also the more uniform texture of needle groundcover permits balls to roll and makes them more visible. Shearing makes screen plantings more efficient; topping them when they near a maximum desired height reduces maintenance (p. 443). Isolated individual trees, small groves, and woodland margins can have the lower third to half of their branches pruned off to give visibility and reduce conflict with straying drives (p. 440). Enough branches must be left for a crown of leaves to make adequate food for the health of each tree. While tall shade trees along a fairway add immeasurably to a course, prominent notices should warn golfers during thunderstorm seasons against taking refuge from rain under such trees lest they be struck by lightning. Rustic summer houses are safer, but if placed at the edge of the woods they should have properly installed lightning rods.

Shrubs. Bushes and golf balls don't mix well. But bushes add so much to the beauty and wildlife of a course that they should be much used where they will not frustrate seekers of stray balls. They can be placed around tees and along the tee ends of fairways. A long, island-like grove in a fairway can be permitted flowering shrubs at the end toward the green. Shrubs close to the green are not popular. Elsewhere on the course, a small patch of shrubbery can be taken in the same sportsmanlike manner as any other hazard, especially such species as highbush blueberries, which have few stems at ground level and provide in addition delicious berries.

Turf. Grass management for golf courses is both art and science. Give special attention to greens, which are usually of an extra-fine short grass like some varieties of bent grass. The shorter the grass, the more care it needs to keep it healthy, because closer cutting removes more of the food-producing leaves. Also, closer cutting means less sun protection for the roots, so that more soil moisture may have to be provided by supplementary watering. Tee areas and greens have more concentrated compaction by golfers' feet than do other parts of the course and require more attention to maintain soil porosity and to reseed worn spots (p. 389).

Small golf courses. Where it is not feasible to put in an entire nine-hole course, smaller courses, though not regulation size, can be very enjoyable, as attested by numerous driving ranges and pitch-'n'-putts. Miniature golf should prove increasingly valuable in our time of increasing land costs and lengthened age span of the population. It is strongly recommended as a sport readily adaptable to a diversity of topographic conditions. As more small farms go out of business because of mechanization and other scientific advances in agriculture, a larger proportion of farmland should be kept unbuilt upon and used for recreational purposes. Small tracts of pastureland can be readily converted to small golf courses, as can small fields on floodplains. Ski slopes can offer "uphill pitch," a very special and challenging kind of golf! (357)

SKI SLOPES AND COASTING SLOPES

One of the best ways to get people to appreciate natural resources is to get them out where they can see them. Winter is an excellent time to see watersheds, trees, and a host of other beautiful and useful aspects of nature. Many more communities can have recreation areas for snow sports if, instead of holding off because of the expense, they let young people contribute their brains and brawn to developing the areas themselves. In regions too warm for a commercially usable amount of snowfall every year, scant snowfall will be no economic tragedy where the making of a winter sports area has been a happy cooperative venture by the community; when the snow does come, it will be all the more enjoyed. Many camp properties today in the northern United States, now unused in winter, are suited to winter sports. Many can be made so on a paying basis now that winter transportation is easier.

Location.   In the northern hemisphere, the coldest side of the hill is usually the northeast-facing slope. In the zone of prevailing westerly winds, this is also the sheltered side, where the slowing wind deposits drifting snow. Here the accumulation lies deep and long, providing the best site for a lengthy skiing and coasting season. Farther north, west- and east-facing slopes may also be suitable. South-facing slopes may be better than none.

Ledges of outcropping rock are to be avoided, of course. The fewer boulders on the surface the better, because they must be removed for safety's sake. When possible, use boulders for stone benches to serve skiers and summer hikers, fill for a parking lot, bumper stones, outdoor fireplaces, terraces, or walls of a skihaus. Rocks not removable in one piece can sometimes be split by sledge or dynamite and removed in pieces. When they must remain, plant a thick patch of evergreen trees on the uphill side and keep them trimmed densely (p. 443), twiggy but high enough to show above the deepest snow, like lighthouses to warn of ledges beneath. Should a skier run out of control, it is better to hit many small branches than a solid tree trunk. Sometimes grading can cover offensive rocks too big to move.

Steepness is a factor. A ski area should have broad, gentle slopes at its base, where it is first approached, so that beginners can learn before going farther and those out of practice can redevelop their control of themselves and their skis before being challenged by steeper slopes or narrow trails. Steeper slopes are harder to clear;

in the East they are more apt to be used for trails than for open-slope skiing. Lay out trails for downhill running so that they afford a neat balance between thrill and safety, with wide places where zig-zagging can reduce speed for those unskilled enough to "take it straight." Banking corners so that they are low on the inside of the curve will make higher speeds safer. At the bottom of the run, there should be adequate run-out space for those who because of fatigue or foolishness find it difficult to stop quickly. Neighboring trails should not converge at their bottoms but should allow for a fanning out of descending skiers. Trails should be rated and posted in terms of their difficulty as novice, intermediate, or expert.

Clearing a ski trail. Downhill trails through woods should be at least fifteen feet wide, with more room at corners. That doesn't leave much room for safety for a pair of seven-foot skis and a pair of ski poles brandished perhaps a little wildly. The wider the better, except that tall overhanging evergreens shade the trail and slightly extend spring skiing. Particularly avoid trees at the outsides of corners; cutting them and letting the sun in encourages bushes which make safer landing than tree trunks in the event of a spill. Bushes, however, have their own hazards, such as catching the ring of an unsuspecting ski pole. Trees felled should be used for construction of shelters, picnic facilities, and firewood; possibly some logs can be taken out for pulp or lumber (p. 417).

Planting. The vegetative groundcover is very significant on ski and coasting slopes. A tree stump laboriously cut below the ground level, chemically treated, and then covered with soil may stick up a dangerous number of inches after rain or snowmelt has eroded the soil around it. The same is true of rocks. Such hazards cannot be tolerated on slopes for winter sports. Grade the surface of the trail or slope to minimize washing (pp. 268, 341). Wherever topsoil is disturbed in construction, plant a hardy grass seed mixture as soon as growing conditions permit. While repeated mowing will favor development of a strong, soil-holding turf, an annual mowing in autumn may suffice. After grasses are well established, thus minimizing the seeding-in of woody plants, mowing every year may not be necessary to maintain the sward, especially if spot-spraying with chemical planticide is used on woody seedlings which do get established. In some instances, controlled burning of well-grassed slopes will be all the maintenance that is needed (p. 431). Where fast turf development is essential, fertilizer can be applied as indicated by chemical soil-testing. On steep slopes, erosion netting can be used (p. 338). Moderate grazing by cattle or sheep is often ecologically sensible for maintenance and harvesting of the grass.

Beauty. In forested country, it is often difficult literally to see the woods for the trees which obscure the view down on farmed and church-steepled valleys and across to distant hills, except in a few places where rocky shoulders or manmade clearings lend a prospect. Even burned areas grow up fast to obscuring brush, except where the soil is thin. Slopes cleared for winter sports give both broad views and narrow vistas of great beauty for those willing to climb the hills. The possibility of creating these views should be considered when designing the layout of slopes and trails. This can be a matter of economic importance as well as personal pleasure, now that so many people feel the need to get away from the city for recreation.

Ski slopes may also contribute ugliness to the rural scene: gashing of a primeval forest; interference with an area needed for scientific research; erection of skyline structures which stick out grotesquely; insensitive draping of lifts across the best views; and advertising signs, which by their number or lack of harmony with the scene cause esthetically sensitive people to shy away from the area. Development of resources rich in beauty should not despoil them. (305)

RIGHT-OF-WAYS

These include strips of land for public roads, railroads, and public and private utility lines such as electricity and gas.

Roads. The value of herblands along roads is discussed above (p. 77) so far as grassed areas are concerned. Sometimes the right-of-way extends beyond the grassed verge, often up unmown banks on the far side of the roadside ditch. What vegetation will cover this bank if it is left alone will depend upon many local ecological conditions. In the humid eastern United States, vegetational development usually commences with annual herbs giving the first cover to the newly graded soil, followed by perennial herbs and then eventually woody plants. The herb stages often afford great beauty to the roadside and are better than woody plants where visibility over them should have high priority. Banks of moss and ferns or of goldenrod and asters add immeasurably to the scene. The herb stages can be maintained by weeding out the woody plants as they appear. In some instances hand weeding may suffice for small areas, and can be rather enjoyable, as one contemplates the possible results. But for more extensive areas, chemical planticides selectively applied make possible long stretches of herblands along highways or lanes (p. 400).

Utility lines. Electric lines, gas lines, and water pipes sometimes follow the road and can be treated as road right-of-way, discussed in the paragraph above. At other times the utility right-of-ways take off across country, representing in the aggregate a vast acreage. These lands are sometimes owned by the utility; at other times the company or government agency will have rights only to run the lines or pipes and to maintain them. When topography permits, a narrow road or at least a trail is maintained in the middle of the right-of-way or thereabouts; and this is best kept as herbland. Where woody plants tend to invade they are usually best weeded with chemical planticides selectively applied so as not to kill the desired herbs or contaminate soil and upset animal populations (p. 400). In some situations, controlled burning periodically removes dried organic matter (p. 431). Mowing and grazing can also be used to keep certain portions of right-of-way in herbs rather than shrubs or trees. Where right-of-ways cross private property, the company or agency may welcome help in maintaining the herbland. Sometimes the entire width of the right-of-way can be made into a beautiful wildflower garden just by selective weeding; sometimes additional native herbs can be introduced by seeding or transplanting. The interest of individuals can help beautify the million acres of right-of-way which are too often single-use scars on the landscape. *(15, 171, 204)*

PASTURES AND HAYFIELDS

These herblands may consist almost entirely of native grasses and forbs, or they may have been plowed and planted to species particularly desirable for livestock. Sometimes, instead of being kept as permanent pasture, a field can be grazed some years and cut for hay in others. Such land management is most often found on hills where sod is needed to protect the soil from the erosion which would take place if they were cultivated, although rich lowland soils may support bountiful livestock farming. The scope of this book does not permit discussion of farming, which is available in many excellent publications. Note, however, the wisdom of including pastures and hayfields on properties where they might not normally be considered, as in parks (p. 55), camps, educational institutions (p. 368), estates, and other private holdings *(439)*

CULTIVATED CROPLANDS

The purchaser or possessor of cultivated land who does not want to continue its cultivation should seriously consider his responsibility for its future. In urbanizing areas, fertile soils capable of producing food, fiber, or other materials should be kept productive, not polluted with the paving of "developments," even though the economics of the moment may seem to demand it. Suburban owners can seek adoption of tax systems enabling them to continue farming or ask for farmland to be taken into public ownership for park purposes. Also investigate government help such as that provided by the "Soil Bank." Sometimes a nearby farmer will lease the land as an adjunct to his farming, or a neighbor interested in part-time farming will be glad to use the field. Perhaps the new owner of cultivated land may not be interested in cropping it — until he tries his hand at it. Part-time farming has joys as well as headaches, especially with the small-sized farm tractors available today; and there may be young people around who would like to help, since employment opportunities for them are scant in many communities.

In humid regions, abandoned cultivated land will revert, sometimes fast, through stages of herbaceous growth to woody vegetation such as alders in damp sites or birches, cherries, and pines in drier sites. To one who has struggled to clear land from forest, such reversion seems a defeat. Cultivated land was hard won before the advent of bulldozers, and even now it is expensive to create from forest. Reversion can usually be arrested without cultivation by grazing, mowing, controlled burning (p. 431), or careful chemical planticiding (p. 400), thus preserving open space and making land relatively easy to put back into cultivation at any later date. Such techniques will maintain the fields as herblands.

On the other hand, perhaps woody growth should be allowed as the wisest land use of a field no longer to be cultivated. Volunteer shrubs and trees will often provide excellent cover and food for wild-life and can in themselves be beautiful (p. 151) and in time provide a beneficial forest cover for the watershed, manageable for timber and other forest crops. You can also plant the site, perhaps to berries or Christmas trees for harvesting, or perhaps reforest it for timber production.

In less humid regions, abandoned cultivated land should be has-tened into grass cover and thence, when climate permits, into shrub-land or woodland if they are desirable (pp. 111, 116, 374).

GARDENS

Tons of literature are available on gardening of many sorts. In this book only the briefest mention is made of gardening—to make sure that the values of gardening are seriously considered by all non-gardeners who are planning use of the land. Should not every con-servationist have experience with a garden at some time in his or her life? In gardens, major conservation problems can be met on a small scale—sometimes with great pleasures along with the inevitable frus-trations of any challenging endeavor. Even the invalid in a wheel-chair who reads about national conservation problems in *Audubon Magazine*, *American Forests*, or the daily paper can with a little help have a windowbox garden that gives firsthand experience with weather, soil, water, growing plants, and even wildlife (insects). And almost every yard can have at least a little garden. In crowded parts of American cities, people with European or Asian back-grounds have tiny yards made delightful with a grapevine trellis over a table, benches, a masonry wall topped with a profusion of flower-ing herbs, and vegetables growing in niches or boxes of soil. To call them herblands may seem farfetched, but they are the best possible steps in the right direction, using the resources at hand to make the land bloom and be fruitful.

The kinds of gardens are innumerable. A trip to the library will indicate many of the possibilities, in terms of such major types as vegetable garden, kitchen garden, rose garden, rock garden, wall garden, English garden, formal garden, and so on. But actually a garden is a very personal affair, so there are as many different types of gardens as there are gardeners. The type of garden is also determined by its environment. This whole book endeavors to call attention to conservation practices of a great variety suited to a large number of different environments, in the hope that at least a few will be to the taste of the reader. The special realm of gardens is for many people the most joyous and productive of herblands; one should be able to find a garden to his or her taste, even if nothing else in this book appeals.

To choose a garden, plan both space and time—time first. An hour a week? Six? A weekend? Except the two weeks (two months?) that you are away in summer? Two months in summer only? An hour a day? Now, where will you find the space to use this time? Turn to Chapter 1. Then get some books on gardening. And may the dogs stay out of your flowerbeds! *(92, 163, 407, 458)*

POSTLUDE TO HERBLANDS

Herbs are little things, weak, dainty. They should be helped to inherit much of the earth. Their lowly stance lets the eye roam to distant views. They make the ground soft underfoot and put milk and bread on the table—and a vase of flowers. They can bring hummingbirds to the edge of the veranda and the color of butter to a child's chin.

Once there was a bus driver who had a twenty-minute wait every day at the country end of his suburban line. Each day after he let his last passenger off, he took his gardening tools from the back of the bus and worked on a little garden patch which he had asked permission to use at the turn-around. Maybe you too can brighten a place by caring for a little herbland.

(See also *37, 502, 580.*)

4 Drylands: Shrublands

Other Plants in Shrublands
Physical Environment of Shrublands
Fauna of Shrublands
Man's Relation to Shrublands
Natural and Relatively Natural Shrublands
Dune Shrubland
  Planning
  Natural areas
  Clearing
  Pruning
  Shearing
  Planting shrubs
  Planting isolated trees
  Planting groves of trees
  Wildlife management
  Protection
Oak Shrubland and Chaparral
  Planning
Clearing
Maintenance by Burning
Forestation
Wildlife Management
Recreation
Heaths
  Planning and utilization
Oldfield Shrublands
  Planning
    For farming again

93

Shrubs are woody plants with two or more stems emerging from the soil at ground level or close to it. Sometimes one stem seems the most important, with the result that the shrub looks tree-like; but usually there are several stems, none of them growing to tree proportions. The term *bush* is often used synonymously with *shrub*; several shrubs together may be termed *shrubbery* or *brush*. Sometimes, by pruning, a shrub can be made to grow tree-like, as with lilac trees in certain types of gardens. Conversely, cutting the top off a young tree can make it bushy. Sometimes a species growing like a tree in one region may make only shrubby growth in others, especially in windy sites like coastal headlands or near treeline on mountains. In other cases in nature, pruning is by rabbits or other wildlife who nibble the tips of stems, making plants more bushy than they would otherwise be. Fire too can alter the growth form of tree-like plants so that they grow as shrubs. On rare occasions a fungus has been known to turn a tree species into a shrub, notably the American chestnut, now found only as a bush or small tree. Shrublands, then, can contain woody plants that are bushy for a number of environmental reasons, aside from their inherited growth form.

OTHER PLANTS IN SHRUBLANDS

In this book, shrublands are those which are primarily bushy, though trees may be scattered through them or they may have open patches with herbs. We refer to intermediate types as "brushy woodland" or "shrubby pasture," or by some other descriptive term. Often shrubs form a distinct layer, or two or more layers, under trees. If the component shrubs are intolerant of shade, the shrubland may be in its old age, being killed out by the shade of trees which have grown up through it. If the shrubs are shade-tolerant, they form undergrowth which is a continuing part of the forest complex; in this book these latter are not considered shrublands, although parts of this section may apply to their conservation. In studying the uses of shrublands, think about their place in the normal development of plant communities. For instance, if a patch of blueberries has inconspicuous little saplings of pine, cherry, and birch in the drier portion and of red maple in the moister part, its blueberry-producing days are definitely numbered if the trees are not eradicated, or at least radically restrained by pruning.

PHYSICAL ENVIRONMENT OF SHRUBLANDS

While the shrubbery of drylands exists in diverse sites, such as southwestern deserts and New England pastures, a few generalities can be made. Shrubs often colonize and survive in quantity in sites too dry for forest growth. The dryness may be the aridity of deserts where rainfall is scant, of arctic tundras where water is unavailable most of the year because it is frozen, or of sand dunes with plenty of rainfall for trees but inadequate soil moisture because rains percolate down rapidly through the coarse pores between the sand grains. Where trees grow well, shrublands are either stages in vegetational development on the way to treelands (when some natural disaster has previously removed the forest or when man has cleared it), or are found where some agent such as wildfire, wildlife, or man keeps repressing the tree growth which would otherwise grow up and shade out the shrubs. In deserts, shrubs sometimes survive as predominate vegetation largely because their roots descend to depths where they tap groundwater too deep for herbs to reach (p. 22).

Some shrublands exist in really wet areas (see Chapter 6). The moors of Britain, for instance, are often very moist, with several species of heather forming a wet heath *(205)*.

FAUNA OF SHRUBLANDS

The advent of shrubs into a bareland or herbland can greatly improve living conditions for many forms of wildlife. The bushes provide protective cover from sun, wind, rain, and snow. They have moderating effect on local climate, increasing humidity and decreasing temperature extremes. They also provide escape cover—sanctuary for the fleet jackrabbit who scurries to the sagebrush when the coyote pounces—as well as food of many sorts. Some provide flowers and fruits in profusion, others leaves and twigs for browsing mammals like deer and rabbits. Any part of a shrub may be the shelter and basic food of some insect on which larger animals feed; they in turn, perhaps, are the diet of still larger animals.

MAN'S RELATION TO SHRUBLANDS

Shrublands usually appear as wastelands from the point of view of direct production, with a few exceptions like blueberries in the Northeast. Growing small fruits (as fruit-bearing shrubs like raspberries are called) brings variety to the diet of many country homes; and these shrubs are occasionally the basis of extensive commercial enterprises. Certain specialty products are made from gathering the fruits of some of the wild-growing shrubs; beach plum jelly and bayberry candles on the Atlantic coast and cactus candy in the southwestern deserts, for example. Some native shrubs are important sources of honey, especially in the Southeast. Mountainlaurel kalmia, salal, and a few other shrubs are harvested for their decorative foliage.

Most native shrubland, however, has indirect values far exceeding its commercial ones. Shrubs are some of our most valuable protectors of soil, minimizing erosion by both wind and water. Their role in regulating the flow of water on watersheds, imperfectly understood, varies from region to region. We need more research on the amounts of water evaporated into the air from the ground by shrubs as compared to trees or herbs. In parts of the West, shrubs have been eliminated in large areas in an attempt to save water. In the East, thought is being given to substituting shrub cover for forests to prevent the larger loss of water from the trees (p. 299). Shrublands are so important to many forms of wildlife that their manipulation is one of the foremost techniques of wildlife management. In forestry, commonly thought of as dealing almost exclusively with trees, the shrub layers, known to foresters as "lesser vegetation," are being increasingly studied for their effects on forest microclimate, soil, wildlife, and production of tree seedlings. Taken from their natural context, shrubs are used by man in many ways, especially around his home. He plants rows of tall shrubs as screens to stop the eye or shut off the wind (p. 279); as hedges to delimit property or its subdivisions with differing land use; as foundation plantings to help relate the design of buildings to the land on which they stand (p. 127); as floral displays; and as attractants for wildlife. For many people, shrubs help make home home. *(42, 122, 270)*

The beauty of shrublands is noteworthy. They brighten man's life on the deserts where the ocotillo blooms, in the azalea gardens of the Deep South, in the rhododendron "helds" (shrubberies) of the Carolinas, in the golden thickets of Scotch broom on the Oregon dunes, on the blueberry heaths of Maine when autumn frosts set them aflame. The heather moors of the British Isles are a sight to be long remembered. At different times in different places the shrubs sing out. But one does not have to travel far or wait long to find beauty in a bush. In summer, turn over one green huckleberry leaf and tip its under surface to the sun to see its Midas glint. In winter, cut a prostrate branch of ground juniper, shake off the snow, and bring it into the house as an over-the-doorway decoration. Take any bare twig of a shrub and study the design of one bud. Is it neatly shingled? Do its budscales meet edge to edge like folded hands? Are naked, embryonic leaves close muffled in brown fuzz? Man's relation to shrublands is incomplete if he uses shrubs only to realize dollars.

NATURAL AND RELATIVELY NATURAL SHRUBLANDS

The best management of natural shrublands is often to leave them as natural as possible. The following pages suggest relatively minor modifications of shrublands. For more artificial approaches to shrublands by planting, see p. 116 and those following.

DUNE SHRUBLAND

Where sandy soils, coastal or interior, have been blown into dunes, shrubs often grow where dune grasses have stabilized the sand sufficiently (p. 60). The shrub species vary from region to region; beach plum and bayberry are found on the North Atlantic coast and coyote brush, Pacific waxmyrtle, and tree lupine on the Pacific Northwest coast. Sand cherry is a typical shrub on Great Lakes shores. In the British Isles one often meets the golden-flowered gorse. Whatever the species, shrubs form thickets giving greater stability than do the dune grasses alone. Given time, they replace the grasses which nursed them. Given more time, they in turn form the natural nursery for trees capable of growing in the sandy soil. But the shrubs may not have time: vicissitudes of the local air currents or the interference of man may cause blowouts; renewed cutting by the wind excavates the sand from between the roots of the bushes, leaving them first dangling and sand-blasted, then dead, fallen, and buried by the unleashed sand. To better admire the struggles of the shrubs which do survive, visit the dunes during a coastal gale. Times of stress determine who will survive.

Planning. Should shrubbery be encouraged to extend into dune-grass zones, increasing the stability of the dunes and providing more cover for wildlife? Should it be reduced to provide a greater area of moving sand with its fascinating dynamics and beautiful contours (p. 61)? Should vegetational development toward treelands be hastened by planting trees amid the shrubbery, by mulching to supplement the natural deposits of leaves and twigs of the bushes, and perhaps by installing drift fences to protect the shrubbery? Or should the shrublands be left natural? Careful planning may allow room for all of the above, plus specific recreational developments like those discussed under *Dune Grasslands* (p. 62).

Natural areas. While dunelands in North America and Western Europe have a great deal in common—for instance strong sun, blowing sand, and grasses—each is different and still has a wealth of unsolved problems for science and a still-to-be-excavated treasure of designs for art. Inevitably some of these values are lost when man unhumbly moves in to manage everything. Plentiful and sizable areas should be left for man to study and appreciate nature when she is left to her own vices—like blowing sand.

Clearing. Unless blowing sand is wanted, any clearing must be done with caution, in very small, protected areas only, preferably on the leeward side of the shrubland or in the center. Since some types of dune shrubs are very flammable (especially European gorse, but also North American species), clear shrubbery around picnic fire sites to provide fuelbreaks. At appropriate places, remove bushes to provide vistas of ocean, distant dunes, or adjacent marshland whose colors and designs add so much to our coastal dunes. Clear pathways through heavy shrubbery to scenic spots, or to allow rambling and nature study. Sometimes patches of bushes can be taken out to set back vegetational development so there will be samples of blowing sand and dune grasses for study and beauty (p. 42).

For species which do not give trouble by vigorous sprouting, loppers should be used for cutting: where people will be walking, cut the stems down in the sand, holding the handles low to give a horizontal cut that will not leave sharp stubs. Sometimes it is preferable to pull shrubs up by the roots: by hand where possible, with beach buggy where trails are wide enough, or with block-and-tackle or other stump-pulling device (p. 424). Chemical planticides are effective where sprouting is a problem. Use cut brush for windbreaks and drift fences on the windward side of shrublands, for helping adjacent dune grasses win their battles with blowing sand, or for wildlife shelters, rustic ramadas, and photographic hides. Cut into tinder and faggots with loppers; cut brush is welcome neatly stacked on the dry-weather upwind sides of picnic sites where sparks will not light it accidentally. Some of the stems, particularly those of certain cacti, are worth drying and saving for their ornamental shapes and weathered browns and bleached grays (p. 435).

Pruning.   Where vistas or broad views are desired, but it is unwise to clear away shrubbery because of danger of wind erosion, judicious pruning can lower the bushes enough to permit looking over them (p. 439). Since tolerance to pruning varies with both species and site, experiment to find how much can be pruned off a species in one year without killing it. Usually pruning should take place during late winter. Avoid extensive pruning on windward sides until experimentation has shown how much resprouting can be counted upon. Pruning and shearing can also be used to maintain the desired width of trails and other openings.

Many shrubs of the dunes and other sandlands have great beauty, which is not revealed when the bushes are crowded together. Near trails and picnic sites, or other spots where they will be appreciated, select promising specimens and prune away competing neighbors to allow fuller growth. In some cases competition for soil moisture may be a factor; then adjacent shrubs can be taken out completely, so long as they are not affording significant protection from wind. Sometimes a shrub standing by itself can be pruned to give a picturesque beauty sought after in some kinds of oriental art. Books on the Japanese art of bonzai show how to use annealed, spiraling wire to hold the carefully selected branches remaining after pruning so that they develop the desired stance. A single dune-top bonzai or a group around a picnic site can add considerable charm.

Shearing.   Shearing dune shrubs can produce quite different and more formal effects. Long-bladed shears snipping the tips off many branches can develop smooth surfaces like hedges along trails and picnic sites. Carefully designed planes and curved surfaces can create great beauty. Maybe a bit formal at the parking lot entrance to a trail, with perhaps two lighthouse-shaped bushes as posts, farther along the design can blend with natural angles of the dunes and the clean horizontal line of an ocean horizon. Foliage density of shear-tolerant plants (those sprouting readily after cutting), can be increased by shearing, for example in shrubs used as windbreaks around picnic sites. Bushes shaped to a gradual flat slope on the windward side deflect wind upward and over an area, much as naturally wind-pruned shrubs do in exposed places. But much of the natural charm of dunelands will be lost if ornamental shearing is carried too far (p. 443).

Planting shrubs.   Carefully selected species can be used to extend dune shrublands, but only where blowing sand has been stilled by dune grasses or is sufficiently slowed by other natural vegetation or drift fences. Shrubs can also be planted in small open spots within dune shrublands, to prevent the enlargement of new blowouts, to heal old blowouts, or to add variety to the kinds of shrubs already present. Native shrubs which can be spared from nearby areas can be dug carefully and transplanted (p. 374), but far better results will usually be obtained from nursery stock. While native species from the nursery are usually preferable, some introduced species have proved admirable under certain conditions. Scotch broom, for instance, has been very successful in the Pacific Northwest and moderately so elsewhere, being hardy on medium-dry to very dry sites where the grasses have stilled the sand. Its gray-green whiskery branches become covered with yellow blooms; the seeds are used by wildlife; and it is happily fire-resistant, unlike the related European gorse (see also p. 104). Scotch broom can even be planted as firebreaks between combustible native plants.

Low-growing shrubs can sometimes grow where taller ones fail. Bearberry can be started from seed or cuttings and forms an attractive evergreen mat which spreads sidewards; it can grow in the Northeast, Lake States, and Pacific Northwest on dry sites. Similar are two species of hudsonia. The gray-green *Hudsonia tomentosa* is a conspicuous part of the dune scene in the Northeast at all seasons, but excels in May when its yellow flowers spread across sand where beachgrass has begun the job of stabilization.

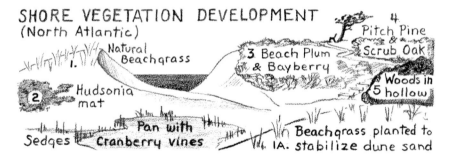

SHORE VEGETATION DEVELOPMENT
(North Atlantic)
1. Natural Beachgrass
2. Hudsonia mat
Sedges — Pan with Cranberry vines
3 Beach Plum & Bayberry
4 Pitch Pine & Scrub Oak
5 Woods in hollow
Beachgrass planted to
1A. stabilize dune sand

In dune hollows where the wind has deflated the sand down close to the water table and surrounding dunes give protection from wind, a wider variety of bushes can be planted. In the Pacific Northwest, red alder, hardhack, and hooker willow are apt to seed in naturally but can perhaps be hastened by planting. In northern California, Pacific waxmyrtle does well in such areas. On the Atlantic coast, shrubs such as serviceberry and chokeberry add beauty with their flowers and wildlife food with their fruits.

Cranberries brighten many a wet dune hollow from Atlantic to Pacific. If weeding the native cranberries does not provide enough of this delightful plant, more of the shrubby vines can be planted. Where there is considerable area of interdune lowlands, it may be possible to carry on commercial cranberry growing. Sometimes, rather than encourage shrubs in interdune pans (wet hollows), it may be desirable to excavate to make small ponds attractive to shorebirds.

Planting isolated trees. Trees growing in numbers up through the shrubs mentioned above may in time shade and kill them. But isolated trees on dunes will seldom attain much height above the shrubs, not having fellows to help them withstand the wind. They either die off at the top or become wind-formed; windward buds are inhibited by the drying effect of the streaming air while leeward branches may extend considerable distances. Wind-formed trees rising now and again above shrubs add considerable interest to the dunescape and are appreciated by perching birds. On the east coast of the United States, pitch pine and sometimes black locust may windform beautifully. In the Pacific Northwest, shore pine and Oregon crabapple adapt to shaping by the prevailing wind. In the British Isles, hawthorn is often wind-shaped, as is Scots pine.

Planting groves of trees. A group of trees will give more protection from the sun than will a single tree—and may even provide uprights for slinging a hammock, though the slow growth of trees in the dune environment may mean that the planter's grandchildren will be the first to have that privilege. It is usually necessary to provide shelter from the wind for young trees, such as drift fence of slats, brush, or wire covered with burlap. As in planting windbreaks on the Great Plains, it is best to have low, dense shrubs on the outside, then taller shrubs, then small trees, and finally in the center of the grove, tree species with the greatest potential height (p. 279). Japanese black pine should be noted for coastal areas because of its resistance to damage from salt spray.

Wildlife management. Variety of shrubs to favor wildlife can be increased by planting, with special attention to species giving good food (such as waxmyrtle and bayberry) and cover (scotch broom). Where the shrubbery is very dense, some careful cutting or planticiding can create *small* openings to be used as flyways by small birds and insects and pathways by larger mammals. Clearing paths helps the observation and study of wildlife; narrow lanes can be cut for setting up nets to catch birds for banding. Because fresh water is often at a premium in dunelands, birdbaths, dug ponds, wells with windmills, "gallinaceous guzzlers," or other watering stations will be appreciated by animals and will concentrate them for viewing (p. 466).

Protection. Wind, fire, and people are the greatest hazards. Wind tends to form blowouts which undermine the shrubs or kill them by sand-blasting and desiccation. Try to slow the wind with brush or slat fences or by planting low shrubs to windward (p. 279).

Fire danger can be very high with dense shrubbery, less where it is sparse. Fuelbreaks made by clearing are desirable, except that if not laid out carefully they may give free rein to wind erosion. Fire access roads and paths through dense shrubbery help with patrol and fire suppression (p. 427). The best protection comes from prevention. Restrict picnic fires and campfires to specified sites. At parking lots and elsewhere, have neat signs calling attention to fire hazard and proper safeguards. Make sure that there are people in the community instructed in fire suppression, organized for fighting brush fires in the dune area. Long-handled shovels are excellent tools in sandlands, for slinging scoopfuls of sand at burning stems and leaves to smother the combustion. A trailside nature center near the point of entry to a recreation area can alert visitors to the interesting and beautiful aspects of the dunelands. Included can be instructions and admonitions relative to fire prevention, trash disposal, treatment of plants, and animals—the country code of outdoor manners. Besides education, patrol is necessary wherever there are large numbers of people.

OAK SHRUBLAND AND CHAPARRAL

A wide variety of shrubs and fire-stunted trees located in various parts of the country are here lumped under this heading, being too diverse for separate treatment. Oak scrub is found throughout the eastern United States in small patches or extensive tracts on sandy coastal areas or inland sand and gravel plains, sometimes known as "barrens" or "shinnery." Oaks predominate, including bear oak and dwarf chestnut oak. In the West, the term "chaparral" applies to vegetation of similar character, although the species are markedly different, including sagebrush, manzanita, mesquite, and ceonothus. In many cases these shrublands seem to be a vegetational response to the aridity of the local climate, as in large areas in the Southwest and in small areas on the south sides of rocky hilltops in the East; but in many instances the scrub is attributable to burning, often repeated wildfire. The species which have survived have the ability to sprout from roots after the stems have burned. *(217, 442)*

Planning. Mostly these shrublands have been unmanaged or mismanaged, having resulted from wildfire or overgrazing. Where an effort has been made to take care of them, they may even have been mistakenly protected from fire to the point where a tremendous accumulation of combustible material makes any wildfire a calamitous conflagration which burns with such heat that even roots of fire-resistant species may be killed. This may mean disaster for the watershed, as in some of the chaparral country of Southern California. It is easier to point to past mistakes than to give sound advice for managing these shrublands. But the first step, as always, is to learn all one can about them: the physical environment, vegetation, wildlife,

We do not know all the pros and cons of sagebrush, so we should approach its "control" experimentally on a small scale. Dubois, Wyoming.

and history of land use. Get these data tabulated and mapped. Then run small experiments, leaving natural areas as experimental control areas for comparison. Then one will be better able to decide wisely whether to try to maintain the area, using its scrubby growth for whatever it may be worth, or to convert the cover to some other type of vegetation, such as grassland or forest, which might be able to survive in the site if properly cared for. Usually it will be best to keep the shrubs.

CLEARING

Messy stuff to clear! Controlled burning can get rid of the innumerable stems if conditions are dry enough—but then the fire is very difficult to control. Also, the burning stimulates an upsurge of new stems from the old roots unless the fire is dangerously hot. Chemical planticiding usually seems to offer the best hope, giving some root-kill (p. 400). Spray only a small area, then let it die. Burn the dead stems while the surrounding vegetation is green and moist, or when snow is on the ground. If such safe conditions do not prevail, remove the stems by cutting (harder than cutting while stems are still alive). Repeated spraying may be necessary to achieve root-kill with some species. Another method is to cut the living stems, using loppers, machete (dangerous!), or mechanical brush cutter; then spray the stumps with planticide to keep them from sprouting. If the proposed land use will permit, leave a few select specimens of the scrub for whatever advantages they may have, such as beauty of bloom or fruit. Often with some of the tangle removed, the eye can begin to appreciate individual plants (p. 114).

MAINTENANCE BY BURNING

To keep the vegetation low, to perpetuate the species composition, and to prevent undue accumulation of combustible duff (leaves and twigs), burning is prescribed (p. 431). Note that in some areas, notably the chaparral of Southern California, there may be *no safe way* to carry out such burning, because of the semi-arid climate and the already existing amount of litter; so do not burn without consulting local foresters. Make suitably wide fuelbreaks and burn only small areas at any one time. Take no chances! Avoid unnecessary damage to wildlife, such as burning during nesting season. Realize that repeated, controlled burning will avoid the far greater disaster by wildfire that is likely if litter is allowed to accumulate over many years. An area maintained by controlled burning can be used as a buffer to protect from wildfire a central natural area which is left unburned (though in the West it may still be kindled by lightning).

FORESTATION

In Europe *coppice* or sprout forest is used because of the demand for its wood, especially for fuel and fencing. In the United States almost no wood products are derived from scrublands as such, but some of the sandy soils are well suited to growing pines for timber and pulp. This requires some clearing to free the young planted pines from competition with shrubs and to provide space for planting and harvesting (see *Clearing*, above). But aside from commercial wood production, it may be interesting to experiment with making small clearings in the scrub and planting trees in them, perhaps just one tree to a clearing, and protecting them from fire, for their landscape effect and advantages to wildlife, and for the scientific interest of finding out what species of trees can survive in such environments when once given a toehold and protected from repeated burning.

WILDLIFE MANAGEMENT

This should often have top priority in these shrublands. Many plants fruit heavily, for instance the scrub oaks, which often produce quantities of acorns ("mast") good for wild turkeys, deer, and other game. Often the cover is thick, giving sanctuary to the hunted. Management can be minimal in many cases. Protection against wildfire is necessary, but controlled burning of small areas at a time can help maintain diversity of environment and "edge" (p. 458). In dry barrens and arid areas, development of watering places is important. Access roads can facilitate censusing, observing, and hunting. Not all such roads should be open to the public because of fire hazard; subsidiary

ones should be gated or chained, opened only for those with permission to enter on legitimate business or pleasure. Where legal,
placement of salt licks can lure animals to spots where they can be
observed and photographed, but over-concentration of animals
should be avoided (p. 457).

RECREATION

These shrublands are often passed by as recreationists seek forests
or shores with their more moderate climates. To many people, shrublands are just messy. Good trails, however, make a big difference;
for when you do not have to battle noisily through the scrub you can
observe the wildlife and the plants. Bridle trails are particularly desirable. Often the added height from a horse's back gives a distant
view so that one does not feel so shut in by the shrubbery. Also,
oak shrublands are often on sandy soil which makes a good tread
for the trail. A series of foot trails laid out as a maze in a small area
will delight children—though it may temporarily frustrate their
parents. A trailside museum can help open people's eyes to the natural beauties of the shrubland. Any picnic or camping areas must
be laid out with great regard for fire hazard, with wide fuelbreaks
maintained in bare mineral soil. Wood for campfires can be prepared
as bundled faggots cut by loppers, pruning saw, or small bow saw
during clearing of trails (p. 426).

HEATHS

A whole family of woody plants takes its common name from the
heather so familiar in the heathlands of Great Britain. The true
heathers *(Calluna* and *Erica)* are not native in America and have
been introduced successfully in only a few places. But the American
flora is rich in other members of the heath family, including blueberries, huckleberries, salal, cranberries, bearberries, mountainlaurel kalmia, azalea, and rhododendron. These share a peculiarity
of iron metabolism which normally makes them successful only on
acidic soils, where they often thrive when other plants will not, creating shrublands which are often very beautiful and occasionally eco-

nomically important. The heaths occur in moist climates where one would expect trees, and indeed under some circumstances vegetation will develop from heath to forest. But often the heath will be stable for decades and even centuries, when tree growth is held back by such environmental factors as high acidity, shallow soil, sweeping winds, rodent damage, or repeated wildfire. Some kinds of heaths are better classified as wetlands rather than drylands, notably cranberry bogs, leatherleaf bogs, and, in Britain, heather moors (p. 175). Others merge with herblands, for instance the tundra heaths where cranberries and bearberry, along with dwarf birches, willows, and alders, mingle with the herbaceous grasses, sedges, and lichens.

The bulk of our heaths in middle latitudes are predominantly blueberry and huckleberry; they occur in burned-over sandy soils or ledgy areas in the spruce-fir forests of the north and mountains further south, or in the Eastern Broadleaf Deciduous Forest Zone, where scrub oaks may form a significant part of the heath so that it merges with the oak shrub discussed above.

Planning and utilization. Arctic-alpine heaths around the timberline of mountains and on exposed coasts coinhabit the herblands discussed above (p. 56). The glossy-leaved mats of bearberry and the pink-flowered runners of mountain cranberry spread from crannies of lichen-covered ledges where bloom the avens and other rare flowers. These areas should almost always be kept natural, their beauty a more than adequate excuse for being. Trails should be marked with stone cairns in case hikers and naturalists are caught in bad weather in these often stormy wilds.

Similar heaths where lowbush blueberry predominates offer luscious fruits which delight the recreationist with nibbles and provide pies for farmers and lumbermen living in the region; these heaths also supply cash crops, on extensive acreage of improved blueberry land in Canada and those northern states which have acidic soils. Controlled burning maintains the land in the heath stage, killing many weeds and insects, returning minerals to the soil in the ashes, and, perhaps most important of all, pruning the bushes by burning off the branch tips. Dry hay or slash (branches cut from trees) is spread evenly and lightly over the heath in late winter or early spring while the ground is still very wet, then ignited. Commercial flame-throwers are used in extensive operations (pp. 431, 433).

In most cases where man strives for larger and larger areas for monoculture (single-crop agriculture), insect pests find the expanses of one crop ideal for living and breeding. Large commercial growers therefore usually expend considerable effort to spray with pesticides and become trapped in a sinister pattern of ever-increasing applications of chemicals which are not subtle enough to fit in with nature's complicated mechanism for parasite control—indeed, chemicals which can poison vast ecoystems. In contrast, the amateur who wants a more relaxed berry patch may do well to maintain some variety of plants in the blueberry heath, for instance leaving some rows of unburned shrubbery to slow the spread of insects. Ground juniper and savin can encroach weedily on blueberry bushes; yet some of the largest berries seem to grow where the prickly sprigs of these evergreens mix with them. Extensive use of fire kills all these evergreens, possibly a desirable procedure for the commercial grower, but not necessarily for the amateur or for the grower with an urge to experiment further with the wonderful ways in which nature produces blueberries.

Blueberries may be picked by hand, the slow process being paid for partly by the beauty of the site, partly by the plinky noise of the first-picked berries on the bottom of the pail and the muffled inrollings as the can fills, partly by the anticipation of muffins and other goodies. Commercial pickers use a blueberry rake made of wood or aluminum; it looks like a dustpan with a comb on its front edge and is used with a scooping motion. Leaves and other litter are winnowed out by a power-driven fan, while the berries pile up deliciously blue in boxes beneath.

Heaths often provide watershed protection after wildfire, before other types of vegetation can cover the barren soil. Also, they are important sources of nectar for honeybees. In the autumn, their foliage is a brilliant red or vermillion. The joys of hiking, horseback riding, painting, and photographing in heath country in the autumn should be better advertised.

Rhododendrons and mountainlaurel kalmias (not true laurels

botanically) are among the taller heaths. Their thick evergreen foliage and prolific blooms have given fame to the hills of the Appalachian uplands and elsewhere; and azaleas (rhododendrons which are usually not evergreen) are among the most brilliant flowering shrubs in the world. These plants are regularly grown in nurseries, and nurserymen often dig them in the wild to retail for foundation plantings, clump plantings, and borders. The evergreen species must be transplanted by the ball and burlap method (p. 382). In their native state these plants look less heath-like than plants described above; they are often taller and have trees mixed in with them. In most instances, they too have to give way to trees which shade them out, except where shallow soil, wind, or wildfire work in their favor. Certain areas in the Appalachians thick with rhododendrons are called rhododendron *helds;* like the grassy balds with which they are sometimes associated, much remains to be learned about their ecology.

Any owner or manager of heathland should give thought to how much of it can be set aside as a natural area for research and untrammeled beauty. *(205).*

OLDFIELD SHRUBLANDS

Where *cultivated farmland* is abandoned, nature promptly begins to reclothe the bare ground. The first plants to show are usually herbs, perhaps mosses or grasses. In climates with sufficient moisture, woody plants start when the herbs have created growing conditions favorable enough for their seeds. Sometimes it is hard to tell just when shrubs and trees germinate, for seedlings may be hidden by the herbs for several years. In fertile soil with plenty of moisture, shrubs and tree seedlings may emerge above the herbs in five years and spread out above them to become the dominant vegetation in less than ten. On sterile soil deficient in moisture, shrubbery may not become dominant for decades, and even then may have open patches where herbs still hold mastery. Where windy or droughty climate, wildfire, or poor soil conditions dictate, the shrub stage may be relatively permanent, as in the types of shrublands discussed above. But under more favorable conditions, young trees will push up through the shrubs, eventually killing them by overshading, and creating forest.

Where *grazed farmland* is abandoned, the succession of vegetational stages is similar. But instead of starting among the pioneer herbs, woody plants have to invade the mat of established pasture grasses. If the grazing land was in poor condition when abandoned, certain trees (like gray birch) and shrubs (like sweetfern) take advantage of bare spots to establish themselves quickly. Plants unable to colonize such barren areas have to wait until the grasses released from grazing grow tall, creating a nursery with more shade and moisture. Sometimes it is years before woody plants can invade the grass cover; other times the transition from herbaceous growth to shrubbery is surprisingly fast, perhaps only a half dozen years. Certain woody plants, those distasteful to cattle, may get a head start before grazing lands are abandoned. Prickly evergreens like ground juniper and redcedar are safe from cattle, though their most succulent spring growth may be sheared off perennially. Hawthorns too become resistant to grazing as they grow older. Curtailed but not killed by grazing, these plants have well-established roots and shoots which help them take over when pastures are abandoned.

Planning. As society changes rapidly these days, land use changes fast. Mechanized farming favors large farms, as do economic considerations. Industrial, commercial, or professional jobs and city glamor attract young people who do not look forward to working the long, hard hours of their farmer parents. Countless small farms have fields no longer tilled and pastures without cattle. Owners commute to livelihoods elsewhere or move away, selling the farm. But there are reverse trends. Many city people, young and old, want to flee from the city, seeking the quietness, better air, and visual beauty of the country. Most of these refugees will settle for the outer edge of the suburbs, not realizing that what is at one moment the outer edge will soon be the center. Much of this suburban growth takes place on the farmlands being abandoned, and by the time the shift in ownership is effected, natural vegetational change presents the new owner with an oldfield shrubland. Another possibility is that several small farms have been bought up to make a large, mechanized one; again the new owner finds shrublands requiring land-use decisions.

For farming again—If the oldfield shrubland is needed for farming again, refer to *Clearing Land of Brush,* in Chapter 14 (p. 421). However, realize that with modern machinery it is not always necessary to follow the bounds of former fields, perhaps laid out when a man and ox sweated mightily to drag stones to make the boundary walls. Look for ways to run long fields along the contours of hills or to bulldoze out stones which earlier, less fortunate farmers had to cultivate or mow around. Procure good topographic and soil maps and aerial photographs. If you can get a recent aerial photograph and also one from several years previous, comparing them can tell you much about the vegetational development on the abandoned farmland. Then get professional help by consulting your local agricultural extension agent and federal soil conservationist about layout of fields as you reclaim the farmland from the brush. But as you plan, do not consider all the shrublands as just so much brush to thwart you and increase the expense of clearing. Some of the shrubbery may be the nursery of valuable timber trees about to push up through the bushes, and some is providing effective watershed protection. Shrubs left as hedgerows can break the cold wind and lengthen the growing season in adjacent fields. Shrub areas create valuable cover and food for wildlife. Certain bushes will provide the family with berries or holiday decorations, and some of them will burst forth with showy and fragrant blooms in their season. And an old wall may be a thing of beauty and of great historical interest. Study its virtues before deciding to cart it away or bury it in a trench.

For suburban shrubbery—As suburbs grow out into the abandoned farmland, many people buy a lot of, say, 50 by 100 feet. It is all green and beautiful, a veritable Eden, flanked by heavenly woods, shrublands, and meadows. Across the little valley there may be a few of the old farm buildings. Six months later, the surrounding area may have the topsoil bulldozed off, basements excavated, and foundations being poured by towering cement-mixing trucks which whack the lower branches off the one or two remaining trees. Things may be better when the soil is back-filled and everybody has planted a lawn and bought shrubs from the same nursery—but the area will never have that rural look again. The edge of the city has swept outward, perhaps without leaving even a patch or strip of rural park for the joy and edification of the children to come. Need it be so? No!

Those oldfield shrublands, if partially conserved, can preserve a bit of the rural environment which may have been a major reason for the suburban purchase. Before planning the location of the new house, garage, garden, or anything else, be sure to inventory what you have acquired in the way of vegetation. If you don't know one plant from another, get help from somebody who does (222). If you can keep contractors from devastating all the natural shrubbery, you may be several hundred dollars ahead in your landscaping, ahead of neighbors who bulldoze everything, pay to have it carted away or burned, and then buy expensive little shrubs which may take years to reach the stature and blooming maturity of what you have saved. And you may have valuable shade trees growing up through the shrubs which will have more vigor and more stable root systems than the spindles others will plant. To be sure, most of your urban-rooted neighbors may think you are crazy for a while, because you are not doing what everybody else does; and some of them may have nightmares over all the poison snakes and rats which they think "that mess of jungle" must harbor. If for no other reason than calming neighbors, you should yourself become familiar with your new shrubland. You must at least make a pretense of managing your "jungle," using some of the following ideas.

Simplification. Nature almost always over-plants. By cutting out or killing with planticides (p. 400) certain shrubs or sapling trees, those remaining will usually grow better, producing thicker foliage and more flowers and fruits. They will be more appreciated by most people because their eyes will focus on them without being distracted by the miscellany of other brush growing around and into them; the landscape becomes easier to appreciate because it is simplified. If one bush can be pointed out to a neighbor and he is told it is an azalea or a zeitpfiller, it will lose much of the terror of the unknown; he may even enjoy looking at it. But which shrubs should go and which should be kept?

Don't remove the last plant of any kind—keep it at least until you have a clear idea of what you want. It may be as valuable as the spice in your kitchen cabinet which you use but once a year. Even one (recognized) plant of poisonivy can be valuable—to educate your neighbors' children.

Design in three dimensions. Consider the width of shrubbery desired along your boundaries, or across a corner, or between an active-play yard and a sitting terrace. Consider also the optimum height, to cut off cold winds (p. 276), to provide privacy from a neighbor's windows (first story only or second story too?), or to throw shade on the children's sandbox. Width and height requirements will help determine which plants you remove and which you leave. Lambkill kalmia seldom grows over three feet tall, whereas mountainlaurel kalmia may reach six to nine feet and some rhododendrons considerably more. You might have all three in your abandoned shrubland! By selective killing you can leave the lambkill only at the edge, then the mountainlaurel, and the rhododendron in the middle, encouraging a shrub mass of simple form which even a pavement-reared neighbor may like. If you don't know the growth potential of your wildlings, try to identify them and then look up their growth in a botany book. *(288, 435)*

Pruning and shearing promote simplicity (p. 439). The wildest of highbush blueberry bushes will look proper when a few dead stems are cut out and it is flanked by lower huckleberry bushes and meadowsweet spiraea kept shapely and weeded of other plants. (p. 397)

Keep the calendar in mind. A clump of filbert (sometimes called hazelnut) may not seem worth keeping until you remember that in early spring this filbert is suddenly hung with golden tassels glinting against its gray stems. A wise rule with plants as well as people is to live with them for a year before you decide that you don't like them. Some day they may reveal their charm.

OTHER SHRUBLANDS

Watch for many other types of native shrubbery. Sometimes one genus of shrub, such as alder, spiraea, mesquite, or sagebrush predominates. At other times a complicated mixture of bushes may form a challenging biotic community, particularly in wet places (p. 179).

Consult local ecologists and taxonomists for help and read ecological books about your region.

Avoid the common tendency to refer to all shrubs as "brush". Find out what kinds are present, what they are like at different seasons, and what they are good for. Then either keep the shrub community entirely intact as a natural shrubland or, if it is large enough, take part of it for working with nature, trying to achieve a simpler design that will be more meaningful to people.

PLANTED COMPARED TO NATURAL SHRUBLANDS

Areas without naturally growing shrubs can sometimes be turned into shrublands by planting shrubs which are native to the region or introduced. The native shrubs can, with time and care, create a very natural type of vegetation. Introduced shrubs, if carefully selected, can create a natural-appearing shrubland which may fit well into the native landscape yet, because of certain attributes of the species selected, may have advantages over native shrublands (for instance, scotch broom planted on the dunes in the Pacific Northwest as described above, p. 101). On the other hand, either native or introduced shrubs can produce highly artificial plantings. Because so much already has been printed in horticultural publications, the following only outlines uses of planted shrublands and indicates suitable references for further help.

USES OF SHRUB PLANTINGS

While various types of plantings have special functions, generally shrubs are used to improve the microclimate, provide visual beauty, create cover and food for wildlife, or supply certain products such as berries. Their relatively low stature as compared to trees allows sun to come in over them, permits more air movement, and often grants a view. Their multiplicity of stems makes for dense growth close to the ground where it can restrict movement of air and the larger animals. A visit to ancient gardens in Europe or the Orient indicates the many centuries that man has appreciated the importance of planting shrubs for both beauty and utility.

SHRUB BORDERS

Of fields along woodlands. Any row of shrubbery along the edge of land with another use can be considered a shrub border. Farmers may have such a row bordering a cultivated field along a woods. The bushes give the field crops less competition for sun and moisture than would trees that were permitted up to the edge of the crops. Also shrubs supply more food and cover for desired game birds and mammals, which may provide a wildlife crop for the farmer either for food or recreational hunting. To be sure, if a farmer plants shrubs in the edge of his field, he will have less area for his field crop; but the low yield of crops close to the woods may not be worth the labor to plant and harvest there, whereas the shrub border needs very little maintenance. Shrubs planted are usually selected for their value to wildlife, for instance autumnolive, a large shrub native of Asia which has sweet-smelling flowers and abundant red berries much sought by birds. Select species hardy in the region of planting and with growth form and color suitable to the site. Consult the references, then your local county agricultural agent and/or U.S.D.A. Soil Conservation Service representative. *(147)*

Of woodlands along fields. These obviously are the same as the above, but looked at from the point of view of the forest. A shrub border on the windward side of a woodland in dry weather will increase the tree growth by reducing the amount of desiccating wind that blows in across the forest floor. While a thick growth of lower branches on the outer trees can perform the same function to a degree, it will neither make such a thick barrier nor provide such a variety of food and cover for wildlife. A shrub border can also provide increased privacy for a woodland picnic or camping area.

Along ponds and streams. The banks of water bodies occurring in farmland are good places to plant shrubs. They serve as habitat for wildlife and help stabilize the soil, especially where cattle would tread down the banks or where streams or wave action would undercut them. Where trees, rather than shrubs, are planted in such sites, they tend as they grow tall to lean out over the water and eventually fall in. Where trees are desired to shade a stream, plant them well back from the bank, with shrubbery along the side of the stream.

Trees should be planted with reference to the sun so they cast their shadows appropriately. While willows are usually the first thought for streambank planting because they thrive in wet places, the top of a bank is often a very well-drained site, sometimes even droughty; many other kinds of shrubs are adapted to planting there. Multi-flora rose, in regions where it is hardy, is a good top-of-the-bank species for a pasture; it restrains the cattle. Several species of viburnums and certain of the shrubby dogwoods are excellent for the sides of banks.

Of lawns and playfields.   In these situations shrubs are primarily for ornament and wildlife, with attention given to species with showy flowers or brilliant or abundant fruits. In some cases, foliage is a major consideration; for instance, sumac leaves turn brilliant reds and oranges in the autumn. Many desirable shrubs will not grow in narrow borders along woodlands because of the shade. If you are unwilling to cut some of the trees, high pruning of their lower branches may let in sufficient sun, especially on the south side of a woodlot. In other cases, one must select shade-tolerant shrubs, such as rhododendrons, azaleas, and for moist areas sweetpepperbush. Japanese barberry is fairly tolerant of shade, but like most plants will grow more thickly and produce more flowers and fruits if given sun; also it is prickly, and prickly shrubs should be avoided along playfields where one may have to retrieve balls from the bushes.

Along roads and bike paths.   Rapidly changing patterns of transportation make it important to consider more carefully just how we use and maintain the narrow strips of land (verges) along lanes and highways, which aggregate millions of acres. Four major factors are safety, cost, productivity, and beauty. Shrubs well located can be helpful with all four. Shrubs have been more expensive than grass for highway departments to plant along new roads. However, with newer planting methods giving higher survival, younger and therefore less expensive planting stock can be used; so we should be seeing more shrubbery along highways. For instance, controlled-release magnesium-ammonium fertilizer can be put in the bottom of each hole at planting to supply nitrogen.

Safety—Shrubs should not restrict vision around sharp corners on roads with fast traffic, or obstruct the view where side roads enter or where children, adult pedestrians, or domestic animals might cross the road. However, in recreational areas it is sometimes possible to lay out roads for one-way traffic only; then bushes can remain close to the road, even on sharp corners, providing a lush tunnel effect quite out of the ordinary. However, restrict speeds on curving stretches to prevent rear-end collisions should a car break down just around a corner without room to pull off the road.

Shrubs planted in the center strip of divided highways prevent headlights from blinding oncoming traffic. Also, evergreen shrubs can be used instead of evergreen trees on the south side of east–west roads in cold climates, where evergreen trees would shade the road and promote dangerous icing. (The use of shrubs as drift fence to minimize snow on roads is discussed below (p. 279).

Cost—On road cuts, planting shrubs stablizes the soil, reducing maintenance on steep grades where it is difficult to grow grass.

The basic choice of vegetative cover along roads is grass, vines, shrubs, or trees. Climate and soils influence the decision, as will the steepness of the grades in road cuts and fills. Grass is a favorite, because it stays low (except in swampy areas), providing good visibility; also it can be maintained rather uniformly by periodic mowing and/or by controlled burning. Vines also stay low; they do not need mowing; but because they often have the disadvantage of making a good seedbed for unwanted trees in moist regions where trees are native, they may require considerable weeding. Shrubs, at least in some instances, can help prevent trees from growing. Fairly stable shrub cover can be maintained by hand weeding or selective planticiding of tree seedlings (p. 400), and at less cost than mowing.

Productivity—Shrub borders along roadsides can produce berries for fresh fruit and preserves and flowers, fruits, and foliage for decoration. They also contribute to the productivity of wildlife by affording them food and cover.

Beauty—Blanket spraying with chemicals along many verges of roads in recent years has created a uniform border of grass—which looks beautiful to the turfsman, chemical salesman, and highway engineer. Of course its beauty is often sensed by others, too. But the beauty of shrubbery along many roads is becoming rarer as grass borders become standard. Masses of shrubs of different shades of green, with a variety of blooms at various seasons and with assorted effects of texture and value, have much to offer in the way of roadside beauty, not only on winding country lanes but also on super speedways where monotony of aspect can be a killer.

HEDGEROWS

This term usually refers to woody vegetation which follows a fence (or forms a living fence) between fields in farmland. Trees in such a row may unduly shade the crops, although some may be wanted for shade, for fence posts, or for other reasons. But a fencerow should consist of shrubs (or trees kept pollarded, p. 441) which will not rob crops of sun and moisture. The shrubs, when dense enough, can serve to restrict cattle, delineate fields of different use, slow down wind, increase moisture in fields by causing snow to drift more deeply, provide small fruits and flowers for ornament and honey production, and give food and cover for wildlife. In many farming areas, hedgerows are *the* major habitat for wildlife, including the songbirds and small game which can be an economic as well as esthetic factor for the farming community. Modern barbed wire and electric fences do not promote wildlife. Where maintenance of such fences requires removal of brush, as it usually does, it is well to plant rows of shrubs parallel to the fence and about twenty-five feet from it; or if old fences run up and down hill, disregard them and plant new hedgerows on the contour to fit in with modern conservation practices for almost all farm operations.

While almost any of the heavily fruiting shrubs adapted to the soil and climate may make good hedgerows, it is fun to study references and talk with nurserymen and extension agents of state universities to compose a hedgerow to be planted from scratch. Select a variety of compatible species to attract a variety of wildlife and to give blooms and fruits at different seasons. For instance, multiflora rose has both enemies and advocates among planters. It flowers and fruits heavily, but planted too far north it will winterkill; in too small a space its sidewards spread crowds adjacent land use; or in too shady a spot it dies. Perhaps gray dogwood or arrowwood viburnum are better suited to some sites. And so it is with other shrubs: a wise choice brings satisfaction. In Britain, hazel, hawthorn, and elder are primary genera in the thousands of miles of hedgerows *(322)*. American species of these genera are equally suitable to America *(581)*.

WINDBREAKS

Windbreaks may be of living trees or shrubs, often preferable to structural fences, which are often too expensive to build and maintain except for short stretches as around a yard. Crops in large fields often need protection from wind. In most cases shrub rows not too far apart will suffice; shrubs do not compete with the crops as much as trees would. In areas exposed to strong winds, like plains, mountainsides, and shores, be careful to select suitable species which can themselves survive the wind. The most wind-hardy shrubs are usually very low-growing (some almost prostrate). These may have to be established first, even though they are not tall enough to have much effect on the wind. Next somewhat taller-growing shrubs can be planted in their lee, with perhaps several subsequent plantings of still-taller kinds until even a row of trees will survive downwind from the wedge-shaped growth of shrubbery. The entire windbreak will then lift winds high above the fields and make a dead-air space where (in colder climates at least) snow will settle deeply, and melting in spring will replenish the soil with moisture. Extensive plantings of this sort are known as *shelterbelts.*

Shorter windbreaks add greatly to the comfort and beauty of farmsteads and ranch houses; even in areas with only moderate winds, they can materially reduce winter fuel bills by creating a warmer microclimate. Also, areas for outdoor recreation can be vastly improved by thoughtful plantings of shrubs (and trees) for windbreaks. Select species for growth form, density, and of course hardiness. Where winter winds are a factor, evergreens are obviously necessary for a major effect (p. 279). Trees will stay shrubby if they are sheared at least once a year. Broad-leaved shrubs also will benefit from judicious snipping of terminal buds to make them branch more compactly (see also p. 443; *581*).

SCREEN PLANTINGS

Where rows of woody plants are meant primarily to block vision and only secondarily, perhaps, to break the wind, they are referred to as screen plantings. They may hide unsightly buildings, provide privacy for backyard activities, lead one's eyes to a focal point in the landscape, form the sides or base framing a vista, create wings and backdrop for an outdoor theatre, make a dark background against which to see flowers or statuary, or provide a ready background for group pictures taken every year (as at schools and camps).

The life-form of the plants used should be considered. While screens are often made of *narrow-leaved evergreen trees* such as hemlock or arborvitae, sometimes *narrow-leaved evergreen shrubs* like yew are good where moderate height will suffice. On level land, a height of six feet is usually adequate for visual screening for people on the ground (as compared to people in second-story windows, for instance), and any taller screen adds maintenance problems. *Broad-leaved evergreen shrubs* such as rhododendron provide interesting coarse textures as well as profuse blooms; they also make excellent cover for wildlife in bad winter weather. But they need more room to spread sideways than do some of the narrow-leaved evergreens like arborvitae and yew. *Deciduous shrubs* such as privet make excellent screens, some up to fifteen feet tall, where the season for visual privacy is within the season of leafing. Privet is inexpensive within its range and is delightfully shear-tolerant so it can be shaped to whim.

When setting out a screen planting, it is tempting to plant them very close together so they will give the desired solid effect soon. They should, however, be spaced far enough apart to provide for healthy living of the plants. This distance varies from species to species and should be determined from books, nurserymen, or extension agents before obtaining plants, so that the number needed can be accurately decided. When an early screening effect is desired, the plants can be given more growing room by setting them out in a double row alternately, if there is adequate width for such a configuration. In other instances, tall annual or perennial herbs like hollyhocks and delphinium can be planted between the shrubs for partial seasonal screening effect until the bushes spread and touch. *(322, 581)*

HEDGES

A hedge is primarily a living fence. (There is no sharp demarcation between a tall hedge and a screen planting.) Usually it marks the edge of land with particular uses—for instance roadway and lawn, back yard and front, playground and ballfield—or land of different ownership (p. 4). Hedges make good boundaries but should be accompanied by stone or metal boundmarks when denoting legal boundaries. Often hedges are meant to restrict the movement of people or animals so that they will conform to the land uses involved. A low hedge around the lawn of a corner lot may look much more pleasant to the neighborhood than a KEEP-OFF-THE-GRASS sign; and a multiflora rose hedge across the back yard makes a beautiful barrier to keep cows from the vegetable garden. Hedges add perfume to the air in time of bloom, prevent dead leaves from blowing onto the lawn, patio, or swimming pool, and, as windbreaks, improve the microclimate of the garden. Across slopes, be sure to provide an opening in the hedge for cold air to drain out on frosty spring and autumn evenings (p. 281).

Attraction to wildlife is a major asset of a hedge. It is fun to watch bees snap the stamens of a low hedge of Japanese barberry (one of the least expensive of the prickly hedge shrubs), and to follow the nesting activities of a family of catbirds in a tall lilac hedge. Hedges make excellent pathways for wildlife, luring them up to the patio birdbath or window feeder.

Hedges require maintenance, the amount varying with the wishes of the owner and the kinds of constituent plants. Each stretch of hedge is usually of only one species, thus simplifying its management. A formal hedge trimmed to smooth planes is attained by frequent careful shearing, whereas an informal hedge of looser texture is maintained at desired size mostly by cutting a few of the older stems periodically at or near ground level or by judicious internal snipping here and there. More or less weeding is necessary as seedlings or suckerings of other species volunteer to join the hedge. The denser and more vigorous the hedge plants, the fewer volunteers will appear; so time is well spent in frequent shearing. Weeding is best done by hand, which usually means hands and knees—and gloves of gauntlet proportions are not amiss when a thorny hedge is involved! When a plant poisonous to the touch (such as poisonivy) appears, root it out with impervious and washable gloves if it is spotted soon enough; but if it is well established, mix some chemical planticide in vaseline and smear it for a few inches all around the base of the stem, thus effecting a root-kill without disrupting the hedge plants. *(45, 322, 581)*

FORMAL GROUP-PLANTING OF SHRUBS

Shrubs can be planted in non-linear patterns. A round clump may make a focus for radiating hedges in a formal garden, or two clumps may stand on either side of a driveway, (where they should not block visibility). Round or oval shrubbery may look well at the base of a pole supporting a birdhouse, mailbox, or sign. Triangular plantings fit well into the corners of a garden. Formality results from the symmetry of the pattern and from care in maintaining the regular shapes. Group-plantings are better than hedges in most cases where one wishes to mix two or more species of shrubs, for instance to give a seasonal succession of blooming. Usually the higher-growing species should be put in the center of a group that stands by itself in an open space and at the back when a group is against a boundary or wall. In addition to flowering at different seasons, the mixture will provide fruits for wildlife at various times of year. For example, a tall Tartarian honeysuckle in the center of a clump may in late spring produce fruits much sought by thrushes and catbirds. A ring of highbush blueberries surrounding it will attract birds in the latter part of the summer (if they can beat the children and pie makers and are not foiled by protective netting). An outer ring of Japanese barberry will hold its red fruits decoratively into late winter or even early spring. They make an excellent emergency food for early spring migrants, who may get caught by a late snowstorm which buries most other food. In another situation, a buckthorn surrounded by gray dogwood and/or coralberry makes an attractive grouping for people and birds alike. Also, one should not forget that a narrow evergreen tree, such as a pyramidal or columnar arborvitae or one of the upright junipers, makes a fine vertical accent in the center of a formal planting of shrubs and will probably be used by small birds for roosting on cold nights.

INFORMAL SHRUBBERIES

Plantings without any conspicuous symmetry are called informal. They should not be completely hit-or-miss, but need not be so regularly set out nor so rigorously maintained. Size, shape, texture of foliage, pattern of limbs and twigs in the leafless season, succession of flowering and fruiting, and (as always) suitability to the living conditions of the site should be considered. As with all plantings it is good to keep a record, preferably on a file-sized map, of the name and date of each plant set out.

SCATTERED SHRUBS

Occasionally where there is enough room, a bare or herbaceous area may be planted to one or many species of shrubs widely enough spaced so that the bare soil or herbs can persist between them, perhaps with grass kept mowed or weeded. Such spacing permits ready harvesting of fruits, such as those of highbush blueberry and huckleberry. It is also well adapted for educational plantings at arboretums, botanical gardens, parks, and schools where people need to be able to walk around a shrub to learn its open-grown shape and other characteristics. These areas are excellent for a game of hide-and-seek for small children, and good habitat for birds and bees; free from competition with surrounding shrubs, the bushes are apt to flower and fruit heavily; and there is maximum "edge" (p. 458) between woody cover and herbaceous areas.

SMALL-FRUIT PLANTINGS

Such plants as raspberries, blackberries, loganberries, currants, gooseberries, and blueberries are known commercially as small fruits. Such plantations nowadays are mostly large-scale enterprises; too few homeowners enjoy their own raspberry patch. Homes and institutions with more lawn than they need can set out small fruits, which are attractive to look at in flower and fruit as well as good to eat. They can be a source of income for young people under sixteen, who sometimes find it hard to get employment because of labor laws and insurance. And the care of small fruits can be a joy to older people who also find it difficult to be obviously useful. Netting protects ripening fruit from birds; but if one does not want to take the harvesting too seriously, one can share the fruit with wild creatures.

FACING PLANTINGS

Sometimes one wants shrubs along a blank wall of a building, to make it more visually interesting, to cool the building in summer (south side) or keep it warmer in winter (north side), to provide flowers or fruits to look beautiful or perhaps to perfume a bedroom window with lilac fragrance on a warm spring night, or to attract wildlife. Do not plant the bushes too close to the wall; leave plenty of room for maintenance, and in some cases for air movement that prevents excessive humidity harmful to the structure. Commonly people fail to allow enough space for sidewards growth. Planting close to the wall can be allowed if one is going to espalier the shrubs (p. 437). A row of shorter shrubs can be planted in front of a line of taller ones. Until the spaces between young shrubs fill in, annual and/or perennial herbs can be used to plug the gaps.

Facing plantings can be used also along masonry boundary walls and high retaining walls. An outdoor fireplace with chimney built against such a wall is fine for barbecues; sometimes a similar structure makes an efficient incinerator, with facing plantings and wing plantings out from it forming a screen. Radiant heat from a fire has a harmful drying effect on leaves and tender twigs (particularly evergreens), so don't plant shrubs too close or let the fire be too hot.

Daylilies and Lilac bushes often persist around sites of old houses.

FOUNDATION PLANTINGS

In early colonial days in America, houses were built low to the ground and mostly lacked plantings of shrubs around the foundations. Later, especially in Victorian times, bigger basements and higher foundations led to the common use of shrubbery to hide the masonry beneath the wooden first stories of many homes and institutions. The twentieth century has seen fluctuating interest in foundation plantings with rapidly changing styles of architecture and landscape architecture. Foundation plantings make the vertical planes of buildings blend with the less uniform planes of the landscape and have a softening visual effect on the hardness of most building materials; these "living walls" outside the non-living walls change with the seasons; and they bring wildlife close to the house where they can be more readily observed.

Foundation plantings, like facing plantings, improve the microclimate. Careful trimming of shear-tolerant plants like yew and arborvitae can make dense foliage shaped with surfaces that shed cold wind. One study of microclimates in England showed that a well-sheared shrub can be ten degrees Fahrenheit warmer in its center than a comparable unsheared one. For a roosting sparrow in a winter night, that could be significant. (284)

Vines on walls. A vine with deciduous leaves, like Bostonivy, can keep sun off a south-facing brick wall in summer and cool it by evaporating moisture into the air; when it sheds its leaves in autumn, sunlight is permitted to heat the bricks. Do not plant vines at the foundations of wooden buildings, however, unless they are to grow on trellises five feet or more from the walls, or else the vines may rot the boards or shingles and pull them down by their weight. Trellises with pivot-hinges at the base permit lowering for care of both vines and trellises. The five-foot space allows room for painters with ladders or for other maintenance.

Vines can cause problems on masonry walls, so people whose primary concern is building maintenance at institutions are apt to discourage any vines. This is unfortunate, considering the positive values of ivy and other vines, which far outweigh the maintenance required. Periodic cutting of some of the older stems prevents the problem of weight before vines become arm-thick. The vine dies above the cut, of course, leaving a dead area. With evergreen vines, this will look brown until the dead leaves fall off, which may take time; so the severed part should usually be pulled down. Deciduous vines on the other hand can be cut in their dormant season so that there are no dead leaves, and the vines can either be pulled down or left up, though it is probably better to pull them down and use this opportunity to repoint (clean and patch) the mortar between bricks wherever it is needed. Periodic pruning of vines around windows is also necessary; and vines should not be allowed to grow up to the eaves or gutters, where even the best-behaved vine is usually out of place.

In weighing the value of vines against maintenance costs, one should reflect not only on the microclimatic effects of vines but also on their visual and other sensory effects, for instance their spreading of natural green over a building and perhaps changing color seasonally. Some vines have sweet-smelling flowers; some have decorative fruits which also serve nesting birds. House-sparrow haters may wish to avoid vines; but people who are willing to face a little lime and who like birdsong in the morning will set out vines along their foundations.

Vines as walls. Older wooden houses often have a veranda (porch with columns), and sometimes a porte cochere (outward extension under which a carriage could drive for shelter when loading and unloading). In summer, the spaces between the columns are sometimes green-walled with the large heart-shaped leaves of the birthwort vine, climbing on vertical wires to give shade and privacy and thus adding greatly to the livability and attractiveness of the old house. Modern building materials and design now more often result in porches enclosed with jalousies which give more control of the environment at different seasons. But in modern architecture there are surely some places for using walls of vines strung on wires, along with the glass and aluminum now so commonly used to blend interior living space with the out-of-doors.

Design of foundation plantings. The many existing books and articles on landscaping present many ideas on patterns for planting along foundations. Commonly, tall narrow evergreens like upright yew, pyramidal or columnar arborvitae, falsecypress, or various upright junipers are used as vertical accents at corners and beside doors; rounded or horizontally growing forms of the above genera are used under windows. Corners often have a clump planting of shrubs around a small tree like a flowering dogwood or hawthorn. Sometimes, to make a house look longer or to shelter an area, a so-called wing planting extends as a screen from a corner—perhaps a row of arborvitae, Scots pine, or spruces if they are hardy in the region. Deciduous shrubs along with the evergreens provide flowers and fruits as well as variation of color and texture of foliage. Spiraeas and Japanese quince are two often-used genera.

It is not necessary to set out foundation plantings that look just like those of everybody else, in a routine style recommended by some nurserymen, who benefit by selling large quantities of a small variety of species. In cold climates, give special attention to putting dense evergreen shrubs where they will protect window feeders located on the side of the house least exposed to cold winds; and plan hedges confluent with the foundation planting at one or two corners of the house to make wildlife pathways to the house so that foundation plantings can hold their full share of birds.

Spacing of shrubs along foundations. As with hedges and facing plantings, it is important that young shrubs be set far enough apart to allow for healthy growth. To prevent that Joshua-tree-on-the-desert look, fill in temporarily with tall-growing annual or perennial herbs, perhaps iris, marigolds, or chrysanthemums, or even taller ones like dahlias and sunflowers between windows. As the shrubs spread sidewards, the flowering herbs may be brought forward from between the bushes, which then make a good background for them (p. 373).

Most people plant shrubs too close to the house, making maintenance difficult. Sometimes it is practical to run a narrow walk immediately against the house and have the shrubs outside the walk, still giving the effect of foundation plantings. Leftover mortar and other limey materials from building should not be dumped in with the backfill against the foundations, in case one may wish to plant acid-soil plants such as rhododendron and azalea, mountainlaurel kalmia, or other members of the heath family often used for landscaping buildings.

Trees in foundation plantings. When very young, some tall forest trees look neat and shrub-like on each side of the door. Beware! They may grow fast to a stature which dwarfs the house, smothers windows, blocks doors, and eventually poses a physical threat to the home in windstorms or thunderstorms. As they get up toward the eaves, they bend away from the house toward the light and become prone to breakage if snow piles up on their upper side. If pines, spruces, and hemlocks and their like are used in foundation plantings, they must be rigorously sheared at least annually to keep them down to size. Even then they are apt to become coarsely twiggy in a few years and will need to be replaced. It is wise to avoid tall forest trees along foundations.

POSTLUDE TO SHRUBLANDS

Shrubs are not just so much messy "brush." While they lack the upstandingness of trees, and refuse to lie down underfoot subserviently as do most herbs, still they have important jobs to perform in the human environment. Many of us need more knowledge about more kinds of shrubs. In the meantime, ignorance will have to be compensated for by tolerance, tolerance of "all that brush."

(See also *93, 123, 238, 245, 257, 313, 353, 502, 549, 550.*)

Without protective vegetation, the bluff will go. So will the lighthouse. Block Island, Rhode Island.

5 Drylands: Treelands

Man's Place in the Forest
Occurrence
Natural Forests of Eastern North America
Northern Narrow-Leaved Evergreen Forest Formation
Broad-Leaved Deciduous Forest Formation
    Northern hardwoods association
    Central hardwoods association
    Southern hardwoods association
Southern Narrow-Leaved Evergreen Forest Formation
Subtropical Broad-Leaved Evergreen Forest
Natural Forests of Western North America
Natural Forests of Britain
Planning
Long-Term Plans
Treeland or Other Land Use?
Closed-Canopy Treeland with Canopy Left Intact
    Clearing beneath canopy
    Pruning
    Controlled burning
    Browsing and grazing
Closed-Canopy Treeland with Canopy Partially Opened
    Creaming versus culling
    Girdling and chemical killing
Closed-Canopy Treeland Clear-Cut
    Leaving seed trees
    Sprouting
    Planting

Open-Canopy Treelands
   Wood production
   Christmas trees
   Fruits, flowers, and greens
   Wildlife
   Watershed
   Recreation
Treeland Recreation
Forest-Trail Recreation
Forest-Clearing Recreation
   Small clearings for active games
   Growing zones between clearings
   Access roads to clearings
   Parking spaces for forest recreation
   Sites for tents, recreational vehicles, and cabins
   Clearings for fireplaces
   Clearings for picnic tables
   Vistas
Recreational Structures for Treelands
   Shelters
   Hides
Trees for Children
Non-Modifying Treeland Recreation
Creating a New Treeland for Recreation

T *rees* are the primary factor in determining forests. But treelands are much more than groups of trees. There are *other living plants*, such as shrubs and herbs on the forest floor, and bacteria, slime-molds, and true fungi which break down dead organic matter and parasitize living organisms. Without these, a forest could not be a forest. *Animals*, too, are an integral part of the community; many species of vertebrates and invertebrates perform essential roles such as distributing seeds, pruning buds, pollinating flowers, curbing the populations of other animals, and assisting the breakdown and recycling of organic matter and inorganic matter.

The *atmosphere*, from which the trees get carbon dioxide for manufacturing their food, is a vital component. Its motion (wind) distributes pollen and seeds, heat and moisture; sometimes it shapes the trees by wind-pruning or lays the treelands low by windthrow. A major characteristic of a forest is its effect on the atmosphere: slowing down wind, piling up snow, cooling the air in summer and warming it in winter, giving off moisture and oxygen, and in other ways modifying the local climate. *Solar energy* powers the treeland community, contributing strongly to the roof of the forest canopy and then losing some of its effectiveness as it sifts down between the leaves or passes through their filtering greenness, which absorbs radiation for food-making and heating. The fungus flora in the dark of the soil uses the sun's energy indirectly as it makes a living from the remains of sun-built organisms.

Water, in the air, in the soil, and in living organisms determines the existence of treelands and their vitality. *Soil* is basic to every forest. A substantial portion of the trees themselves is hidden by it, anchored by it, and supplied with life-giving water and minerals by it. There is much more to a forest than meets the eye above ground.

134

A forest is an amazing amalgamation of living and nonliving entities. When we cut one tree from a forest, we influence every one of the components mentioned above to a greater or lesser extent, just as removing one human tooth may change the shape of a face, influence digestion, and even alter a personality. Each component organism of the forest has its niche in the community, sharing the natural resources with all others. *(128, 187, 403)*

MAN'S PLACE IN THE FOREST

Can man still fit into treeland communities now that he has changed animal-skin clothing for synthetic fibers, and a stone axe for a power chain saw? Certainly, but he must have both wisdom and humility, work with nature and not against it, being sensitive to the importance of components other than himself in the forest community. Wise use of forest resources is a complicated challenge to man's complicated brain. There is much research to be done, much trial with some inevitable error. To practice successful forest conservation we must learn the maximum from those who have gone before, as well as contribute our own bit to the understanding of man's place in the forest *(468)*.

OCCURRENCE

Forests need more *moisture* than most other types of vegetation. Treelands grow in climates with 20 or more inches of rainfall annually. Along the drier edges of these zones (such as the prairies of the Midwest and the lower and eastern slopes of mountains in the West), trees grow scattered or in groves in what is called savannah (p. 63). Within zones of adequate moisture, forests occur almost everywhere that the soil is deep enough for anchorage and sustenance, so long as man has not established an inimical land use (farming, roads, airports, industries, housing, and so on). Of course, forests are temporarily razed by fire or windthrow, or killed back by insect attack or fungus disease, or excluded by a dense growth of grasses or other low plants which colonize the area first, or held in

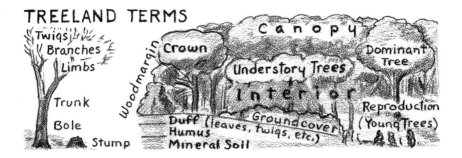

TREELAND TERMS

Twigs
Branches
Limbs
Trunk
Bole
Stump

Woodmargin

Crown

Canopy

Understory Trees

Dominant Tree

Interior

Duff (leaves, twigs, etc.)
Humus
Mineral Soil

Groundcover

Reproduction
(Young Trees)

check along the ocean by salt spray or at timberline by wind. But usually, where there are 20 or more inches of annual rainfall without excessive evaporation, nature produces treelands.

Forests also need *time* to mature. A brushy field may have 40 inches of annual rainfall, a rich loam, and be heavily stocked with little trees. It has all the makings of a forest and may well be managed as such; but it needs time, years and years of it. Two years can produce a fair lawn, but not a forest. We find fifty-year-old forests only where trees have been protected for fifty years. Hundred-year-old forests occur much less frequently because they must have been protected twice as long. Primeval forests dating back to precolonial times are so rare in the United States that we should preserve all of them for both scientific study and esthetic reasons. Americans can envy the "Ancient and Ornamental Woodlands" of England, protected for over three hundred years.

Some forests occur over vast expanses, like the taiga (p. 137) of spruces and firs stretching from New Brunswick to Alaska. Others form patches in appropriate local environments. A group of as few as three trees in your back yard can well be considered a miniature forest and managed as such.

Whether forest occurs all around your farm or village or exists only as a small patch along the river or behind the city dump, that forest is one of nature's greatest gifts to man. If there seem to be reasons for destroying it, study them. If "progress" points to their removal, be sure to save adequate samples for science and tracts for recreation, watershed, and wildlife management. If no forests occur in your region, find out why not. Perhaps they will grow if you start them!

NATURAL FORESTS OF EASTERN NORTH AMERICA

Forests vary tremendously, largely in response to climate but also because of geologic history, present soil conditions, and human activity. They are usually classified by characteristics of their predominant trees, particularly the foliage as it has developed in response to climate. Narrow-leaved trees like pines and spruces tend to be better adapted to droughty conditions than broad-leaved ones like oaks and maples. Thus we find the narrow-leaved ones in the far north and on mountaintops where liquid water is imprisoned as ice much of the year, and farther south on sandy lands which hold little water. The largest stretches of similar forest are called *formations*. Frequently-occurring variations of considerable extent within formations are known as *associations*. Following are brief characterizations of some formations, and of a few of their associations.

NORTHERN NARROW-LEAVED EVERGREEN FOREST FORMATION

Spruces and firs predominate with an admixture of larch, arborvitae, and hemlock. Because these trees are cone-bearing, this formation is often called the Northern Coniferous Forest. Geographers and vegetationists use the term *taiga*. Its southern limit at sea level is in eastern Maine, but in the Appalachian Mountains it stretches south to Georgia and in the Rockies to Colorado. Associated with the evergreens are paper birch, aspen, willow, and beech; they are broad-leaved trees which are not evergreen but have deciduous leaves (that is, leaves which die and mostly fall off at the beginning of the unfavorable season). They are commonest in the earlier stages of vegetational development, as in burns or along waterways or rock outcrops. Normally developed soils in this forest region are called *podzols* and are characterized by a thick top layer of needles, often lush with mosses and lichens, overlying a mineral soil whose top layer is grayish, with much of the water-soluble material washed down and out because of the acidic nature of the needles.

The animal life of any forest is as much a part of it as the trees. In the taiga there are red squirrels, lynx, fox, snowshoe rabbits, porcupines, and of course mice among the typical mammals exerting their many influences on vegetation and soil as well as on each other. Juncos, white-throated or white-crowned sparrows, thrushes, and red-breasted nuthatches are characteristic forest birds. Woodboring beetles and their ichneumon parasites are common insects; they keep the equilibrium of the forest, attack the vulnerable and make way for the vigorous. Human activities are centered on the extractive industries of lumbering, mining, and trapping and on forest recreation, especially as related to rivers, lakes, and mountains.

BROAD-LEAVED DECIDUOUS FOREST FORMATION

Oaks and maples are typical of a vast area extending south from the taiga to the pine forests of the South, and from the prairies of the Midwest to the Atlantic. In the southern Appalachians a great variety of trees and associated shrubs and herbs occur because this area served as a refuge during past geologic ages when inundating seas destroyed life in the Mississippi Lowland and the Atlantic Coastal Plain, and more recently when glacial ice sheets buried and scoured lands to the north. Subsequently certain species have moved outward to recolonize these various areas, forming more or less distinct Forest Associations within the formation. *(69)*

Northern hardwoods association. *Hardwood*, a lumberman's term, denotes a deciduous tree whether or not the wood is actually hard. (Pines, spruces, and the like are called "softwoods." They often mingle with the "hardwoods.") American beech, sugar maple, and three species of birches (paper, yellow, and black) are characteristic. Hemlock and white pine, although not broad-leaved deciduous trees, are frequent forest components. Red maple and American elm may be abundant on moist sites, though the latter has been killed out in many places by a fungus, Dutch Elm Disease. White ash and red oak are locally common where the soil is suitable. Pin cherry and aspen are plentiful in early stages of vegetational development after fire. This and the following are among the most brilliantly colored forest associations in the world when their foliage turns in the autumn. The sugar maple is one of the most conspicuous as well as one of the most economically important of the hardwoods.

Central hardwoods association. This association, typical of the central Appalachians, extends north to southern New England and west into the Ozarks and the prairies. Many species of oak, several hickories, and formerly American chestnut (prior to the coming of the chestnut blight early in the century) are the typical hardwoods. Beech, sugar maple, and hemlock may be part of a climax stage of forest development (p. 372), which is very rare these days. White pine occurs as stands of nearly pure pine in old fields or as isolated specimens among the hardwoods (if given time—which seldom happens now). Buckeye, mulberry, and hackberry are common in the wooded valleys and ridges of the Midwest. Gray birch and eastern redcedar are frequent in early stages of vegetational development.

Southern hardwoods association. Tuliptree, black gum, sweetgum, persimmon, and additional species of oak, such as willow oak, join to make the great variety of species found in the southern Appalachians and stretching out along the fertile bottomlands of rivers on the Atlantic and Gulf Coastal Plains.

These forest associations occur primarily on Red and Yellow Podzolic Soils whose duff is thickened each autumn as the leaves fall but thins out rapidly each ensuing summer as the many earthworms (rare under coniferous trees) and other agents incorporate the organic matter with the mineral soil to make a rich humus layer. A great variety of animal life is an integral part of the forest, with increasing variety southward.

SOUTHERN NARROW-LEAVED EVERGREEN FOREST FORMATION

The great southern pine forests stretch from Virginia to Texas across the Atlantic and Gulf Coastal Plains, extending north into Arkansas in the Mississippi Valley. Longleaf, slash, loblolly, shortleaf, and Virginia pine are the prevalent species. Some of the broad-leaved deciduous trees listed above range far south into this region, and southern broad-leaved evergreens such as live oak, magnolia, and holly are common locally.

The soils of the southern pine forests are coastal plain sediments not directly affected by glaciation. They are often sandy, strongly leached of their soluble elements, and frequently bright red where their iron has been heavily oxidized ("rusted") in the better-drained sites. The fauna of the upland pine forests, including such typical species as the pinewoods sparrow, is more meagre than that of the bottomland gum forests of the Southern Hardwoods Association which share the same region.

SUBTROPICAL BROAD-LEAVED EVERGREEN FOREST

Southern Florida has many trees foreign to the rest of the Eastern United States. Palms and many other subtropical trees create a noteworthy forest of considerable variety but relatively little economic usefulness. Because of the flatness of the country, an elevation of only a few inches may make the difference between a dryland forest type and a wetland type such as mangrove. Poisonous reptiles and toxic plants add to the interest of these forests but make caution a necessity in their manipulation.

NATURAL FORESTS OF WESTERN NORTH AMERICA

Treelands in the western continental United States have not arranged themselves into quite such large neat areas as have eastern treelands, mostly because of the great mountain ranges, where climatic conditions depend on latitude, altitude, and aspect. These factors determine the amount of heat and moisture available to organisms. More northern latitudes are of course cooler, with more condensation of moisture into rain, fog, or snow, correspondingly less evaporation, and a resultant greater availability of water during the growing season. Similarly, higher altitudes are cooler and moister; and north- and northeast-facing slopes are also cooler and moister. But be on the lookout for plenty of interesting exceptions where other factors determine what lives where.

"Life Zones" in the West were first described under that name by the biologist C. Hart Merriam, as he sought to recognize and map the areas inhabited by plants and by the animals associated with them. Many other scientists have refined his initial work—or rejected it as too simple. Although overly simple for many purposes,

In time, a young forest can heal an old burn—if the soil has not all washed away. Glacier National Park, Montana.

three of Merriam's Life Zones provide useful patterns for the study of western forests:

Canadian Life Zone: needle-leaved evergreen forests of spruce-fir and associated species at high altitudes in the Rockies, Cascades, and Sierra (southward extensions of taiga; see p. 137).

Transition Life Zone: needle-leaved trees with some broad-leaved trees; often ponderosa pine with several other kinds such as western larch, Douglasfir, and any of several oaks. Warmer and drier than the Canadian Zone; usually found farther south or lower on slopes.

Sonoran Life Zone (named after the State of Sonora in northern Mexico): the hottest and driest of these three life zones, often with pinyon pine, various junipers, and/or small broad-leaved trees such as mesquite. Trees and shrubs are often widely scattered, so the treelands do not look like northern or eastern types of forest. These treelands occur in the Southwest and farther north in arid intermontane basins and lower slopes of mountains, extending higher on the drier sides of mountains (usually easterly) than on the moister side (usually toward the Pacific).

Largely because of the aridity of much of the West and the mostly north-south arrangement of mountain ranges (at right angles to moisture-bearing winds from the Pacific), the treeland patterns are too complex to express here other than in generalities. The references listed, however, will enable you to puzzle out the local forest associations to an extent meaningful for intelligent land-use planning. In the meantime, the Life Zone classification reminds us that the distribution of living things is influenced primarily by climate and topography, even though many other factors are at work secondarily.

A special word is in order about the treelands of the Pacific Northwest, extending from northern California northward through coastal Oregon, Washington, British Columbia, and Alaska. Here a narrow-leaved evergreen forest much warmer and wetter than normal Canadian taiga produces, in a mighty temperate rainforest, some of the tallest trees on earth, including coast redwood, Douglasfir, western hemlock, and sitka spruce. The average reader of this book will never fell one of the giants; but feeling like an ant walking on the forest floor, she or he may find ways to work with rather than against the subtle forces of nature in this most humbling treeland. By working in a small way (as with seedlings) or by joining with others in community projects, the conservationist may find ways to insure that wise land use prevails. The greatest treelands pose the greatest challenges.

NATURAL FORESTS OF BRITAIN

Compared to the United States, Britain has had a much longer history in which its forests have been markedly modified. In the U.S. we say (rather loosely) that the Stone Age American Indian was a natural part of the landscape and that the forests began to lose their naturalness with the coming of Europeans and their metal culture. In Britain, the postglacial forests of oak and beech were modified from ancient times by a combination of clearing and introduction of additional plants from the Continent. Even the English yew, from which Robin Hood reputedly made his trusty bow, is looked upon as an introduced species; and the Scots pine may be the only truly native evergreen needletree.

The problems of British forestry in terms of native and introduced species cannot be dealt with adequately here. Mention must be made, however, of the so-called Ancient and Ornamental Woodlands which Britons have preserved at such sites as The New Forest and The Forest of Dean. They are precious and pay tribute to their custodians over many centuries. While not so wild as primeval forests of North America, they are evidence of men and nature working together, and surely their beauty does not suffer by comparison with any forests this side of heaven. *(420, 429, 442)*

Even a few shade trees around a house can be managed as a treeland. Surry, Maine.

PLANNING

What do you want from your treeland? Income, rural appearance, moderated climate, seclusion, companionship with other living things? A source of lumber, pulp, fuel, and other wood products? Protected watershed, nature sanctuary, hunting preserve, research area, source of inspiration, or showplace? It is humbling to be faced with a piece of woodland or forest and have to decide what to do with it. In older woods, nature has invested so much time; in younger woods, the trees have so much future. And there you stand with the ability to change it all. Introduce one pregnant leaf beetle, one fungus, one spark. With one swift signature sell all the standing timber to the first bidder. Or set up a scientific plan of long-term multiple-use management to keep the area both productive and beautiful. Face to face with a forest, professional foresters often feel ignorant and inadequate. Don't be surprised if you lack confidence at the beginning. But with humility and courage you can help nature achieve new wonders. *(253, 286, 359)*

Whether your woods is a very small grove or hundreds of acres, get the facts, or as many as you can gather in an organized and there-

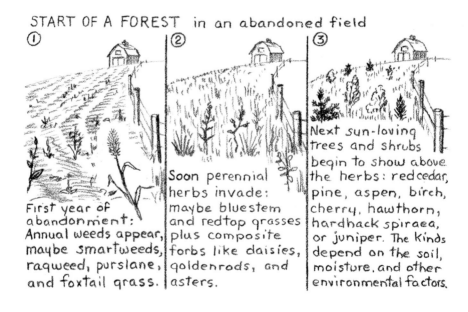

START OF A FOREST in an abandoned field

① First year of abandonment: Annual weeds appear, maybe smartweeds, ragweed, purslane, and foxtail grass.

② Soon perennial herbs invade: maybe bluestem and redtop grasses plus composite forbs like daisies, goldenrods, and asters.

③ Next sun-loving trees and shrubs begin to show above the herbs: redcedar, pine, aspen, birch, cherry, hawthorn, hardhack spiraea, or juniper. The kinds depend on the soil, moisture, and other environmental factors.

fore potentially useful way (see 67). If the treeland is not relatively uniform, study it unit by unit (491). Then for each unit try to decide which should be the primary use and which ones secondary, each fitting in with the primary use and not conflicting unduly with the other secondary uses.

LONG-TERM PLANS

It takes time to grow trees, and sometimes generations of trees to produce a certain forest type. Take the long view. Each forest or woodland has a past; plans for the future management of the forest should be based on that past if you want to work *with* nature. While inventorying the trees and other components of the forest, figure out how long the present trees have been growing and what the environment was like when these trees were seedlings or sprouts. Did they seed into a neglected pasture or abandoned field (p. 372)? Did they start in a mineral soil laid bare by wildfire (p. 22)? Did they begin as shade-tolerant seedlings under their lofty parents in some deep forest? Clues to the past may include: fire scars and char on the bases of old trunks; stumps of felled trees; stumps with sprouts; upturned root systems of windthrown trees; scars of logger's chains wrapped

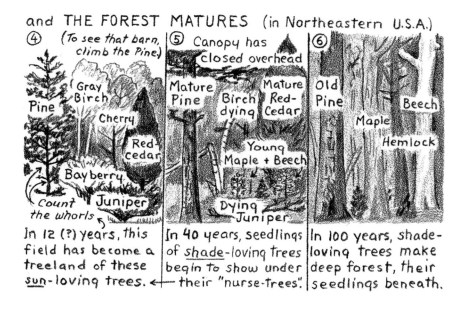

and THE FOREST MATURES (in Northeastern U.S.A.)

④ (To see that barn, climb the Pine.)
Gray Birch
Pine
Cherry
Red Cedar
Bayberry
Count the whorls
Juniper

⑤ Canopy has closed overhead
Mature Pine   Birch dying   Mature Red- Cedar
Young Maple + Beech
Dying Juniper

⑥
Old Pine
Maple
Beech
Hemlock

In 12 (?) years, this field has become a treeland of these sun-loving trees. ← | In 40 years, seedlings of shade-loving trees begin to show under their "nurse-trees". | In 100 years, shade- loving trees make deep forest, their seedlings beneath.

around trunks; scars from some surveyor's blazes; old walls, posts, or strands of wire delimiting old farm units; ruts of old roads through woods; abandoned cellar holes and wells; old dam sites and bridge abutments. In your mind's eye, live with the forest through its past and you will be better able to understand its present and plan its future. Set your plans down on paper, with maps *(67)*.

With natural treelands as with other natural environments, the foremost question should be, "How much of this area can be kept in a natural, or relatively natural, condition?" Whenever possible, some parcels managed by nature alone should be set aside as samples for comparison with man-managed ones and as areas for non-mod-ifying types of recreation (nature observation, hiking, photography, sketching, meditation, and the like).

TREELAND OR OTHER LAND USE?

Whenever part of the treeland is not to be left natural, the question arises whether to leave it as managed treeland or to clear part or all of it for some other type of land use. Weigh all that trees have to offer against the values of cutting them down to create other environ-ments; see the chapters *Barelands*, *Herblands*, and *Shrublands*, which it would be useful to consult at this point in planning. If you decide to convert to non-treelands, study the above sections of this chapter, then note in Chapter 14, *Plant Management*, the sections on *Clearing Land*, *Harvesting*, and *Handling Cut Brush and Slash*. Try to harvest the trees so as to make best use of them and to leave the land in the best condition possible for the new land use. In converting part of a forest to non-treeland use, do not cause unnecessary damage to adjacent areas left as treeland. Too large a forest opening on an ex-posed hillside or shore may let the wind in enough to cause almost total blowdown of the woods left standing; carelessly piled slash from a clearing operation may cause a fire hazard that jeopardizes the remaining forest.

CLOSED-CANOPY TREELAND WITH CANOPY LEFT INTACT

Clearing beneath canopy. In a woodland with large trees, the present landscape can be markedly improved for certain purposes

CLOSED-CANOPY TREELANDS: Canopies left intact

Canopy

Undergrowth

Natural Area

Cleared below by cutting

Browseline

Grassy Groundcover

or browsing

by cutting down some or all of the smaller trees which do not reach up into the canopy. If the trees of the canopy are ultimately to be harvested for lumber, it sometimes helps their growth to remove overtopped trees which reach into the bottom of the canopy but do not attain its top, so-called thinning from below (p. 409). This also increases the appearance of height of the trees forming the canopy and exposes to view their large, strong trunks. To give more feeling of space within the forest and more circulation of air, especially where the cutting is carried right to the edge of the woodland, fell understory trees and remove saplings of shade-tolerant species which would have eventually formed canopy. This practice is sometimes recommended for recreation areas where, although shade from the canopy is important, space is needed for visual effect, air circulation, or active play (p. 157). Cautions: (1) Markedly reducing undergrowth right to the windward edge of a forest speeds the drying of the soil and therefore may retard growth rate of many trees on drier sites, making them more susceptible to diseases. (2) Underclearing promotes soil compaction and its attendant increased runoff; be especially careful on slopes (p. 338). (3) Stumps and roots of cut woody plants may sprout vigorously, so that the effects of cutting are quickly nullified. Careful spraying with planticide of freshly cut stumps can eliminate the sprouting; but keep the poison off leaves, stems, and roots of plants to be left growing (p. 400). (4) Even though the canopy is left intact, the future structure and composition of the woods will be markedly altered by cutting undergrowth. If no undergrowth is permitted, openings in the canopy will develop as old trees die or blow down. To form a subsequent canopy, leave selected vigorous saplings of shade-tolerant trees. (5) Some of the plants in the understory or groundcover may be highly desirable, for instance flowering dogwood with its beautiful growth form, flowers, and fruits. Don't cut blindly.

Pruning.   Pruning lower branches of canopy trees promotes the feeling of height and space and will also improve the quality of the lumber should the trees of the canopy ever be harvested (p. 440).

Controlled burning.   In certain forest types, notably some southern and western pinelands but also pitch pine woods and jack pine in the Northeast, controlled burning under mature trees when the soil is wet favors fire-resistant herbs and shrubs while eliminating competing ones. The result is a simplified, more uniform groundcover with parklike effect economically attained. Prescribed burning must be intelligently carried out or it will kill or damage the mature trees or possibly escape into an adjacent land-use unit which might be ruined by wildfire. And much careful experimentation is still needed to determine the role of controlled burning (see *Prescribed Burning*, p. 431).

Browsing and grazing.   Goats and deer are browsers; they eat twigs and bark as well as leaves. When confined, they can eat a big change into the landscape of a forest! Goats will even feed on prickly junipers and poisonivy. If one doesn't mind being tied down by animal husbandry, these animals are recommended for creating and maintaining openings in the lower forest, at first only to the height that they can reach, then higher, as devoured saplings fail to replace the dying trees above. To keep the animals healthy and working, there must be enough browse all year, or supplementary feed must be supplied. There must be water available or supplied. And fencing will usually be needed unless animals are tethered. Cattle are primarily grazers rather than browsers, mostly avoiding twigs. But a cow will eat a whole tree if it is a seedling only a few inches tall, and so can have a pronounced effect on the future structure and composition of the forest. Where enough herbage has grown up as a result of browsing, burning, cutting, or seeding, cattle can help retain a parklike effect under tall trees. They may, however, have adverse effects on the canopy trees because their feeding opens up the woods to drying winds and their feet may overly compact the soil.

CLOSED-CANOPY TREELAND WITH CANOPY PARTIALLY OPENED

Felling or killing selected trees in the canopy has pronounced effects on a woodland. (1) Adjacent trees have reduced competition and the branches with food-making foliage tend to spread sideways into the opening; well fed, they are thus able to add thicker rings of wood to their trunks each growing season and are less susceptible to disease. (2) Light shafting down through the opening stimulates growth of plants in the understory or on the forest floor. Sapling trees under the hole in the canopy tend to grow straight and vigorous. Shrubs and/or herbs grow lush with the added solar energy. Vines may climb faster and even gain the canopy. Populations of many kinds of animals flourish around the edge of this newly created micro-environment, with its enriched variety and productivity. When thus opening the canopy, trees to be eliminated may be selected to harvest as lumber, fuel, or pulp. The remaining trees are future-crop trees, often referred to just as "crop trees" (p. 407).

Creaming versus culling. A short-sighted operator may select for immediate harvest the best trees and leave the worst, a so-called creaming operation. A conscientious forester, however, will care-fully note all the future-crop trees and leave them, while harvesting whatever he can from the competing trees which he removes, a so-called culling and thinning operation. The treelands resulting from these two methods, creaming and culling, may have about the same species composition, but their growth form and vitality will be much at variance, as will their future productivity (p. 409).

Girdling and chemical killing. Where the value of the wood of

CLOSED-CANOPY TREELANDS: Canopies opened

New problems and new possibilities !

Sunlight

Vigorous young growth

Small opening

Just cut, so no new growth yet

Connected openings

Regrowth will come

Recently clear-cut

National Forest timber cutting has left scattered seed trees to start a new crop and has bulldozed into piles and burned the debris left after harvesting the merchantable timber from this patch of forest. Shoshone National Forest, Wyoming.

trees removed would be less than the cost of removing them, they can be killed and allowed to rot in place. Cut around the base of the trunk through the inner bark to the wood, making the ring wide enough so that new growth cannot bridge over it, say an inch. This process is called girdling (p. 399). Or use a planticide, carefully spraying all around the bottom ten inches of the trunk; this can be done at any season, but in woods with thick undergrowth it is easier to get the spray in to the right place when deciduous leaves have fallen (p. 400). The dead standing trees are attractive to many forms of wildlife, and may blossom forth with colorful fungi and lichens. Note, however, that large dead trees are hazardous if left standing along trails.

CLOSED-CANOPY TREELAND CLEAR-CUT

It is possible to keep forest as forest land yet cut down all the trees. This operation, called clear-cutting, was standard lumbering proce-

dure for centuries in the United States; it is still a valid mode in a
few situations, although selective cutting has usually proved more
sensible. Clear-cutting permits easier and cheaper harvesting because
of the working space afforded where trees have already been felled.
Also, the immediate harvest is greater. Clear-cutting, however, has
ruined too many environments, creating many ecological problems,
especially erosion. By contrast, selective cutting is initially more
expensive because the lumbermen have to work between the future-
crop trees, which must not be damaged, and less can be harvested
at any one time. But of course selective cutting can be repeated more
often than the tree-generation required for regrowth after clear-
cutting; the forest is maintained and its vitality and form improved
even as it is being harvested.

Leaving seed trees.   When clear-cutting non-sprouting species
such as conifers, leave some trees to scatter seeds in the cleared area.
Isolated trees may be left here and there; but because they are often
susceptible to windthrow, seed trees are often left in strips or patches
of uncut woods.

Sprouting.   Partly because many hardwoods species such as those
of oak, maple, hickory, elm, chestnut, basswood, and ash sprout
readily from cut stumps, developing a coppice woodland which is
difficult to handle, hardwoods are less often clear-cut than softwoods
such as pine, spruce, and fir. However, rapid suckering of hardwood
stumps quickly creates good wildlife cover. In Europe, coppicing has
been used for centuries as a type of forest management supplying
faggots for fuel (avoiding the need to split kindling) and wattles for
laying hedges. Also, experimentation is indicating ways of improving the future timber growth of sproutwoods by selective de-sprout-
ing.

Planting.   If the forest is to be perpetuated, artificial reforestation
is used after clear-cutting when natural reseeding and sprouting are
inadequate to stock the new stand of trees (p. 374).

OPEN-CANOPY TREELANDS

When trees grow far enough apart that their branches do not touch,
the canopy is described as open. In humid regions this occurs nat-

(Top) Short-lived gray birches create a tangle too complicated for many to enjoy. (Bottom) A similar area carefully simplified by the Youth Conservation Corps appears more beautiful to people driving by. However, too much "cleaning up" is to be avoided. Moosehorn National Wildlife Refuge, Calais, Maine.

urally where trees have seeded into abandoned fields, pastures, or other open areas (meaning areas without trees). As the trees mature, their spreading branches normally close the canopy. (In more arid regions, mature trees may be widely scattered, indicating insufficient water for supporting denser stands of trees.) In the humid East, open-canopy treelands usually represent a stage in vegetational development wherein the dominant trees are young shade-intolerant ones such as pine, redcedar, aspen, birch, and cherry, which started in a seedbed of pioneer herbs. Many shade-intolerant shrubs are usually associated with them, for instance juniper, sweetfern, sumac, blueberry, spiraea, and blackberry. It is a treeland which may look more like a brushy field one decade and more like a young forest the next. Its temporary nature is even better understood when one notes the little seedlings of shade-tolerant trees (such as hemlock, maple, beech, and certain oaks) becoming established in the shadow underneath the shade-intolerant trees listed above. In time these little ones grow up through the "nurse trees" which shade them and they will then shade out and kill their shade-intolerant benefactors. Thus the open-canopy woodland represents a period of forest adolescence, and as such it is a time when a great variety of conservation practices can mold the future of the environment.

Wood production. To develop a treeland for a harvest of structural wood or pulp, the density of stocking with suitable species is important. Nature may have seeded too heavily or too sparsely. With too many little trees, there is strong competition as the canopy closes; many become stunted, broken, diseased, and finally dead, while the survivors are battle-scarred and therefore of inferior quality. Thinning the trees carefully while the canopy is still open can greatly improve the subsequent harvest (p. 405). If, on the other hand, the treeland is too sparsely stocked by nature, the larger open spaces between trees can be interplanted to young trees of suitable species, usually fast-growing conifers such as pine, spruce, fir, or larch. It will not pay to plant timber trees unless their growth rate will assure them an ultimate place in the canopy; for if the natural trees are growing fast and close the canopy over the planted ones, those planted will be suppressed and grow only very slowly. When either thinning or interplanting, be sure to estimate both the sideward and upward growth of the trees. Crowding causes competition, but trees with too much space around them spread sideways with large limbs while their trunks grow less tall; this causes a disproportionate amount of wood to develop in the hard-to-harvest branches instead of in tall, straight trunks. Note too that both thinning and planting can influence the species composition of a maturing woodlot, desirable species being released from competition with less desirable ones, or more desirable ones being added to those supplied by nature. *(199, 406, 471)*

Christmas trees. In this country, most trees decorated for Christmas are small, dense conifers, especially pine, fir, spruce, and redcedar. They are best grown in full-sunlight, shade-grown specimens being scrawnier. In open-canopy treelands you can often find naturally seeded little trees which make excellent Christmas trees. Their growth is benefited by releasing them from competition with any surrounding trees or shrubs which make them grow asymmetrically or might overtop and shade them. Their density of foliage can be increased by shearing each spring (p. 443). If the stand is understocked with evergreens and has sufficient open spaces, additional little conifers can be planted (p. 378).

Fruits, flowers, and greens. Watch the blooms, fruits, foliage, and twig patterns of the different seasons. Some of the most beautiful flowering and fruiting trees and shrubs grow in open-canopy treelands. Judicious releasing and pruning can help bring out their attractive growth form or increase the quantity or quality of blooms and fruits. Watch for the wild cherries whose dark gray or reddish trunks become clothed with their floral kimonos, followed by fruits which help to lure robins and other thrushes away from cultivated fruits. Look for sumacs, coarse when leafless but feathery green in spring and summer, turning vermillion or scarlet in the autumn. Search out the bayberries, whose gray fruits feed over a hundred kinds of birds, and which you can harvest for making hand-dipped candles in the Puritan tradition. These plants and many others can be encouraged to provide for continuing years if you arrest the normal vegetational development by keeping the canopy from closing over, thus letting each selected plant reach a magnificent maturity rarely allowed by unaided nature.

Wildlife. Open-canopy treelands are excellent for many kinds of wildlife and for relatively easy observation of them. The edge between different environments which so promotes dense wildlife populations (p. 458) is extensive, with many vertical edges around the openings between trees as well as the horizontal edge atop the crowns and the peripheral edge of the treeland. Sunlight striking through to the ground stimulates considerable undergrowth, often rich with many species of plants attractive to a great variety of wildlife. The openings make it relatively easy to see birds and tree-climbing mammals in the treetops, so difficult in a tall, closed woodland. Wildlife management includes cutting away competing plants *(releasing)* around trees and shrubs which are favorites for desired species of wildlife (p. 457), clearing trails for easier and quieter observation of animals (p. 256), selective cutting, pruning, and planticiding to maintain or create openings for increased edge effect (p. 458), and maybe supplying feeding stations and water (see Chapter 15).

Watershed. Open-canopy treelands on soil which is deep, fertile, and moist enough to create good groundcover make relatively good watersheds because of the accumulating organic matter and the porosity of soil well penetrated by roots. In more arid places, the scattered woody vegetation may be interspersed with quite bare areas with rapid runoff; planting suitable species in these openings may help if there is adequate water for them. Contour ditching (p. 353), terracing (p. 343), mulching (p. 340), and other watershed management techniques may also be used without destroying the existing tree cover. Where open-canopy treelands border drinking water supplies, selective cutting, pruning, weeding, and planting encourage needle-leaved evergreens. These are preferred along the edges of reservoirs because their narrow leaves, falling more nearly vertically than broad leaves, do not blow into the water much; hence they do not give the water an undesirable color and taste. Evergreens also act as a drift fence to prevent broad leaves from blowing into the water. As with all watersheds, protection from fire is important.

Existing openings can help in laying out fire access roads and fuel-breaks.

Recreation. Open-canopy treelands lend themselves to a variety of easily attained landscape effects suitable for trails, vistas, and picnic areas. The interplay of sun and shade and the variety of vegetation give many opportunities to the skilled landscape artist and many challenges for experimentation by the beginner. Modes of recreation can be as numerous as the tastes of imaginative people. Young people will enjoy tree-climbing because the trees are apt to be still low-branching and vigorous, with a minimum of dangerous dead wood. An abundance of wild fruits for jam and jelly will lure gatherers and cooks. Recreational forest management or plant training will provide outlets for the talents and energies of many people, while others will find peace sitting on a sunny rustic bench at a turn of the trail, watching birds, butterflies, and the changing seasons. The whole family can enjoy a barbecue spot in a suitable opening. If it is used for an evening campfire and sing, you may need to pollard surrounding trees (p. 441) because their upward growth will obscure more and more of the sunset sky and the constellations which glitter more brightly as the embers fade.

TREELAND RECREATION

Forests provide recreation based primarily on forest climate, beauty, and native plants and animals. Trees moderate local climate, making it cooler in hot weather and warmer in cold weather than nearby open spaces, providing greater comfort for either quiet enjoyment or active games which do not require large cleared areas. The living walls and leafy canopy give snugness and privacy, the forest floor a resilient carpet. Each leaf and twig and every animal adds a bit of beauty or interest. We can find stimulus or relaxation in our woods, in many ways. The person learning the joys of using a sharp axe and the photographer of trees experimenting with a new lens have different needs, each valid. To manage our woods to give as many satisfactions as possible, we need good planning, sensitive development according to priorities, and administration which diverse people can understand. *(166, 528)*

FOREST-TRAIL RECREATION

Treelands for trail recreation need more or less linear clearing and/or marking of routes for any of several uses: strolling, hiking, cross-country running, cross-country skiing, snowshoeing, riding animals, bicycling, motorcycling, snowmobiling, nature watching, nature study, and nature arts. In most cases, avoid motorized vehicles except for emergencies and patrol. Give special attention to esthetic aspects of trail design (p. 251).

FOREST-CLEARING RECREATION

Wider areas need to be more or less cleared of tree trunks, low limbs, undergrowth, and stumps for activities such as quoits, tetherball, and horseshoes; small-court games such as badminton, deck tennis, and volleyball; outdoor eating and sleeping groups ("camping" in a narrow sense); folk dancing; outdoor theatricals, musicals, and other performances for small gatherings. Decentralize activities so that clearings are well scattered, with growing zones between (p. 158) to minimize wear and preserve the forest environment. Poor layout and careless management can change a beautiful treeland into a beaten-down desert. (See Chapter 14 for methods of clearing.)

Small clearings for active games. *For summer coolness,* leave the canopy as intact as possible. If the trees are tall enough, clear out just the underbrush and prune branches to the required height. But if the trees are still too small to overarch, make narrow east–west clearings with as many tall trees as possible on the south side for shade. Favor these by releasing them from competition (p. 410) and by pruning, mulching, fertilizing, and fencing to hasten their becoming fine shade trees. When you can, leave a few trees pruned high right in the clearing to become overarching shaders, with ground rules for games designed to make the trees part of the fun rather than obstacles causing complaint. For greater comfort on hot days, trim out to windward to increase air circulation through the clearing, realizing though that this will make it cooler in cold weather (p. 281).

For winter warmth run small clearings north–south, with evergreens as windbreaks (p. 279) along the west and north sides. Have only deciduous trees on the south so that their bare limbs will let in sun. South-facing slopes are the warmest.

To minimize soil compaction, which decreases insoak (p. 304) and increases erosion and sickliness of shade trees: (1) Make clearings for active games only in level places, when possible. (2) Grade sloping areas to make them as level as possible without disturbance to tree roots. Do not fill against tree trunks! (3) Mulch to help water penetration (p. 340). (4) Do not let water from adjacent areas flow onto the clearing. (5) Plan roads and trails so that they do not conduct water into the clearing (p. 252). (6) Keep paths in good condition so that people stay on them and do not trample growing zones (below) bordering the clearings. (7) Fence off adjacent growing zones *before* it seems necessary.

Growing zones between clearings. Forest-clearing recreation should be decentralized enough to permit continued happy existence of typical forest plants and animals. Too many such recreation areas become devoid of undergrowth and the shade trees die from soil compaction. The areas become hot and dusty in dry weather and muddy in wet. Growing zones provide privacy for campsites and separate areas for different age groups and different activities, curtail dust and noise, slow the wind, attract wildlife to areas where people may sit quietly, and provide maximum variety and beauty in the forest scene.

Avoid trampling, fuel-gathering, cutting toasting forks, collecting craft and campcraft materials, and picking flowers, except when thoughtfully controlled. Rustic fencing can help. Sturdy sitting-fences and standum-sittums do double duty by providing perches for spectators.

Replanting is advisable in treeland areas which have been too heavily used. Make fences *before* planting to protect new plants. Use shade-tolerant species, for instance hemlock, beech, and sugar maple, some viburnums in cooler climates, and inkberry farther south. Rhododendrons and azaleas are useful and beautiful on acid soils. Sweetpepperbush does well on moist, sandy soils. Japanese barberry is hardy in many sites, as is Tartarian honeysuckle. In the Pacific Northwest, salal is one of the most helpful shrubs. Along sunny edges of clearings, many sun-loving plants help fend off people and contribute intriguing life to the growing zones (see *Planting*, Ch. 14).

Access roads to clearings.   Approaches should cause minimum disruption of the forest. One-way roads (p. 266) need only narrow clearings; they curve between large trees and other natural features with greater ease and safety than two-way roads. They provide solitude by avoiding oncoming traffic. Have occasional turnouts (laybys).

Roads and trails on slopes should run obliquely rather than straight up and down and should be maintained with a high crown and gutters to keep water from flowing down where the traffic runs (See Chapter 9). Poorly laid out roads and trails not only erode but also cause sedimentation problems where they level off downhill.

Parking spaces for forest recreation.   If the site permits, make only small clearings for parking, preferably numerous single-car parking spurs (p. 24) along the road at a 60-degree angle and with bumper log or stop-stones at the end. Thus spreading out the parking means some cars will be farther from a recreation clearing than if there were a large central parking lot, but the shadier microclimate and sylvan esthetics will for many people be worth the longer walk to their cars. To keep foot traffic off the road, run a "nature sidewalk" paralleling the road some twenty feet or more away wherever topographically feasible. Each camping site for a tent or recreation vehicle should have its individual parking space well screened from adjacent campsites by growing zones (p. 158). Whenever possible, use hand labor to avoid disruptive bull-dozing. Take a little longer; do a little better. *(552)*

Sites for tents, recreational vehicles, and cabins.   Some clearing is necessary to make floor space and walking space and to keep branches from touching canvas or walls. In moist climates, cutting may be needed to assure sunlight part of the day, preferably in the morning, to dry out the site. Do not start to clear until the locations of access paths, outdoor fireplaces, and eating areas are firmly mapped out, for all of these must be planned with reference to each other! For instance, prevailing winds during seasons of most use should blow the smoke from the fireplace away from tent and table

rather than into them. Well-planned sites cause minimum disturbance of forest growth, leaving maximum growing zones for native
flora and fauna. If faulty planning requires relocation of tent, table,
fireplace, or trails, more vegetation has to be cleared. Repeated mistakes turn the treeland recreation area into a desert of compacted
earth. This often happens as more people pressure rural regions.

A site can often be improved by selective cutting and pruning of
trees and by pruning and releasing (p. 410) berry-bearing and ornamental shrubs. When tall treelands have too few lower branches or
undergrowth for privacy, keeping out wind, maintaining soil porosity, and so on, cut tree species capable of sprouting quickly (p. 438)
to provide low vegetation. Trees cut in spring often sprout more
vigorously than those cut in autumn; and old or sickly trees may
fail to sprout. The trees to be cut to stimulate sprouting should be
thoughtfully selected to provide the desired kind of vegetation in
the desired place.

Planting shrubs native to an area often improves the site, increasing privacy and adding beauty, berries, or a sustained supply of
toasting forks, dough-twist sticks, and other campcraft materials.
These should be carefully harvested with an understanding of how
to stimulate the plants to replace the materials taken (p. 435). *(14,
375, 454)*

Clearings for fireplaces.   The woodland fireplace itself should
always be small. A forest is no place for bonfires! To serve many
people at one time, build several small fires, well spaced. The size of
a clearing for a fire will depend upon the combustibility of the
surrounding vegetation. Clear no more than necessary—but err on
the safe side by clearing enough. Many people clear too far sideways
but not enough overhead, forgetting that the updraft of hot air can
wither leaves and kill branches high above. Remove the closest small
trees and shrubbery and carefully prune over the fireplace the lower
branches of the bigger trees which are left. Rake away the duff of
dead leaves and twigs right down to mineral soil for several feet in
radius, the distance depending upon the size of likely (and unlikely)
fires and the combustibility of surroundings. Use the duff to give
additional mulch to some other part of the recreation area. Make
sure that users of fireplaces are informed about wise use of fire.

Clearings for picnic tables. Picnic areas should be flat enough to hold tables and benches with some additional walking-around room. On hilly terrain, this requires terracing by cutting and filling, with or without retaining walls (p. 343). When terracing, first rake the duff to one side. Then, after leveling the mineral soil, replace the duff to make the soil absorbent and to give the site a natural look. Some people make the mistake of raking duff away from eating areas; it is as clean as the mineral soil beneath and it helps prevent dust and mud. For heavily used eating areas where enough duff cannot be maintained, it is good practice to have a poured cement slab under each table and its benches. Sometimes it is wise to raise the grade of low-lying land to develop a picnic site. Such a locale may be mosquitoey, but this may be compensated for by the greater wealth of other wildlife observable there.

Vistas. Sometimes a clearing should be made primarily for its visual effect. It may be just a hole in the canopy to let a shaft of sunlight into deep forest. More often it is a vista, an opening which focuses on some distant point of beauty, perhaps a paper birch backed by evergreens, an outcrop of rock set about by ferns, a bit of lake shore down through the trees, a glimpse of a sunny meadow, or a distant mountain.

The cutting should be carefully planned and then done a little at a time to watch how the effect is coming. Be concerned not only with the view being revealed but also with the nature of the frame. The bottom of the vista frame may be the duff of the forest floor; if so, be careful, if a hill is involved, not to let it become a trail. Because a vista must always be straight, it is natural that people will use the clearing as a straight path; but on a hill a straight path often leads to bad erosion. So leave enough underbrush to discourage walking down or up the vista, and supplement it with rustic fencing if necessary. Usually it is best to encourage a total groundcover of shrubs. (Little hardwood trees should be pulled out or killed with weedicide as they come up; cutting them just stimulates them to grow more sprouts. Little coniferous trees, however, can usually be eliminated by cutting.) A frame bottom of topped trees is difficult to maintain at the desired level, but it can be beautiful and practical on steep slopes.

Side frames of vistas are easiest to maintain when composed of tall trunks with branches pruned off on the vista side. A different effect, harder to maintain, is created by shearing branches on the sides of the vista, progressively more difficult as the side plants grow taller. The top of the vista frame can be either the sky or branches spreading from the trees at the sides, or from overhead at the point of viewing (if there is only one such point). Some cutting of overhead branches may be necessary as they lengthen and bend down from their increasing weight and leverage. The nearer end of a vista clearing can be narrower than the farther end in cases where the view is to be seen from one spot, such as a bench, summerhouse, or tent doorway.

RECREATIONAL STRUCTURES FOR TREELANDS

Considerable creative endeavor can go into furnishing a recreational woodlot; but one should not let his enthusiasm for manmade contraptions obscure the natural scene. A brilliant red soft-drink machine looks out of place; but metal waste receptacles painted in greens, browns, grays, or other colors which harmonize with the natural environment are sometimes acceptable. Wood, natural material in treelands, is suitable for many kinds of rustic furnishings. Living wood can sometimes, with patience, be trained to make seats, tables, and true jungle-gyms (p. 164). Cut wood for permanent furniture should almost always have the bark removed, no matter how attractive it may seem, so that the wood can be treated with chemical preservatives to retard decay. Rotten furniture is dangerous because it can collapse suddenly. Besides, it is a waste of time to spend much effort on a structure and then have it soon rot. Stone makes enduring and beautiful benches, fireplaces, and table legs if carefully laid. Because of their permanence, take care planning location of stone structures, to be sure that they become an appropriate part of the scene.

Play equipment suited to woodlands can include swings (suspended from eye-bolts through large branches, not tied over the branches); suspended log horses (tied to four trees); rustic jungle-gyms; miniature log houses securely spiked or bolted together and often open-roofed; low balancing rails made of logs; and sandboxes with debarked logs to restrain the sand.

Animal feeding stations and baths, fountains, and statuary can be added to the list of forest furnishings if congruous with the treeland setting.

Shelters. The season of recreational usefulness can be extended if you create protection from cold winds by planting a windbreak, by solid fencing, or by building a lean-to, Adirondack shelter, or cabin. A summerhouse open on two or more sides provides protection from summer rainshowers. If it has a cooking-style fireplace, less disruption will result from showers during summer cookouts. Sometimes the same chimney can be used for an additional, unprotected fair-weather fireplace on its outside, with a separate or partially separate flue. The summerhouse can give valuable protection also from the sun when trees are still too young to give shade; and when screened it gives respite from biting insects. Don't forget that for young people particularly there is probably no shelter so intriguing as a tree house. *(43)*

A shelter can be far more than a place for outdoor eating. It can be a place for reading, writing, sketching, and music, and a center for making nature observations and records. It is well to plan a locker for a book of nature writings, pencil and paper, and other suitable appurtenances of the arts and sciences.

Hides. A hide (also called a "blind") can greatly increase the enjoyment of watching wildlife by keeping the occupant camouflaged. In woodlands, such an observation post can have the added advantage of being built in trees above the ground. Many of the most interesting treeland phenomena go on in treetops, missed by earthbound people.

TREES FOR CHILDREN

Feats of daring and balance are important for children in developing strength, coordination, and self-confidence. They should have opportunities beyond a rectangular jungle-gym of smooth pipe and the tops of city fences. For the youngest, a felled tree trunk with one end a foot or two off the ground can provide hours of delight, especially

TREE GYMS

Unpruned Apple

Brace—

Pruned for climbing

Swing

Hung Horse

Bolted Saplings

Let grow

if two or three large side branches are left on it. When a little older, they enjoy two to four trees felled informally crisscross, some with their tops several feet off the ground, high enough to be a little scary. Some pruning will help, but strategic branches should be left for holding on.

Some children will be ready for low-branching trees growing nearby where grownups can give them reminders: (1) to stay near the trunk, because of increased leverage and weaker limbs as one goes out on them; (2) always to hold on with at least one hand, preferably two; (3) never to use a dead branch for support unless it has been well tested; (4) to distribute one's weight on two or more branches when it is necessary to climb on thin ones; and (5) to recognize tree species with strong wood and ones with weak wood (such as poplar, aspen, and young pine).

Certain kinds of trees should be encouraged as climbing trees for children. Catalpas and apples are two of the best because they branch low, have well-spaced branches, and are strong. Superfluous small branches should be pruned off, especially on apple trees, which are apt to have many suckers and sharp spur shoots. In time, careful training of branches can make imaginatively wonderful climbing trees for ensuing generations. Gray birches are great for climbing and swinging, but only where they are plentiful and their bent shape will not mar the landscape, or when the bent trees can be set upright again after swinging by strenuous up-pushing with a long forked pole.

NON-MODIFYING TREELAND RECREATION

Treelands for the following need little, if any, alteration: berry-picking, limited flower gathering, hunting, tracking, stalking, orienteering with map and compass courses, nature watching, nature study, nature arts, and wilderness camping. In our culture, bent on subduing nature rather than on finding a humbler way of relating to it, there is need to promote non-consumptive recreation.

Conservation of treelands for non-modifying recreation consists primarily of protecting the forests from fire *(67, 140)* and from people, especially those who wish to develop them for other uses. It is important in treeland planning to designate natural areas and to perpetuate them as such. Write to The Nature Conservancy, Suite 1030, The Federal Building, 1522 K St., N.W., Washington, D.C. 20005, for literature on values of natural areas and for help in setting them aside. Help may also be available from organizations such as Audubon groups at the state and local level.

CREATING A NEW TREELAND FOR RECREATION

A new woodland meant primarily for recreation will usually be a grove in an open area. It may also function as a windbreak or screen planting to cut off less desirable views. Topography, soil type, groundwater conditions, and prevailing wind directions determine the tree species which can be successfully planted. While sites and personal tastes differ, the following may be worth special thought.

Plant pines or spruces five or six feet apart on the side which is windward in dry and cold weather (pitch pine or Japanese black pine if exposed to salt spray from the ocean). Keep them bushy by cutting off one third of the "candle" of new growth each spring. In the shelter they provide, clumps of any of the light-barked species of birches can be set twenty to twenty-five feet apart. Between the birches plant catalpas and/or horsechestnuts (buckeye), both beautiful when in flower against the dark evergreens and both good for climbing by children. Little children enjoy making garlands of the catalpa flowers and playing various games with the nuts of the horsechestnuts. The catalpa is fast-growing, even on sandy soils. Downwind from these trees, plant longer-lived species to form the center of the grove, with such genera as oak, beech, maple, tuliptree, and sycamore. Avoid such fast-growing and brittle trees as silver maple, poplar, cottonwood unless these are the only ones adapted to the region. Faster-growing trees can be spotted in between the longer-lived ones but should be removed after some years to let the oaks and the like spread out. It is sometimes better to use flowering and fruiting shrubs to fill in, for they will cause fewer problems of removal later and may produce enjoyable flowers and fruits sooner than most trees. Fruit trees may be planted on the downwind edge to complete the recreational grove. Apple trees, a favorite for children to climb, can be pruned for that purpose, and their flowers add beauty even when you do not wish to bother to spray them repeatedly to insure insect-free fruits. While these kinds of trees are suited to the northeastern United States, southern Canada and the northern Rocky Mountains, the reasons for choosing them can be applied in other regions to the species of trees hardy there. The biggest problems in developing new recreational treelands will come in those climates where trees are hardest to grow, areas with less than thirty inches of annual rainfall. There it will be necessary to use hardy species such as the Chinese and Siberian elms, hackberry, and, in desert regions, specialized trees such as date palms. (Groundwater close to the surface or irrigation water can increase the numbers of hardy species so that dates and other palms can be grown.) The harder the job of establishing a treeland and of protecting it until it attains tree stature, the greater the pleasures that may be derived from it.

Any tree has recreational value if enjoyed. The problem is knowing what a desired species needs to make *it* happy. Tree books, books on landscape design, journals, and local nurserymen can help. Look to see what others have planted and how successful they have been; but also be willing to make well-thought-out experiments of your own. Involve the whole family in researching, planning, and planting for recreation. Let each express preferences; then reach compromises. Mother may want the main grove of pines like the ones where she grew up. Johnny may want the entire grove of locusts, sourwood, basswood, and other trees for his honey bees. And so on. More fun! Then considerable work with nature.

(See also *83, 170, 234, 298, 327, 335, 383, 447, 571, 587.*)

6 Wetlands

Observation towers
Hides (blinds)
Launching ramps and docks
Water-Control Structures
Impoundments
Flood control
Irrigation
Fire protection
Wildlife management
Groundwater control
Esthetics
Vegetation Management
Clearing
Planting
Constructed Wetlands
Topography
Soil permeability
Water-producing potential of the watershed
Artificial impoundments
Skating rinks
Sewage lagoons
Basins excavated for groundwater and surface water
Impoundments along coasts
Saving Samples of Natural Wetlands

Wetlands in this book are lands covered with shallow water for a considerable portion of each year, or lands whose groundwater rises so high that it is near or at the surface much of the time. The edges of wetlands move as water comes and goes, making them difficult to demark. Wet land changes to dry land as a marsh shrinks toward its center, as a wet meadow drops its water table in a dry spell. So for recognizing wetlands, there is is not only a problem of changing boundaries but also a puzzle of time. How long each year does an area have to be wet to be identified as a wetland? Or does it have to be wet *each* year? Frequency of wetting can be an important factor. So can depth of water. A marsh with a six-inch depth may look like a grassy meadow from a distance but look wet from close by and logically be recognized as a wetland, whereas a marsh with three feet of water may have considerable open water showing and be referred to as a pond. At some intermediate depth we get involved with a "marshy pond" or "deep marsh," which it may or may not be helpful to call a wetland rather than a body of water. It is more important to recognize wetlands as ill-defined rather than to try to formulate a complicated definition. In fact, much of their charm as well as their utility is based on their ambiguous position between dry land and water.

USES AND MISUSES

The old complaint about the muddy Mississippi River having too much soil in it to make it drinkable and too much water to make it plowable reminds us of a common attitude toward wetlands. They are usually too shallow to fish and too wet to farm in conventional occidental ways. However, rice paddies of the Orient, fish ponds rotated with tilled crops in the Rhône Valley of France, and polders in the Netherlands have illustrated that where density of population and high land value make it seem worth while, men with a favorable attitude can put to use what has been thought of as wasteland. *(89)*

Primitive cultures have used wetlands for hunting waterfowl, shorebirds, beaver, muskrat, and moose; for harvesting grasses for thatch and baskets; and for gathering wildrice fruits, cattail rhizomes, and other foods. Later agriculture used them for marsh hay, retting of flax, and rice culture. Industrial society, less appreciative of wetlands as wetlands, has drained and filled them for innumerable purposes, including agriculture, commerce, housing, industry, transportation, and waste disposal. Now more people have a better understanding of watershed values of wetlands and of our need of them for education and recreation. In many built-up places, wetlands are the only areas left where urban people can feel wind unbroken by buildings and hear the whistle of waterfowl wings. As development, sedimentation from eroding areas, and pollution take their toll, efforts are being made to create new wetlands by flooding drylands of supposedly lesser value; but still the outlook for wetlands is critical *(285)*.

Wetlands for education.   When people are ill-advised, it is partly the fault of educational institutions. Wetlands have been neglected. Schools, colleges, universities, churches, and synagogues need to set aside wetlands as natural areas and experimental areas for education. While these can also be used for recreation, the primary use must be education and other uses must not conflict. Often educational administrators have taken no interest in wetlands until some informed person has shown what can be done with one. Even a small back-yard wetland may become a helpful demonstration. *(470)*

Wetlands for recreation.   Artists, naturalists, and wildfowlers know the joys of wetlands, but most people do not. Too often they fear swamps and turn up their noses at marshes. As parks, wildlife refuges, and nature centers expand their interpretive work, more people are coming to wetlands to enjoy seeing them. But working with wetlands can be fun too.

Wetlands as watersheds.   No matter what a wetland is used for, it is part of a watershed, often a most significant part. Its retention

of water can cause such problems as stagnant water where mosquitoes breed or groundwater which filters into basements of buildings. These detrimental factors, however, must be considered in relation to the wetland's value in retaining water during times of
excessive runoff, holding back floods, allowing streams to spread
harmlessly rather than concentrate destructively in narrow valleys,
and absorbing much of the energy of flood tides (as do coastal
marshes) so that waves do not eat away shores and their human
settlements. In droughts when streams run low and interstream
soils and vegetation are parched, these wetlands can sometimes
supply water for irrigation and fire control which may save a community from destruction. In such times, people are more apt to see
mosquito problems in proportion. They may even understand that a
wet basement often indicates a building built in the wrong place.
Indeed, communities cannot be considered well adjusted to their
environment unless their land use takes wetlands into consideration
and deals with them understandingly.

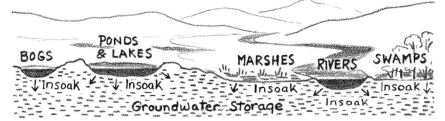

WATER STORAGE by wetlands and water bodies

KINDS OF WETLANDS

The United States Fish and Wildlife Service recognizes twenty kinds
of wetlands, determined by such factors as whether they are coastal
or inland; fresh, brackish, or saline; stagnant (bogs and fens); flowing
(marshes and swamps); grassy (marshes); or wooded (swamps).
Latitudinal variations are also significant, influencing physical and
chemical processes and determining the kinds of plants and animals
in wetland ecosystems.

Coastal wetlands. These usually occur on coastal plains, as on the East and Gulf Coasts of the United States. Some coastal plains extend far inland, but wetlands a few miles back from the sea lose their coastal characteristics, like salinity. Some coastal wetlands are not on plains but in estuaries and deltas where rivers meet the sea or a large lake.

A coastal wetland usually has a barrier beach of gravel or sand thrown up by wave action along its outer margin. This spit or bar is breached here and there where streams maintain their channels through it. Severe storms may cut new breaches where storm tides rush through. Alongshore currents and, to some extent, winds fill in these cuts unless streams or dredging keep them open. Barrier beaches are significant parts of the anatomy of coastal wetlands. Their bare sands are beautiful and hence recreationally important. They monitor the mixing of fresh water coming down in streams or seeping through the soil with salt water flooding in from the sea. They allow nutritive stream sediments to accumulate, and marsh vegetation to grow protected from wave action. Millions of people go to beaches and give little thought to the geological drama where

A prairie slough is an island of wetness in a rolling sea of grass, a haven for a great variety of plants and animals which could not survive in the surrounding cultivated fields. Tipton, Iowa.

land and sea meet. Much interpretive work needs to be done to help shore visitors appreciate the coastal marshes lying thinly protected behind their barrier beaches. *(508)*

Wetlands of undrained basins.   Each wetland lies in a basin, usually a valley with a stream running through it. In arid country, intermontane basins may lack streams, except during the rare but often heavy rains which may bring temporary water that collects as a *playa*. In glaciated terrain, small basins called *kettle holes* slope inward from all sides so there is no low side from which water can drain out. These kettles resulted from the melting of blocks of ice stranded, in late glacial times, on the bottoms of former glacial lakes or on outwash plains developed where glaciers stopped. Kettles have stagnant water; they are fed by springs or surface runoff into them rather than by a through-flowing stream. In humid regions, kettles usually have *bogs* with vegetation growing in acid water. In the drier grassland prairies of the northern Midwest, kettles are called *potholes* or *sloughs;* their water is more basic and more fertile. In Britain, such wetlands with basic water from limestone rocks are called *fens.*

Wetlands along streams.   How much wetland exists along a stream depends largely on the stream's maturity (p. 211). Youthful streams have almost none, because of their narrow valleys and steep gradient. Mature streams, by contrast, may have considerable wetlands on their floodplains; and an old stream with a very wide valley may have miles of marshes and swamps along its old channels, in abandoned meanders called *bayous* or *backwaters* or *oxbow lakes* (p. 212).

Sometimes lands that should be wetlands by the rules of the river are diked off, drained, and used for crops—which makes sense because of the rich silts and because then the only major loss in time of floods may be crops. At other times, floodplain wetlands are filled for residential, commercial, and industrial development, with devastating losses in floods. Now communities seeking a sound ecological basis have zoning laws to prevent unwise developments on wetlands "which belong to the river." Even a tiny stream may be mature and have a floodplain with a mini-wetland. Perhaps you can find one near you on which you can demonstrate wise wetland use.

MOVEMENT OF WATER

Bogs typically are stagnant. A marsh along a stream typically has moving water. A marsh beside a large lake may have very little downstream movement yet be kept from stagnation by lateral and vertical movements of water within the lake, created by wind friction on the surface, by relative heating and cooling of the water, and by lateral seepage of water from surrounding higher land. Shallow marshes in regions with little rain may sometimes stagnate.

DEPTH OF WATER

Shallow water is the rule in most wetlands. In bogs, however, the water may be many feet deep; the appearance of land can be caused by vegetation forming a floating mat. Shallow marshes have less than a foot of water and deep marshes from one to three feet under average conditions. Of course there is no sharp division between the two; a deep marsh may have a shallow marsh along its edge, for instance. The depth helps determine the kinds of plants and animals which will flourish.

SOME CHEMICAL FACTORS

Salinity involves the amounts and kinds of salts dissolved in the water. Salts have pronounced effects on organisms, some of which evolved in fresh water, some in sea water or salt lakes inland, and some in the brackish water of river estuaries and inland ponds of arid regions. Salty waters are alkaline (basic or limy), indicated on the pH scale with a number higher than 7, the neutral point. Fresh waters may be either alkaline, because of calcium salts or related compounds which make the water "hard"; or they may be acidic, with a pH lower than 7, and are then termed "soft" waters.

The amount of oxygen dissolved in water makes a great difference to aquatic life. Colder waters can hold more oxygen than warmer ones. Because wetlands usually have shallow water, which heats faster than deep, they are often low in oxygen and cannot support fish like trout which require an abundance of this element.

Many other substances can be important, for instance the heavy metals like lead, mercury, and copper. If you are not chemically trained, get assistance from schools or colleges in testing the waters in your wetlands. Chemistry often provides important clues to their wise management.

BOG VEGETATION

The stagnant, acidic water of bogs has a limited, highly specialized flora of which sphagnum, also called peat moss, is primary. Early in the bog's vegetational development this plant grows along the edge as a somewhat lumpy carpet of pale green or occasionally pink, its vertical stems sometimes several inches tall and forming a deep, wet plush. The scaly leaves have a remarkable ability to hold water, as gathering a handful and squeezing will demonstrate. Continuing growth extends the sphagnum as a protruding shelf into the water, eventually covering the entire surface as a floating mat, the water hidden beneath. In shallow depressions the bog may become filled with the dark brown organic remains of the sphagnum, forming deposits of *peat*, which is burned in fuel-poor northern countries and widely sold in bales as an organic soil additive for gardeners.

VEGETATIONAL DEVELOPMENT : BOG

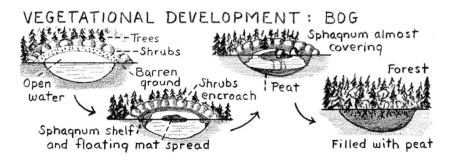

Shrubs invade the sphagnum mat, especially members of the heath family: cranberry, blueberry, leatherleaf, rhodora, labradortea. These and other bushes form a woody shrub-bog stage (p. 179). Acid-tolerant trees, especially spruces and larches, also find the sphagnum a good seedbed. Young trees appear droll as you approach them on the sphagnum mat, for they bow to you in seemingly polite welcome. Their roots grow outward in the sphagnum beyond the extent of their branches; this network of roots is depressed by your foot, making the bog mat quake and the trees tip toward you. When exploring bogs, carry a pole, for occasionally a place in the mat will lack roots enough to support you; the pole will keep you from disappearing forever.

More people would have the fun of bog-walking were it not for the *marginal moat* of northern bogs, a ring of open water one to several yards wide close to shore which effectively isolates the floating mat from anybody on shore who is scared of wet feet. Bridging the moat is a favorite challenge for young people. They should be encouraged in the enterprise, but taught the dangers of bog mats and how to cope with them—just as children should be taught to use a sharp knife when they are old enough to keep their minds on its dangers. One way to bridge a moat is to fell (p. 411) a bankside tree across it. Children also inevitably think of rafts, whose use should be supervised as much as necessary.

The moat often has pondweeds, duckweeds, bladderworts, and algae. In the protection of the sphagnum mat some of the most beautiful orchids flourish. Here too are insectivorous plants: the tiny sundews with sparkling drops of death-sticky exudate awaiting small insects; pitcher plants with a point of no return for insects part way down their cavernous leaves, where down-bent hairs prevent escape from digestive liquids beneath; and, in the southern United States, the Venus flytrap, as deadly to insects as it is beautiful to us. Associated with the wondrously specialized plants are many little animals which make the bog their home. Bees harvest nectar in the white sprays of leatherleaf, and redwinged blackbirds nest in the buttonbush.

WET MEADOW VEGETATION

Grasses are predominant in wet meadows, but sedges of many kinds may also be major components (p. 177). Rushes, spikerushes, and many kinds of forbs often join them. Wet meadows occur in grassland regions where the watertable is high much of the year, as along

VEGETATIONAL DEVELOPMENT: MARSH

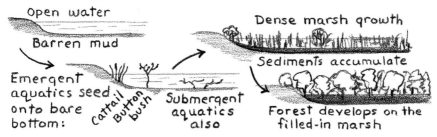

Open water

Barren mud

Emergent aquatics seed onto bare bottom: Cattail Buttonbush

Submergent aquatics also

Dense marsh growth

Sediments accumulate

Forest develops on the filled-in marsh

the edges of sloughs in the prairie states. In more humid regions where woody growth predominates, these meadows occur where grazing maintains herbaceous plants in wet places, or where haying or burning favors grasses. Fresh meadows occur inland in humid regions, salt meadows along the sea coast, blending into shallow coastal marsh. Some of the most beautiful wet meadows are high on mountains where abundant clouds and shallow soil create a high water table locally (p. 297). In the far north, a similar wetland is far more extensive—the wet tundra (p. 50).

MARSH VEGETATION

Grasses and grasslike plants are typical of marshes; their stems and narrow leaves are more or less vertical. The most familiar are cattails, bulrushes, tule, and three-squares, sedges, and reeds, all widely distributed. Forbs include arrowheads, pickerelweed, and smartweeds. The seeds of all these can germinate on muddy bottoms of shallow water and grow up as *emergent vegetation*—marsh pioneers,

A few EMERGENT AQUATICS of MARSHES

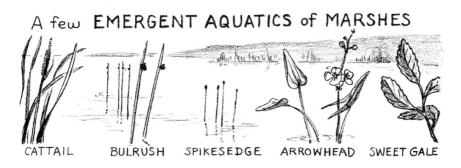

CATTAIL   BULRUSH   SPIKESEDGE   ARROWHEAD   SWEET GALE

Some FLOATING AQUATICS

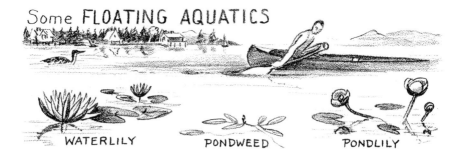

WATERLILY   PONDWEED   PONDLILY

colonizing shallow areas. Salt marshes may be largely cordgrass and/or saltgrass, while fresh marshes may have predominantly wildrice or cutgrass *(508)*. Whatever kinds are present in your marsh, they will have their special habits contributing to the seasonal aspects of the marsh flora and to the activities of the marsh fauna. Emergent vegetation is not only important cover but also a major source of food for wildlife. For people, emergent vegetation is also important in lessening shore erosion, breaking the force of waves and forming marsh peat which stabilizes the bottom.

Floating aquatic plants may be found among the emergent marsh plants or in zones by themselves; examples are waterlilies, pondlilies, and pondweeds. These are rooted to the bottom and have vertical stems to their horizontally floating leaves—seats for frogs and many aquatic insects. Others are free-floating, the tiny duckweeds for example. Unfortunately, at times, some kinds become bad pests—waterchestnut and waterhyacinth for example—clogging shallow waterways and swimming areas. *(258)*

Submerged aquatic plants form a third group in marshes. Bladderworts, watermilfoils, and many algae are examples. These, too, have a variety of roles in paludal theatrics. The bladderworts have, in addition to beautiful emergent flowers, tiny swollen sacs which trap minute water animals. Algae are basic to many food webs in the marsh waters which are the breeding and hunting territory of so many forms of aquatic life, from the little amoeba to the great blue heron. To push a canoe up a twisty channel through the reeds is to enter a world of excitement too few people know. Sometimes only children stop to think what it will be like when "progress" has finished filling the marsh. Where will the heron stand then? *(289)*

SWAMP VEGETATION

The conspicuous growth of swamps is woody, but beneath the trees and shrubs there is often a rich herbaceous flora. *Shrubswamps* have relatively low woody plants, fifteen or so feet high at the tallest; these may be all shrubs or may be shrubs with young trees mixed in. *Treeswamps* have large trees, usually with an understory of shrubs and young trees, and a layer of herbs beneath. *(67)*

Development of swamp vegetation in *stagnant water* may start in a bog of open water being colonized by sphagnum, which acts as a nursery for heath shrubs such as leatherleaf. In time these shrubs nurse seedlings of spruce and larch, which grow into treeswamp. After a long time the accumulating plant debris may fill the bog and permit a forest of shade-tolerant trees to grow up through the conifers. This forest of trees such as beech, sugar maple, and hemlock is the ultimate stage; it persists a long time, reproducing itself until destroyed by some disaster such as fire, windthrow, or felling by man.

Development of swamp vegetation in *flowing water* may start in a marsh of open water pioneered by buttonbush, a specialized shrub whose seeds are adapted to sprouting under two or three feet of water. Buttonbush slows the current, catching silt and organic matter. The marsh becomes shallower, suited to cattails, some bulrushes, and deep-water grasses such as wildrice. Clumps of tussock sedge may lift their bumpy-wobbly heads, making little islands where spiraea bushes and red maple tree seedlings germinate. Years later, the shrubswamp has developed into a red maple treeswamp, prob-

Dragonfly — At rest, wings extended

Damselfly — At rest, wings up

mating flight

ably with other trees such as elm and birch mixed in. One or two hundred years later still, a climax forest of beech, maple, and hemlock may occupy the site of what was once open water, the swamp too gone.

Development of swamp vegetation on *wet land* rather than open water may begin with alder and willow pioneering fresh silts, sands, and gravels deposited by a stream, or invading wet meadows. In time, they nurse more shade-tolerant plants, such as red maple, which grow up through them and shade them out, thus converting the shrubswamp to treeswamp. Ultimately a climax forest of beech, maple, and hemlock may dominate, perpetuating itself in its own shade until destroyed.

The above brief descriptions of a succession of stages of vegetational development apply to cool, humid regions. In warm, moist climates the shrub and tree species will of course be different. In drier climates, the long-persevering climax may be grassland rather than forest.

The rate of vegetational change should be kept in mind as an important factor in wetland management. An alder swamp may turn into maple treeswamp in twenty-five years; a buttonbush shrubswamp may persist for a hundred years or more. Climax forest may last five hundred years—if people care for it that long.

HANDS-OFF MANAGEMENT

In these days of denaturalization, the best management of wetlands is often to keep them natural. In remote areas this may mean doing nothing but paying low taxes, or, for land in public ownership, legally declaring it wilderness. But most areas of concern are close to people, millions of them, and such areas need continuing hard work just to keep them natural. Their management consists less in altering topography and vegetation and more in managing people. With today's pressures, that is certainly not do-nothing management!

Inventory. First, as always, find out what your natural wetland has to offer. Analyze its contribution to its watershed and airshed, its objects for scientific research, its subjects for artistic revelation, its sanctuary for plants and animals, and its potential for non-modifying recreation. Get help from others in inventorying (67).

Getting legal title. If you do not yourself own the wetland, find out who does, confirming ownership with the tax assessor and/or registry of deeds. If the owner or owners are not or will not be committed to keeping the wetland natural, try to transfer ownership to a preservation-oriented group, public or private, such as an Audubon society, nature conservancy, conservation commission, or watershed association.

Posting the boundaries. The edge of a wetland is its first line of defense. Neat, simple signs are often best set on posts in the water a little way from shore, where they are less subject to vandalism than on land. The top of the post can be used for a box for swallows or wood ducks, thus emphasizing positive values of the wetland for wildlife. (It may be a question whether the artificial home constitutes a breach of the naturalness of the area. Where scientific studies are being made of the natural ecology, such houses are not recommended.) In climates where strong ice develops, cut a hole in the ice and through it drive the sign post into the bottom.

Patrolling. A narrow but well-kept "fishermen's trail" along the edge of the wetland facillitates patrolling. If fishing is not allowed, a path is better kept back from the water or wet spots, with branch trails down to points for observation of the shore and water. A tower often gives excellent supervision over a large area and reduces need for trails. Sometimes an easily climbable or beladdered tree can hold an observation platform or seat. A canoe can quietly and effectively patrol many wetlands. For speedy coverage of very large areas, a shallow-draft boat with airthrust motor is efficient but impairs natural values.

Fencing. Fences are offensive and expensive in time even if not in dollars. Use as few as possible, but they are sometimes necessary, especially where the public comes from a larger region than can be reached by local educational efforts to interpret the wetland. Occasionally it is necessary to have a fence high enough so that people do not throw trash over it! Where livestock graze an adjacent area, a fence is a must, perhaps including a stock lane to one place for watering if the farmer has no other source of water for his animals. Fences to keep wild animals in a natural area inevitably cause loss of naturalness, because the animals are not free to disperse in response to their population increase, diminishing food supply, or other naturally occurring factors.

Watching the watershed.   Ideally a natural wetland should have a watershed above it with only natural vegetation. Too seldom is this possible. A wetland may have farmland, woods, or maybe twenty city blocks draining into it. Try to promote a watershed with surface runoff and seepage of groundwater which will not damage your hands-off wetland. Flooding, desiccation, sedimentation, and pollution must be guarded against; unwise development and wildfire are major causes. *(569, 320)*

INTERPRETATION

Interpretation.   The greatest threat to natural wetlands is people who do not understand them. They must be given firsthand, pleasurable, and informative experiences with wetlands. Methods are beyond the scope of this book, but you can get help from many sources. You will find local, regional, and national conservation groups anxious to aid you. The American Nature Study Society, Association of Interpretive Naturalists, National Wildlife Federation, Nature Conservancy, and Wildlife Management Institute publish materials which should be in your local library. Local garden clubs, bird clubs, sportsmen's clubs, youth groups, and service clubs should be given a chance to help with interpretive work, gathering information about the area and sharing it with the community through guided trips, lectures, photographic contests, art exhibits, articles for the press, and so on.

Participation. If local people feel locked out of a natural wetland, it will be continually threatened, for such is human nature. People should be invited not only to interpret the area but also to assist with whatever else needs to be done, including posting, patrolling, and fencing. A wetland with such backing in the community has little to fear from man.

MAN-MODIFIED WETLANDS

Rather than being left natural as discussed above, an existing wetland can be altered so as to make it better fulfill certain purposes, perhaps production of waterfowl, flood control, experimentation for research, outdoor education for schools, or view for a restaurant. Such are often just extensions of the values of natural wetlands which we can extend if we are willing to diminish other values. We must set up priorities for various uses.

FACILITIES FOR RESEARCH, EDUCATION, AND RECREATION

Trails, buildings, and other facilities can often be created with minimal disturbance of the naturalness of a wetland. At other times, major modifications may be needed; if so, they should be designed to blend ecologically with the natural scene, to preserve as many of the natural values as possible.

Trails. Access to wetlands is often difficult without special equipment such as rubber boots or a boat, yet it is important that a larger segment of the population be able to visit wetlands to learn to understand and appreciate them. Good trails are not just a matter of dry feet and encouragement for the skeptical. They must also provide access for the busy scientist, perhaps with delicate apparatus to be kept dry, and for the photographer with his precious equipment.

Students of wildlife will appreciate being able to walk systematically and quietly along cleared trails. Teachers with their pupils will benefit from good trails. Making trails (p. 256) is often hard work but it also can be fun. Some of the best community support comes when people get outdoors on a weekend or weekday evening to work together, as the Appalachian Mountain Club and other trail groups do.

Boating channels. Paths for shallow-draft boats can be cleared of vegetation as described in Chapter 9, but it may be necessary to deepen the water. Make only minimal channels, because they can cause major disruptions in the ecology, as by modifying currents. Digging is difficult even in shallow water, so take advantage of droughts and drawdowns to dig by hand. When a large job requires machinery, a dragline working from solid ground or mats is useful. In coastal areas, a hydraulic dredge may be used. Explosives properly spaced in a row can blow an excellent ditch, with skill and luck. The way the charges are laid can determine, within limits, whether the blown material will make a high spoilbank useful as a causeway (p. 184), or will be broadcast across the adjacent wetland. Usually, whatever method of excavation is used, it is beneficial to use dug material to build causeways, dikes (p. 190), or islands.

Islands. Islands add immeasurably to wetlands. Innately intriguing, they provide variety in the landscape and point the imagination toward adventure. Wildlife profits more tangibly from an island because it creates edge (p. 458). Sometimes an island can be created by raising the water level enough to flood the neck of a promontory. More often an island must be built up with fill dug from the wetland or brought in from neighboring upland (p. 208). Usually, the higher

the island the better, except that it will require more fill, time, and/or money. A few inches above water level may suffice to keep feet dry and give an artist a place to set up an easel. A foot or two will be better for spreading sleeping bags of scouts and other visiting groups. A higher ridge built along the windward edge can provide a lookout (67) for studying wildlife; once piled up and protected from erosion, it does not need maintenance as does a tower (see below). Any banks of fill should be vegetated or riprapped to hold the soil. A gate across a causeway or bridge to an island gives some control over access to it, to provide protection for plants and animals.

Observation towers. Raised structures for observation can be more or less ambitious, ranging from a strong box to stand on to get one's eyes a few inches above the tall marsh grasses, to a prefabricated steel tower such as forest rangers use. Safety is important, so slipshod construction should not be tolerated in home-made towers. A six-by-six-foot platform on piles with sides and roof makes a fine hide for studying wildlife, for photography, or for overnight sleeping. Camouflage will add to its utility and prevent its being an eyesore.

Hides (blinds). A hide conceals people studying wildlife. Photographers and duck hunters especially may be experts at making camouflaged hollows, lean-tos, tents, or even cabins for observing or hunting. Temporary hides, seldom recommended for conservation reasons in frequently used natural areas, can be made by laying fresh-cut branches over one or more poles to make a place to creep into. A simple portable hide can be made from an air mattress, an appropriately colored cloth or tarp, three to six stiff but springy wires or saplings about five feet long, and some big safety pins. This hooped hide is good for waiting and watching lying down. A classic hide is the umbrella type, a large umbrella on a pole with a wraparound skirt reaching the ground. Small holes allow observation and ventilation. A large beach umbrella or cabana is excellent, though often its blatant coloring may need changing to fit the environment. Guy ropes may be needed.

A fox-hole-type hide is dug where it is not too wet, the excavated earth being piled to form the upper wall. Sticks and branches make a camouflaged roof which must be replaced from time to time; a more

permanent roof can be made from boards, exterior plywood, corrugated plastic panels, or canvas. If the top is not waterproof, provide a drain in the floor. Other hides can be made log cabin fashion
or laid up of local stone to blend with the surroundings. Some hides
are built in trees, sometimes with thatch of local reeds or grasses to
minimize weight.

Quiet, patient waiting, so necessary for getting to know the ways
of wild animals, is aided by some comfort, perhaps a folding stool
or chair, air mattress, or cushion. Because patience has been defined
as "the art of doing something else while you wait," a good book,
notebook, or sketching pad is an aid.

Hides should be carefully located either to command a wide view
or one which promises close looks at animals, as by a much-used
water hole. Position relative to the sun is important: westward-
facing hides for morning observation, eastward-facing for evenings,
with northward-facing ones best for general all-day use (in the
northern hemisphere). A mid-marsh blind may face in all directions.

Launching ramps and docks.   Boats often provide the best access
and observation in wetlands (see *Shores*, Chapter 8).

WATER-CONTROL STRUCTURES

Depth of water and rate of flow largely determine a wetland. Under
natural conditions, climate and the topography and vegetation of the
watershed are controlling. Man can use water-control structures to
make either minor or major changes. *Dams* are built across a valley
and withhold water on the upstream side. *Dikes* do not go all the
way across a valley but impound water in only part of it, sometimes
on one side, and sometimes on both sides. A constructed *levee* is a
dike running along the bank of a stream's normal channel, designed
to keep a river from flooding onto its floodplain, or occasionally
to keep water from returning to the river. Any major changes should
be made only after detailed biological and engineering studies to indicate probable ecological changes involving runoff, groundwater,
erosion, vegetation, and animal life. Nature is too complex to tamper
with imprudently. *(533)*

Impoundments.   Innumerable possibilities are presented by the many diverse sites which can be flooded. The following are those most commonly important.

Flood control. A dam can hold back flood waters to the extent that it is not already full before the flood. Its significance for flood control depends upon how empty it is when the flood comes. A dam for flood control only (that is, with an empty basin) has no effect on a wetland or dryland above it until a flood comes, and then the effects are temporary, except for such matters as the deposition of sediment. Such a dam is often called a single-purpose dam. In flood-prone areas, it is better to move human structural developments such as homes and industries off the floodplain than continually to fight the river. But numerous small flood-control dams upstream are sometimes recommended to supplement such other watershed management measures as maintaining suitable contours on farmland and absorptive vegetative cover.

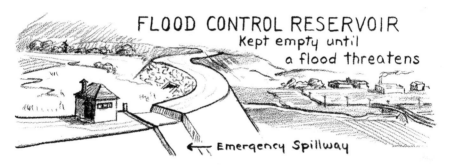

FLOOD CONTROL RESERVOIR
Kept empty until
a flood threatens

← Emergency Spillway

Irrigation. In warm regions where rice can be grown, flowing water onto fields makes a special agricultural wetland. The special problems of agriculture are beyond the scope of this book and should be tackled with the help of agricultural extension agents. A school within the rice-growing states can benefit from making and maintaining its own rice paddy. Commercial cranberry culture uses flooding of bogs to protect crops from frost, by diverting a stream or pumping from a pond or well. A school cranberry bog is a fine project in such states as Massachusetts, West Virginia, Wisconsin, and Oregon—complete with educational irrigation. Irrigation is basic to the agricultural economy in many dry regions. Even in the humid eastern United States, it is increasingly used to compensate for drought or to increase yields of certain crops at certain seasons. Wetlands can sometimes be flooded to a greater depth as a source of irrigation water.

Fire protection. Occasionally a wetland can be flooded for added fire protection of a precious contiguous area during high fire danger. Along with raising the water level, one can make access roads to pumping stations to help fire-fighters.

Wildlife management. Given a good home, wildlife manages itself. What is good for some kinds of animals is bad for others. A six-inch rise of water in a wetland makes surprising changes in habitat, drowning out some forms and encouraging new species. Fish, furbearers, and waterfowl are the animals for whom wetlands are most often managed, and there is much literature already on the subject. In general, establishing water level from six inches to two feet deep is recommended for attracting most forms of frequently desired wildlife; use a dam or dike permitting small alterations at various times of year and under various weather conditions. A valve in a corrugated pipe or flashboards in a concrete gate are commonly used for fluctuating water levels. Some careful fluctuation can make a difference in mosquito populations in some sites. A biennial draw-down of relatively infertile waters to expose mudflats can induce natural seeding of some duck-food plants such as smartweeds, rice cutgrass, and wild-millet, whose seeds can then be made available to ducks by gradual flooding in the autumn. A series of dikes making ponds with different depths helps create the diversity which draws a variety of wildlife. Ponds made in pairs allow for keeping one pond full while the other is drawn down, so that both water areas and flats with growing food plants are available at all times. *(175, 302)*

Groundwater control. Flooding to hold back water in time of plenty can help maintain higher water tables than would exist without dams. With increasing demands upon our water supplies, retention of water on and *in* the land is of growing importance. In most cases, numerous local impoundments are preferred to a few gigantic ones.

Esthetics. Water brings its own particular forms of beauty, both in itself and in the design of reeds and wild wings. You can put a little sod dam across a wet meadow and thus make an expanding mirror to catch a sunset; lay a few logs across a brook and make a deep pool of cool water where trout can lie; dike a bit of marsh for a frog symphony and for a home for a wild goose family.

VEGETATION MANAGEMENT

A natural wetland may be a bog, fen, marsh, shrubswamp, or swamp (p. 175) because of its topography, vegetational development, and/or man's modifications thereof. And man can make major modifications! A small rise in water level can kill essentially all the trees of certain kinds in swamps. (Note the dead forests which beavers have flooded.) Drainage can too; and so can fire, chemical planticides, power saws, and bulldozers. Each can be viewed as a threat to a swamp; but each is also a potential tool for creating desired change; for instance, converting a swamp to a shrubswamp or marsh, perhaps to attract different forms of wildlife, or to open up a view of distant hills to be reflected in a little open water, or even to reduce the transpiration of water into the air by trees, thus conserving precious water. Carefully planned vegetation control can greatly increase some values of wetlands—while inevitably decreasing others. Be sure to leave some natural areas, reminders of what we do *not* know about working with nature.

Clearing. (See also *Wetlands*, p. 180). Removing unwanted vegetation is most easily done in winter if thick ice forms, in dry spells if such occur, or during drawdowns if there is a water-control structure. In clearing shrublands or treelands, remove or burn woody material prior to flooding, because its presence in large quantities in the water can create undesirable chemical conditions such as too-great acidity (low pH) from organic acids, and staining of the water, which reduces sunlight penetration necessary for food-making by green plants such as algae. Without their photosynthesis there may be insufficient oxygen for fish and other aquatic animals. (In some cases, however, with clay soils which create turbidity by remaining in suspension, leaving some decaying organic matter allows the formation of carbonic acid; this helps precipitate the tiny clay particles, thus clearing the water.)

Creating diversity of vegetation increases the variety and numbers of wildlife. Therefore an extensive cattail marsh may be lacking in birds and mammals compared to what it might have if cattails were curtailed in patches so that other plants could invade. It is not easy, though, to eradicate cattails. Combined planticiding and burning has been somewhat successful; repeated treatments are necessary because of the food reserves in the cattails' wide-spreading underground stems. Blasting with dynamite or a mixture of ammonium nitrate and Number 2 diesel oil creates potholes of open water and at least temporarily clears out marsh vegetation. Cattails diked off from brackish water can be flooded with it and the area used instead for growing such plants as widgeongrass to attract waterfowl. To create temporary open water in extensive marshes, mowing, burning, grazing, or treading by foot or machine have been locally successful.

Planting.   Much has been learned about attracting waterfowl by planting food plants such as wildrice, smartweeds, and pondweeds. A wide variety of plants are available for diverse sites, so consult references *(188, 258, 309, 427)*. Whatever is planted should be planted with an experimental attitude — just as one goes fishing with no certainty of success. Study the plants' environment and how they behave in it. If the first attempt does not succeed, make some rational modification and try again, just as a fisherman will change his bait. One must always have a somewhat experimental attitude when working with nature.

CONSTRUCTED WETLANDS

Many parts of the world have no wetlands at all, and others have wetlands inadequate for the purposes of the land manager. Man's needs and ingenuity are such that wetlands have been constructed in some very improbable places. But first look for probable sites.

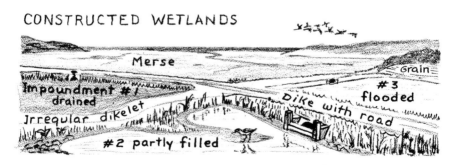

Topography.   Look for potential basins which can be flooded. The flatter an area is, the wider the impoundment which can be created for a given increase in depth. A long, low dam or dike across a broad lowland usually creates fewer engineering problems than a taller dam in a narrower valley. One rule for wildlife wetlands is that the basin should be shaped so that at least 75 per cent of it would normally be flooded by water less than two feet deep when an appropriate water control structure is installed. With infertile soils, the water should usually be held shallower than two feet to permit good growth of emergent aquatic plants.

Soil permeability.   A porous soil such as gravel or pure sand may cause seepage out the bottom. This may not be a major problem if water comes into the impoundment fast enough to replenish the loss. Clay soils are less pervious and therefore make good bottoms and cores of dams.

Water-producing potential of the watershed.   Past experience of local people can help; but for any major construction, you should get engineering help in computing the low, average, and maximum runoffs expected from the watershed. A U.S. Soil Conservation Service employee can tell you how to proceed. The *minimum amount* of water available in a dry season is important. Sometimes you will be glad to settle for an intermittent wetland (one which is dry in summer or perhaps longer in droughts)—which is better than none— but a permanent water body is preferable. The *maximum amount* of water may be barely enough, so that every drop must be saved; but the maximum may be a grave threat in the form of a flood—a serious consideration (p. 297).

Artificial impoundments.   In addition to the more natural impoundments, such as those made on floodplains of mature streams, small wetlands can be constructed in many little basins occurring naturally, with water piped in by gravity or pump, or in artificial basins to which water can be supplied. The size may be anything from a few acres down to something satisfying to the mudpie set in the back yard. Large excavated basins will require a bulldozer and/or dragline, but delightful mini-wetlands can be dug a little at a time with a shovel, or all at once by a number of people at a digging party. Many more schools, parks, and camps should have miniature ex-

perimental wetlands where children and adults too can learn fundamental conservation lessons. Where a natural stream is lacking,
supply an artificial outlet as well as inlet, with consideration of any
erosion problems (p. 305). In addition to an overflow, install a drainpipe at the bottom to prevent stagnation and permit cleaning when
and if necessary.

Skating rinks.   In cold climates, hockey and figure-skating rinks
can be made with a shallow dike. Given an adequate water supply
for keeping it full all year, even such a small area can make a pretty
marsh. The water should be drained in autumn long enough to cut
the vegetation so it will not project through the ice. Such a marsh-
rink makes safe skating for the youngest skaters.

Sewage lagoons.   As populations mount and water becomes more
precious, more thought is given to waste disposal and its conversion
into useful materials through recycling. With better understanding
of how nature breaks down materials into their simpler reusable
elements, we can better imitate her. Sewage lagoons, oxidation
ponds, and the like use the actions of naturally occurring microbes
to break down liquid organic wastes and those in suspension so as
to remove objectionable properties such as odor and disease. In
these shallow impoundments, algae receive abundant sunlight and
flourish on the rich supply of minerals like phosphates in the sewage.
Bacteria and water molds use the oxygen supplied by the plants'
photosynthesis for their own life processes, which break down the
organic matter in the sewage. In so doing they produce carbon dioxide, which the plants must have for their oxygen-making photosynthesis. By feeding our sewage back into nature's processes, we admit we are an intimate part of nature. Benefits are numerous, in
addition to disposing of potentially noxious wastes. We may in
some cases harvest algae. We can filter and reuse the water. And
sewage lagoons attract such beautiful forms of wildlife as the shorebirds, who might otherwise be absent from the area. In constructing
sewage lagoons, keep dikes low and the surrounding vegetation low
to maximize wind action which beneficially stirs the water surface.

Basins excavated for groundwater and surface water.   The United
States Department of Agriculture's Soil Conservation Service (see
the Yellow Pages) has pioneered and promoted with great success

farm ponds made by a bulldozer or dragline. Wetlands can be established by similar techniques at both farm and non-farm sites by excavating to only a foot or two below the water table in dry seasons. Often such a wetland can be adjacent to a regulation farm pond. *(10)* Study the native vegetation to find where the water table is close to the surface, as indicated by willows, alders, and sensitive-fern, for instance. After excavation, plants especially attractive to wildlife can be introduced.

Impoundments along coasts. Along the edges of coastal marshes, impoundments can be designed to retain sea water from high tide through the low-tide period to make a permanent saline environment favoring species unable to benefit from the intertidal zone. They can be built also to retain some fresh water from inflowing streams and thus provide brackish environments. Further advantage to some forms of wildlife results from the ditch-pools created by excavating materials for the dikes, the deeper water supplying still another environment to enrich the fauna and flora.

SAVING SAMPLES OF NATURAL WETLANDS

In our enthusiasm for constructing wetlands, we must be sure to save abundant and extensive samples of natural wetlands. For all our abilities to move earth and water, we must humbly realize how much we still have to learn about the intricacies of undisturbed nature. It often surprises us.

(See also *28, 129, 145, 232, 260, 282, 285, 389, 427, 430, 522.*)

7 *Water Areas*

Water has provided both survival and fascination since the paleo-lithic infancy of the human race. Water holes, fords and confluences of streams, deltas, these are where anthropologists look for the few remaining primitive peoples and where archeologists dig for lost cultures. Today the geography of water still outlines the geography of man. But now as never before, man can change the geography of water and thereby alter his own patterns of habitation on earth. In the wise use of water lies the future of the human race. *(107)*

The oceans, seas, lakes, and great rivers of the world are mentioned only briefly in this book, in the chapter *Shores*. Areas which are shallowly wet much of the year are dealt with in the preceding chapter. The subject of this chapter is ponds and streams. Lucky is the land which has them and wise the owner who uses them.

The smaller the body of water the easier it is to work with. The little water areas of this chapter can provide little lessons in water-conserving practices, big opportunities in a small way. Some wise person said that a man is grown when he no longer enjoys walking in puddles. Perhaps a man's mind has become too set when he no longer enjoys working in puddles: there is so much to learn from them. *(87)*

NATURAL PONDS

Many classifications of natural ponds are more or less possible, because of the diversity of their characteristics. Take size, for instance. A *puddle* is a very small, shallow pond, usually with standing rather than running water. A *pool* may also be very small but usually has the dignity of greater depth. A *spring* is also small, a site where groundwater comes to the surface and forms a pool; though a larger pond may have several springs. A *water hole* is comparable; the term is used more in arid regions. A *pond* in a restricted sense is usually larger than the above but smaller than a *lake*. There is no sharp line to say when a pond is grown up enough to be a lake—perhaps when large enough to enjoy whitecaps in a fresh breeze? Localities may have their own understandings in such matters. For instance, Maine and Massachusetts have laws relating to "great ponds" established by colonial ordinance in 1641-47 as being larger than ten acres. Be sensitive to local usage so that you avoid calling somebody's lake a puddle.

Classification by chemical composition gives useful terms like *fresh pond, brackish pond,* and *salt* or *saline pond.* This last type occurs at the sea coast or in arid areas inland where evaporation brings salts to the surface and runoff concentrates them in low places where water accumulates.

Geological origin gives special names. A *tarn* is a mountainside pond where a mountain glacier left a hollow in its U-shaped valley. A *finger lake* lies in an elongated depression lower down a glacial valley. A *kettle hole* pond (p. 173) fills a rounded depression where a stranded iceberg or buried ice block melted. A *pothole* is either a similar formation (in the prairie states and provinces) or a cavity in the bedrock of a turbulent youthful stream caused by the grinding action of swirling pebbles. A *sink* may be either a pond in a dissolved depression in limestone bedrock or a small saline pond in an arid region. A *slough* when rhymed with "moo" is a marshy pond, especially in the western United States; while a *slough* rhymed with "cow" is a more general term for a mucky-ucky place, a term perhaps more poetic than geologic. An *oxbow* is a pond or lake formed in a bypassed meander of a mature stream (p. 212). A look around home territory or a sharp eye while traveling may reveal these and other kinds of natural ponds, each with its own intriguing attributes, history, and future. *(16, 87, 256, 419)*

VALUES OF NATURAL PONDS

What worth you see in a pond of course depends upon who you are and what you want. Try listing the following benefits, and any others you think of, in order of their importance to *you* for some pond which you know or imagine. Realize that withdrawing a substantial amount of water from a natural pond diminishes its naturalness, to some degree impairing natural values.

Water for domestic use. Early settlers dipped their bucket into a pond to get water for drinking, cooking, and washing. People were few and far between, so pollution was no problem. Today some people are still without the convenience of piped-in water. They miss a lot; but so do those who never stand at the bank's edge and dip, sensing the sounds, smells, and sights of nature by a natural pond. One good reason for going camping is to have such an experience — if the campsite is by an unpolluted pond.

Or consider drawing water from a well with a bucket on a rope, with echoes of spilled water splashing back down into the fragrant shadows between the stones. If the nearby pond helps keep the water table up, there will be water in the well. Most ponds do not really stop at their banks, in a sense; the water extends sideways in the pores of the soil and bedrock. So to draw water from the well is often to draw it indirectly from the pond, hopefully an unpolluted one with its watershed managed so that it yields water all year long.

Perhaps the water is pumped to the house through a pipe running out into the pond. A windmill could do the pumping if it were on a hill or in open fields where the wind could get a run at it. When metal windmills came in, they were clanky and creaky. Then discovery of petroleum and invention of the internal combustion motor brought different sounds and smells as gasoline pumps took over. In one way the pond came closer to the house; but in another it became more distant. It takes real imagination to see waterlily pads and frogs when you turn on the shower or washing machine. And a glass of water may, because of protective chlorine, taste more like something out of a bottle than out of a pond.

Water for fire protection. You can never know when a destructive fire may start. It pays to be prepared. In cities there are water mains and hydrants, often taken for granted by city people. In the country the tank truck may be garaged miles away; and when the pumper truck comes it must have a place to put in its intake hose. In the meantime, a bucket-line of family and neighbors may stretch from the pond to the house, barn, or woodlot and save the day. Or a little pond may give forest-fire fighters a place to start a backfire to stop a wildfire which has crowned in the pines, roaring across the country as though nothing could stop it. Who can put a dollar value on a pond at times like these? Yet many are filled or drained by people in haste to "develop" the country.

Water for livestock. Maybe you were or are a farmer, so you know the value of a pond for your animals. A little natural pond can be basic to a farm. Or maybe you are not a farmer and never want to be. But might you be a parent whose child wants a pony? Or have you dreamed of a goat instead of a lawnmower?

Water for crops. Irrigation has made possible the settlement of much of the semi-arid and arid western United States. Ranchers do not need to be told about irrigation. But people in ranch houses in eastern suburbs are surprised and irritated when a fast-growing community finds itself faced with water shortages and officials place restrictions on irrigating their lawns. Turf yields a crop of pleasure— when it is green. When drought conditions prevail and over-consumption thirsts for all available water, a community needs hydrologic understanding and restraint to avoid pumping its natural ponds dry, reducing even farther the falling water table. The farmer and the orchardist also, even in the humid east, are increasingly turning to irrigation, to beat competitive markets with early harvests and premium quality crops. This makes a bigger demand on natural ponds.

Water for industry. In colonial days, industry was often carried on in the home—spinning, basketry, furniture-making. The natural pond was used for retting flax for weaving; water molds rotted the flax stems' cementing materials and left separate fibers for making linen. In stagnant natural ponds where iron bacteria worked, men dug bog iron for the primitive metallurgy which helped subdue an all-wild continent. But today most industry is institutionalized and government-regulated, using prodigious quantities of water. The smaller ponds are almost entirely unneeded by industries—so they think. Only occasionally does a pond supply water for some cooling process or a place to store logs for a small sawmill; more often, it receives some effluent on its way to a stream used to carry off waste materials. Most industries are not interested in natural ponds any more. But they should be, for three reasons. (1) As communities need more water, industries are apt to tap groundwater by drilling wells; and natural ponds help recharge the supply of groundwater. (2) Most industrial personnel will perform more happily and efficiently if the industrial grounds include a natural pond near which they can relax during lunch hour or before or after shop is open. (3) An industry should be an integral part of a community, with its overall good at heart. Because natural ponds have so many other values for a community, industries, instead of filling and draining them should for enlightened self-interest protect them.

Flood control. Natural ponds usually have a natural drainage-way across a low spot in the natural dam. When water comes into the pond faster than it leaves, the water level rises only to the height of the drainageway because this spillway drains off the excess. At this height the pond is described as full. A *full* pond is seldom of use for flood control, because it cannot retain additional water to reduce the flooding downstream. An exception occurs when a pond has a very shallow basin, say with extensive bordering marshes, and the drainageway by contrast is steep-sided and narrow; floodwaters may then pile up at the exit enough to back up considerable water in the shallow basin. A six-inch rise flooding an acre of lowland beside a one-acre pond will temporarily store 343,200 gallons of floodwater (an acre-foot).

Significant is the flood-controlling capacity of a natural pond when it is *not full*, as at the end of a dry spell. Depending upon its size, it may have a large capacity for floodwater retention before it rises to the height of the drainageway. Unfortunately most cities have filled in their natural ponds along with sealing most of the pores in their soils with paving. The rapid runoff resulting overtaxes storm drains and floods communities downstream. Flood-storage capacity has been doubly destroyed, in the porous soils and in the natural ponds.

Drought control. It takes varying amounts of time for water to soak into the land and to seep down to the saturated zone whose top is known as the water table. The height of the water table is often of little concern until a drought lowers it; then worried persons wonder with each shower whether some will sink in to replenish the natural groundwater reservoirs and raise the water table. With a light-textured (sandy) soil, much of the rainfall may sink in fast; with a heavier (clayey) soil most of the water may run off in a hurry. Every little natural pond, puddle or pool or playa, is a lingering place for water where it can take the time necessary to soak into the ground to help recharge the water table. Do not hurry to fill or drain so-called useless natural ponds.

Wildlife of natural ponds. Mosquitos? Yes, they are likely to be there in season, and those not eaten by fish below the surface or by phoebes and swallows above may well be looking for blood to make possible the continuation of their species. But they are such a small part of the biota of a pond that they should be seen in perspective and swatted proportionately, not eliminated by murdering the pond. Dozens or even hundreds of natural forms besides mosquitos live in a pond, to be sought after and admired, for instance the incomparable fairy shrimp. These other organisms have beauty of design to thrill everybody who stops to look closely. (And did you ever look closely at a mosquito?) *(243, 348, 369, 437)*

Sometimes we need the economic benefit of harvesting "surplus" animals produced by a pond, for instance muskrats, fish, or waterfowl. Managed ponds may give a bigger harvest, but a natural pond may have a greater variety.

Plant life of natural ponds. A pond is a sort of island in a world of dryness. It has that island fascination. What has come to its shores in the course of evolution? What castaway plants have survived along its edge or in its mothering waters? Along the shore of whatever pond is nearest you, there are species of plants well known to botanists. Well known? Yes, so far as identification to species goes, but not in terms of, say, their biochemistry, which may hardly be known at all. Ignorance is bliss when it beckons curiosity. Who knows what important drugs or pesticides might one day be isolated from some rare aquatic plant trying to cling to the shores of the little pond near your home, perhaps the pond even now designated on drawing boards to be filled for a parking lot for Buy Everything, Incorporated, the new supercenter for already saturated shoppers? *(188, 258, 437)*

Recreation at natural ponds.   Everybody who in his or her youth has played around a natural pond knows some of the pleasures to be derived from one, but many of our urban millions have not had such experiences. Urban "progress" has usually meant getting rid of the ponds or at least denaturalizing them with concrete rims and maybe a Japanese bridge. For sure, a child can have fun in a bath-tub or spend good hours sailing model boats in a round pool with a fountain in the center. But the country boy or girl can do far more, more than can be suggested here, and so can adults. Rather than restricting our thinking to such obvious winter uses as figure skating, social skating, hockey, and fishing through the ice, and the summer uses of boating, swimming, and fishing, let us explore also the many subtler pleasures which a natural pond may offer: the artist's joy in the upside-down world of reflections; the poet's challenge to select some item from the natural scene and find words to relate it meaning-fully to the universe; the photographer's preoccupation with record-ing the gyrations of whirlygig beetles; the child's fascination with the air bubbles in sandwich ice.

Landscape effects.   Only a few of the many obvious visual land-scape effects of the natural pond can be even mentioned here: the flatness of the water surface, giving a base line against which all vertical elements in the landscape can be sensed; the reflectivity of the water surface, so that even the downcast can see the sky; the irregular angularities where rocks intersect the plane of water; the gentle curve where sand and silt or clay is lapped by water; the softened shoreline where uncounted reeds stand upright or where the shrubs hang over; the stiffly bowed wings of a shorebird coming in to teeter on the beach. To those who have known intimately these views of their environment there comes a feeling of release from the manmade milieu of urban artifacts. They want to make sure that enough natural ponds are saved by our society to minister to the hu-man nervous system when its million-year biological history rebels at urban constraints.

MAN-MODIFIED PONDS

How natural does a pond need to be? Most people prefer an environ-ment intermediate between Times Square and wilderness. How and in what ways to tame the wild for the highest quality of living is a question that becomes increasingly thoughtworthy. Civilized sandwiches brought to a solitary woodland pool can make a long day there much happier; but one scattered six-pack of empty beer cans will defile it.

Purposes should guide any modifications. List the purposes and assign priorities, noting that all uses are not compatible. A pond kept full as a reservoir is no help for floodwater impoundment. A pond for raising stocked fish should not have shallow water attracting waterfowl, unless it is diked off to keep small fish from too easily escaping the large predatory fish.

Raising pond level. Higher water may be an improvement to permit swimming; to increase storage capacity for domestic use, cattle, irrigation, or fire protection; to make the water cooler; or to increase the sideward spread of the pond, providing more shallows and wetlands for wildlife, for modifying the local climate, or for visual landscape effect.

Dams. In a natural pond with an outlet, the outlet must be raised with a dam high enough to attain the desired new water level and strong enough to hold impounded water (p. 306). If there is another naturally low spot higher than the first but lower than the desired water level, that too will have to be dammed. You will also want a spillway so that water can overflow after the pond is filled to its new height. Often you will need an adjustable gate to alter the water level.

Changing water levels with a dam—A gate with flashboards or valve to regulate height is helpful. When flooding can be anticipated, as in spring with meltwater from winter snows, the pond can be drawn down to provide storage of potential floodwater. For mosquito control, fluctuation of water level reduces the number of wigglers (mosquito larvae). For waterfowl management, summer drawdown promotes growth of food plants (p. 319). For fish management, reducing the pond facilitates seining out unwanted species prior to restocking. For retrieval of items lost overboard and for general cleaning, it is good to be able to drain the pond. To lower the level, flashboards are removed, then, for filling, replaced. Natural vegetation and fauna will not follow their normal development where water levels are artificially maintained; more control means less naturalness. Before making major changes, get help from an ecologist.

Changing water levels without a dam—Where there is no normal overflow from a natural pond, for instance in a kettle hole (p. 173), the water level cannot be raised by damming. Possibilities include: (1) diverting water by pipe or ditch from or into an adjacent watershed; (2) pumping up groundwater from a deep water table not directly related to the pond; or (3) increasing the runoff on the pond's watershed by reducing the transpiring vegetation or by paving. These methods are all tricky or expensive or both. For instance, increasing the runoff at one season may result in less release of groundwater into the basin in a dry season. It is best to leave water levels natural in such basins except to pump out excess water in a flood if necessary.

Deepening ponds. Greater depth for swimming and increased storage capacity can sometimes be attained by excavating at least a portion of the pond bottom, either with a dragline or, if the pond can be pumped or drained, with a bulldozer. Dynamiting by a skilled and licensed operator may be effective, but be sure first that the pond bottom is not an impervious layer above a permeable one; more than one attempted deepening by dynamite has cracked such a bottom and caused the loss of the whole pond by drainage. Small pools can be scooped out with pick, shovel, and wheelbarrow, benefiting the digger's physique if the pond is dug with patience a little at a time. A little pond more slowly come by with handwork often has charms lacking in a machine-made one.

Using excavated material—Deposits of dug material are *spoilbanks.* They can be eyesores or assets. Use rocks and soil as part of the landscaping plan of the pond (p. 183). Clay makes a good impervious core to prevent seepage through a dam. Sands may make a beach. Gravels can be used for trails, roads, and parking lots. Instead of always filling low spots, pile up a spoilbank suitable for an observation mound or a ridge-like bank to shelter a picnic site from cold winds. Stabilize deposited banks so they do not wash down or erode from wave action.

Vegetation management. Shallow ponds may have excessive rooted vegetation hindering swimming, boating, fishing, and, in colder regions, skating. Control may include excavation to a greater depth, underwater mowing, careful use of planticides (p. 400), and, in managed fish ponds, heavy fertilization so that denser growth of algae shades out the rooted plants. Algae themselves, however, may be a problem where swimming is important. Chemical modification of the water may be necessary to control them, but realize that chemicals may affect other organisms too.

Management of fish, waterfowl, and other wildlife. There is much literature available to help plan ponds to suit the species most desired. In general, have an irregular shoreline and a variety of depths of water to provide for an abundance of different kinds of plants for food and cover (pp. 188, 460). *(302)*

CONSTRUCTED PONDS

Water is such a valuable asset to man that over the centuries he has invented many ingenious devices for impounding it for a variety of uses. The hydraulic niceties of Roman baths made more than two thousand years ago are amazing, as are ancient fish ponds and rice paddies in the Orient. But the second half of our century shows man going after water as never before, with growing populations, accelerating demand, and technical abilities and power undreamed of by the ancients. Because water is so often the key to both quantity and quality of life, today's conservationist should not limit his thinking to the brief outline presented here but should keep an eye open for other possibilities for impounding water.

Small wildlife pools. Perhaps the conservationist's smallest pond is a hummingbird feeder, made of a plastic vial or pill bottle with a flower-like red disk of metal or plastic at its top. Fill it with a

honey-and-water or sugar-and-water mixture and hang it at the edge of garden shrubbery. Though small, it will illustrate how a little liquid can alter the distribution of animals. Birdbaths are a little more pond-like; they can range from electrically heated ones at northern window feeders to pedestal pottery or plastic ones and sizable shallow concrete pools in gardens. The latter should include some shelving shore where a bird can wade in to a depth appropriate to his leg length to take his fluttering bath.

Gallinaceous guzzlers.   The name suggests the amount of imagination needed to invent a water supply in desert areas for desert quail and other small wildlife. A large catchment area is paved to promote condensation of atmospheric moisture at night and to prevent insoak. This concrete apron declines gently to an underground pool. In this grotto the water is protected from evaporation by sun and wind, yet is accessible from the downwind side for the wildlife.

Dew ponds.   On British moors, stone-paved catchment basins have long been used to precipitate atmospheric moisture and lead it into pools from which sheep can drink. These were the forerunners of the extensive runoff pavements funneling precipitation for human use into cisterns, as in Bermuda. In suitable climates such water-gathering devices can probably find increased use. In desert climates, the clear air promotes atmospheric cooling by outward radiation of heat at night; this condenses much of the small amount of water in the air. Desert campers can obtain emergency water with a sheet of plastic about six by six feet suspended funnelform in a six-foot-wide hole in the ground, with pieces of succulent vegetation beneath it. In this case moisture condenses on the under side of the plastic and drips into a container under the sheet's apex—a good trick for human conservation when in a tight spot in a vast dry country.

Underground storage of water.   The term "pond" is seldom used for subterranean water (although "pool" is used for underground oil). But out-of-sight, uncontaminated water sources are of growing importance and must not be overlooked. Water stored naturally in the pores of the soil and rocks is comparable to that in clouds and oceans as a very large and integrated part of the planetary water system. We can make somewhat artificial use of underground water storage if we carefully recharge water-bearing strata of rock or porous ground by pumping used water, as clean as possible, back into it by way of wells. Also, we can construct underground cisterns or even larger reservoirs by excavating bedrock or pouring concrete. Water thus stored is kept constantly cool and is protected from atmospheric pollution, including radioactive dust. The difficulties and hazards of excavating rock are such that professional engineers must be involved for any storage chamber larger than a few cubic feet.

Ponds from damming streams. Until recent years, most artificial ponds have been made by damming streams. The size of the impoundment depends upon the length of the dam, the breadth of the stream's valley, the lengthwise slope of the valley, and the height of the dam. The extent of the pond will also depend upon whether the climate and the collecting area of the watershed upstream will keep the pond full. The pond may shrink fast if the watershed above erodes and fills the basin with sediment, as too many dam-builders have discovered to their sorrow.

Characteristics and values of the new pond—To consider intelligently the desirability of making a pond where there is none in a stream, think of such matters as its extent, cubic capacity, probable water temperature and oxygen supply, fertility, natural seasonal fluctuations, and steepness of banks relative to access, erosion, and habitat for vegetation. Consider also the aquatic vegetation which will persist, naturally colonize, or be plantable, and the animals, both domestic and wild, which may use the pond. These physical and biological factors of the new pond environment must be related to projected human uses, such as: flood control, reservoir for domestic use, irrigation, watering stock, fire protection, raising fish, attracting waterfowl, furbearers, and other wildlife, recreational boating, swimming, fishing, skating, nature photography, sketching, meditating, and others.

Consequences of impoundment—But the above complicated considerations of the values of the pond are not enough. The expected values received must exceed or at least equal the worth of the stream and its valley at this point *without a dam*. Often the values of streams and their valleys are taken for granted. Articulate appreciation for natural values often comes only after a natural resource has been eliminated, spoiled, or at least seriously threatened.

Flooding destroys whole biotic communities. Will there be other samples of the lowland vegetation types such as marsh, shrubswamp, and swamp, and will these still be extensive enough to provide the needs of their animals? (Moose in western mountains are classic examples of wildlife who have been threatened by flooding of their winter feeding ranges in the valleys.) If the answer is "No," then you must struggle to evaluate the worth of these plants and animals as weighed against the values of new species which may come with the new pond. If you want a good argument, start a debate between those who prefer stream fishing and those who prefer lake fishing. Some of the problems are unanswerable; yet if we wish to make marked changes in environments, we must consciously deliberate their net worth and articulate them to the communities involved.

Consider too any downstream changes a pond might create. If the pond is kept full, downstream effects will be minimal and perhaps negligible except for the risk of a flash flood were the dam to break. If, however, the pond level is fluctuated by a control gate, then variations in stream flow below the dam may be important. Can adequate water be maintained at all times for any boating, for survival of existing populations of fish and other aquatic organisms, for keeping up the immediate water table, and for esthetics?

Preparation for flooding—Within the projected pool there may be rare plants which can be transplanted out. If islands form during flooding, it may be necessary to rescue stranded wildlife which cannot swim or fly. Give attention to geological sites where special rocks or minerals should be collected prior to flooding. Archeological sites should be photographed and thoroughly studied before inundation, for human history can be more precious than glinting minerals. Consideration should be given to diking off particularly valuable areas to exempt them from flooding. For clearing vegetation, see p. 421.

Grading before flooding—It is easier to modify depth and shoreline before inundation than after. Consider excavating a little harbor for a punt or other boats. A ditch-like slip is good for a canoe, perhaps rustically roofed to fit the scene and give protection. A beach safe for swimming and with clean sand may be possible. Install any launching ramps if it is to be a large pond open for boating. Plan for nesting and loafing islands for waterfowl, jutting peninsulas for fishermen and frog-stalking young people, and dikes to separate manageable wetlands from the pond itself (p. 188). Shape banks to minimize erosion (p. 341).

Excavated ponds. During the drought and depression years of the 1930's, the United States Soil Conservation Service pioneered farm ponds to fit the land-use capability systems designed to help farmers make better use of their natural resources. On each cooperating farm, studies were made of such factors as acreages, slopes, soil types, vegetative cover, wildlife, streams, groundwater, and the farmers' interests. This knowledge of the farms' watersheds led to the realization that a little digging in the right place could sometimes reach down to the water table and a few feet below, and that groundwater plus runoff from conservationally handled surface could keep a little pond full, without any stream. Since World War II the "bulldozer explosion" has provided abundant digging power and thousands of farm ponds have been made. Similar ponds have found use on non-farm areas such as estates, parks, golf courses, wildlife sanctuaries, nature centers, schools, and camps.

Dug ponds are used for water storage and many of the other purposes noted above for natural ponds and other man-modified ponds. Because no one pond can function for all purposes, special designs have been worked out to provide best for different high-priority functions in any situation. For instance, ponds for fish management are mostly steep-banked, while those for waterfowl have extensive shallows, preferably sloping up gently in places to fields of grain. Excellent printed instructions and advice are available from the U.S. Department of Agriculture's Soil Conservation Service. Help can also be obtained from the Sports Fishing Institute and Wildlife Management Institute, Izaak Walton League, National Audubon Society, and other organizations.

NATURAL STREAMS

The general term *stream* is used for any flow of water which is more or less channeled, no matter how temporary and small or vast and enduring. In this book streams are limited to those of fresh water.

Currents in ponds and lakes, while significant at times, are omitted from this discussion.

Temporary and permanent streams. Where a watershed gathers enough water to keep a stream running only part of the year, we speak of a temporary or *intermittent stream*. If very small, perhaps running only during or immediately after a heavy rain or snowmelt, it is a *rill*. In arid regions where the streams may run only when there is a desert cloudburst (often far upstream), we speak of a dry river or *wash*, and the river is often recognized more by its dry bed than by its water. *Arroyo* is a Spanish-derived term referring to a small valley with usually dry bed, and often interchangeable with the term *canyon*. On maps with hydrography (literally "water-writing"), intermittent streams large enough to be shown are marked with broken lines. A continuous line is used to delineate *permanent streams*, those which always maintain a flow of water. Occasionally in semi-arid areas the upper part of a stream's course will be permanent where it is fed by precipitation in mountains, while its lower course will be intermittent, with distributaries vanishing into a dry basin. Such streams must be viewed differently from those of humid regions, which are small in their upper reaches and increase with the confluence of each tributary until they are largest at the mouth, where they empty into a body of water. Distributaries in the lower extremities of a humid-region stream do occur in slow-flowing portions of floodplains and deltas where there is much deposition of sediments; the stream will dump some of its load and block its own channel, then form a new one. Some of these *braiding channels* are intermittent. Many other terms apply to streams; for instance small ones are called brooks and large ones rivers, with no clear distinction. Creek, run, and bayou are other frequent designations. *(36)*

Stream gradients. The steepness of the hill down which a stream runs is significant. An imaginary sideways view of a stream's course shows its *long profile*, as compared with the *short profile* across the stream's bed. A stream's course is typically steeper in its upper reaches and flattens downstream, but this will depend upon the terrain it traverses.

The shape of a valley as it relates to the stream in it has intrigued people since long before John Wesley Powell first rafted down that most improbable valley, the Grand Canyon of the Colorado River.

Conservationists are helped by considering the forces of the past which have made the patterns of the present landscape, for they often have to work with these same forces today.

Eroding and carrying power. Water running down steep slopes differs mightily from water running down gentle ones. It is far more erosive because its velocity is greater, which gives it more power. When a stream doubles its velocity it can carry about 64 times as much eroded material or *load*. If it triples its velocity it will move 729 times as much sediment. In mathematical terms, we say that the carrying ability of a stream varies as the 6th power of its velocity: $CA \propto V^6$. For instance, when doubling the velocity we have $2 \times 2 = 4$, $\times 2 = 8$, $\times 2 = 16$, $\times 2 = 32$, and $\times 2 = 64$. When tripling the velocity: $3 \times 3 = 9$, $\times 3 = 27$, $\times 3 = 81$, $\times 3 = 243$, $\times 3 = 729$.

Deltas and alluvial fans. When a stream slows down, its carrying power is correspondingly reduced by the sixth-power rule. That is why there is so much depositing of a stream's load where it enters a lake or ocean; friction with that body of water slows the stream, which forms a triangular *delta*. An *alluvial fan* is a similar triangular deposit on land where a stream, having descended a hill, is slowed down when it meets a plain at its foot.

A stream is not only influenced in these ways by its terrain, in these cases its steepness, but also it influences its terrain, by cutting and building and thus modifying its own valley. Much of the shape of the world around us has been sculptured or built up by streams as they erode or deposit. Watching them at work helps us understand some of the most important forces of our environment and enables us to work with them rather than against them.

Youthful streams. Streams with steep gradient are termed youthful. They have dash. The long profile is steep and the short profile V-shaped, as is the valley which the stream carves. The water cuts headward toward its sources and ever deeper along the center of its bed, and the sides too erode as the stream tears along. Youthful streams have irregular beds with rapids, riffles, and sometimes waterfalls. They are beloved by white-water canoeists because of their speed, rocky hazards, and swirling currents. These are the brooks and little rivers sought by fishermen looking for trout, who need the cool water and high oxygen content. In hot weather the fish lie deep in the plunge pool under a waterfall; in the evening they feed on caddice-flies in the shallows along a gravel bar. Trees, or at least shrubs, bestow some shade on most youthful streams, helping keep them cool. Mosses and ferns relish the moisture on the banks, making them emerald green between the outcroppings. But one cannot so easily describe a stream. At another season it might look quite different, with grotesque splashed-ice formations and black water hustling along thin silver edges of ice between soft mounds of snow on the hard boulders. Each time of year will bring different delights— not to mention less joyous matters, such as the black flies which breed in fast water and plague thin-furred mammals in spring.

Mature streams.   Less precipitous and more unhurried streams occur on leveler terrain. The youthful down-cutting has given way to more sideways gnawing, with the result that a *floodplain* has been formed. The streambed has been graded so that the long profile is smooth and only subtly curved. The short profile shows a flat-bottom stream with low banks; these may be topped by a *natural levee* a little elevated above the floodplain. The stream channel undulates, each curve called a *meander*. On the inside of the curve a *slip-off slope* builds gradually toward the center of the stream because of deposits, whereas on the outside of the curve the faster current chews the side, making a *nipped bank*, which is often undercut and steep. Meander loops move downstream because there is more eroding on the downstream side of the curve, which eventually cuts through the *meander neck* of land and suddenly gives the stream a relatively straight short-cut. The former loopy channel is then abandoned and may form an *oxbow lake*. Now the shortened stream flows faster, with more energy, more eroding and carrying power. So no sooner does the stream straighten out across the meander neck than it increases its side-chewing and begins to meander again.

Floodplain formation.   The floodplain is made by the mature river looping sideways back and forth between its confining hills. The valley gets lower and lower, much as hair gets shorter and shorter when a beginning barber tries to even out his mistakes. A *river terrace* is left at the higher previous level in those places where the meander loops may not swing all the way to the valley wall in

Dumped-stone riprap in the foreground protects the nipped bank on the outside curve of a youthful stream. On the opposite bank, gravels have been naturally deposited on the stream's slip-off slope on the inside of the curve. Glacier National Park, Montana.

any one series of swings across the valley. *Terrace cusps* are left as curvy-toothed projections of terraces where they have been bitten out by succeeding meanders.

Floodplain deposits. When a mature stream floods, its rushing waters are slowed by friction with the bank where they lap over it. Reduced velocity means reduced carrying power, so at this point the stream has to dump some of its load. Gradually a natural levee builds up along the tops of the banks, often marked by willows, cottonwoods, elms, sycamores, and silver maples (within their ranges). Back from the levees, the floodwaters spread out within the confines of the valley, depositing a thin layer of fertile silt. For thousands of years human agriculture has depended on this flood-renewed fertility in such valleys of mature rivers as those of Mesopotamia, Egypt, India, China, and Vietnam.

Terraces on floodplains often include materials other than silt. Where a stream has cut down through a former lake bed, you can sometimes find *clay banks*, originally deposited far from the old lake shore, where only the finest sediments carried a long way in suspension could reach; *sand banks* deposited from more turbulent waters nearer shore; and *gravel banks* close to the former lake shores, where these heavy materials were deposited as deltas. Often coarser and finer materials are found sorted into layers (in clays called *varves*) resulting from a stream whose velocity was changing with weather and seasons.

Drainage patterns. Streams follow the natural law that fluids must run downhill because of gravity. They are victims of their environment, ruled by the amount of slope. But there are other enslaving environmental factors. Some materials are harder to erode

DRAINAGE PATTERNS

humid   arid
region   region

tributaries

dis-
tributaries

mouth

DENDRITIC   TRELLIS   RADIAL   ANNULAR

than others. One result is that a stream may have attained maturity in soft rocks along part of its course, yet still be youthful in another section where its bed is of harder rocks.

Dendritic drainage—Underlying rock also influences the patterns of streams in respect to their direction and manner of branching. Commonest is the dendritic pattern, a tree-like arrangement of *main stem* and *tributary streams* on relatively uniform sloping planes. You can often see these patterns in minature in parking-lot sediments.

Trellis drainage—Where hard and soft rocks are interlayered, as in the folded Appalachian Mountains, major streams follow the long valleys but occasionally cut across a ridge through a *water gap* to the next long valley. Tributary streams flow down the valley sides and join the master streams at close to right angles.

Radial, annular, and other drainages—Radial patterns develop down conical hills, volcanoes for instance, or piles of clayey soil left by a dump truck. In special cases where sedimentary rocks have been pushed up in a dome, as in the Black Hills of South Dakota, annular (ring-like) drainage develops, streams forming almost-circles with occasional water gaps where they join. Other, intermediate patterns occur, often on a very small scale in the yard at school or ball field at camp or in your own back yard. *(185)*

Chemistry of streams. The molecular orderliness of the universe impresses conservationists again and again, but few are trained to handle the details involved. Not many who can complain to congressmen about pollution can also test a water sample for various elements and compounds. When we cannot ourselves do chemical analyses, we should know when and where to get them *(565)* and what to do with the results. The invisible chemical bits which form streams are as important as more obvious physical manifestations like floods and droughts. Water is the so-called universal solvent; it picks up molecules of almost everything.

Biology of streams. Stream chemistry, though complex, is simple compared to stream biology. The material loosely called protoplasm is the most complicated and variable material known. "Life" is the sum of the continual changes of protoplasm, the events of give-and-take with the environment. There are a multitude of forms of life in streams, all more or less succeeding in their constant interchange of

Beaver dams flood water over swamps, killing the trees but creating ponds with bordering marshes rich in solar energy, nutrients, and plants and animals. West Lebanon, New Hampshire.

materials with the water according to their evolutionary learnings. In a natural stream, the species for the most part are successfully perpetuated even while the individuals may "fail" and die.

Changes in physical environment, as when a stream passes from youth to maturity, bring changes of plant and animal life. That strange mountain bird, the water ouzel or dipper, who nests under overhanging waterfalls in youthful streams, will give way in a million years or so to the avocet in the marshes, for the mature river with its wetlands will develop in the same place after the mountains have been worn down. That recent animal, man, has barely begun with his newfound scientific wisdom to study the slowly changing biota of streams as nature has evolved them. How many caddice-flies from the brook bottom does it take to raise a nestful of ouzels? How many crustacea from a marsh give an avocet the energy to migrate a thousand miles?

To canoe or wade along a little stream is to have a chance to study the variety that time has made in living things adapted to different environments. Where the current slows and allows clay particles to settle into mud, there may be rooted aquatic plants such as bulrushes, up which dragonfly nymphs crawl just before they split their skins and liberate their adult wings. Where the stream speeds up, it may run glassy clear over a gravel bar where a fish hovers in one place by constant adjustment to the current, his sense of pressure keeping him always headed into it. And around the bend a deer may be drinking, muzzle in the water but ears attuned to danger as ears of the wildfolk must always be. (540, 559)

Values of natural streams.   Many of the values of natural streams are similar to those of natural ponds (p. 197). But a stream has special attributes, of which the flow of water is the most distinctive. In the back-country bayou of a mature stream, the current may be scarcely noticeable; and a frozen mountain brook may betray its hurrying only to the ear. At times a stream's current may catch attention only in the greatness and turbulence of its flooding. But to be a stream it must have a current.

How does a natural stream compare with one which, having been dammed, takes orders from man? In some ways it is less useful. It does not provide power or a reservoir of water. Its flooding waters are uncontrolled by dams, dikes, or levees. It does not remove sewage or waste chemicals or excess heat or the streets' gutter-water. Why not make all natural streams captive to serve us? First, man cannot be sure that what he now thinks best, for instance a power dam, will always be best. Water power may become to some degree obsolete. Hydroelectric impoundments are useless as soon as they are full of silt, as are reservoirs for other purposes. Fifty years hence people may not want hundreds of senescent waterworks to contend with but might prefer free-flowing streams. Second, unless man has natural streams left for comparison, he lacks one basis for evaluating his captive ones. Third, variety not only adds spice to life, it may at times have survival value. Availability of the physical and biological characters of free-flowing streams may have unforeseen values; humility as to our ignorance ought to make us preserve some streams in their natural state. Fourth, some streams large enough for canoes or even larger boats should be left navigable without artificial obstructions such as dams, even though dammed streams may be supplied with locks for lifting and lowering boats. And fifth, to those who are sensitive to the role of design in the landscape, the unduplicability of a natural stream is a source of wonder and inspiration.

Recreation in natural streams.   If you ever swam in a pool beneath a waterfall, or studied the shallows and deeps of a brook to see where the trout lazed, or waded with your children on the slip-off slope of a meander, then there is no need to tell you the pleasures thereof. If you have not had such experiences, may you have them soon.

MAN-MODIFIED STREAMS

Purposes of stream management.   After serious study of the reasons for leaving a stream in its natural condition, it may appear that some stretches of it should be managed to make it contribute more to human welfare, both now and in the long-term future. Usually multipurpose management will be best, with carefully determined priorities for the various uses.

Flood control—If a stream goes on a rampage that destroys property and even human life, certain questions should be raised. Is the stream itself at fault or its tributaries? If excessive waters pour from the tributaries, is it their fault, or have their watersheds been made too unabsorptive by wildfire, unwise farming practices, poor forestry, strip-mining, drainage dislocation by highway construction, urban paving, or fillings and draining which have destroyed natural retention reservoirs? If so, should any modifications of the stream itself be made until these sources of trouble have been attended to? Has the flood loss of property and life resulted from people mistakenly using the floodplain for structures and activities unsuited to a flood-created environment which rightfully belongs to the river? Would efforts be more wisely spent trying to manage people rather than the river? After conscience-satisfying answers to the above are obtained, then and only then can you plan carefully any necessary modifications such as dams, dikes, and levees on the river itself *(89)*.

Erosion control—Normal, natural erosion by a stream can offend man. Accelerated erosion can horrify him. In the latter case, first attention (as with flood control, above) should be paid to the watershed above, to hold back and slow down excessive runoff. Then it may occasionally still be necessary for erosion to be curbed at the site of the stream's gnawing.

Sedimentation control—Excessive sedimentation can be a great problem; it fills reservoirs and clogs channels and ditches. It results, first, from water running too fast somewhere upstream, thus giving it energy to pick up and transport clay or silt, or even coarser particles such as sand and gravel; and, second, from its having slowed down, thus causing it to lose energy and deposit its load. First measures should be to protect the upstream watershed so that runoff is as slow and clear as possible. Then if deposition persists, efforts must be made to keep the current at the site moving fast enough to retain its load in suspension. Help may come from narrowing the channel, cleaning obstructions from the channel, steepening the long profile (p. 210) of the stream, adding water from another source, or using deflectors (p. 314). *(79)*

Reservoirs—Effective distribution of water resources is one of the greatest physical and social challenges for mankind. Even a little home-made pool in a suburban stream can help, not only as a reservoir of water but also as a holder of all that goes with it, including frogs and phoebes.

Navigation—Streams in humid regions have usually been the first lines of travel, since they are relatively free of vegetation. A canoe, dugout, or raft supplied the luxury of a downhill ride without expenditure of energy; and even upstream going permitted transport of loads difficult to carry overland. Today the water routes on great rivers are still economical and relaxing, even though some of the picturesque scenes of Indian canoe, voyageur longboat, and stern-wheeler are gone.

When a dam goes across a previously navigable stream, it stops through river traffic unless a *lock* is installed to lift and lower boats hydraulically, an expensive proposition used less than formerly, when canals were more important commercially. Today recreational boating may make it desirable to reconstruct some of the unused waterways and also to construct new ones. A new dam, however, while thwarting river traffic, may back up waters, making lake traffic possible, if not for commercial transportation at least for recreational boating which may take on a commercial character by producing local income. *(237)*

River navigation needs attention to be paid to safe and efficient landings, channel dredging, and channel marking, plus watershed management to insure regulated stream flow that avoids low waters and floods. Sometimes these can be miniature considerations on small streams, as in barely canoeable brooks between wooded lakes or up winding creeks in marshes. *(521)*

Fish management—Streams do not lend themselves to the relatively isolated control that ponds do, but their fisheries can be important both commercially and recreationally. Instead of making a simplified habitat and stocking, fertilizing, and fishing it as is done with an artificial fish pond, a conservationist must accept the natural characteristics of a stream and its fish life and delicately work with them. For instance, some fish, the *anadromous* ones, come upstream from the ocean to mate and lay eggs (salmon, shad, and herring, for example), while others, the *catadromous* ones, swim downstream and out to sea to spawn (eels, for example). One dam without an adequate fish passageway, a fish ladder or lift, can completely destroy the migratory fish resource upstream and may contribute to the downstream demise of the fishery also.

Maintaining a supportive stream environment for fish must include thought for the geology of the stream. Removing vast quantities of gravel from the streambed for concrete dams, bridges, and highways can alter bottom conditions and stream flow patterns disastrously for fish populations. Some fish use gravel beds for spawning. Running heavy machinery across streams stirs up sediment, clogging the gills of fish and causing turbidity which cuts off sunlight from the plants which are so important in the biochemistry of life-supporting waters.

The quantity of water has critical limits for fish; this is a real problem where power dams want to maintain a full pool for maximum power during low-water periods. Fish are not happy in dry streambeds.

Pollution by chemicals, dump effluent, or sewage, which poisons fish or their food, uses up oxygen, or chokes the water by excessively stimulating plant life may mean death for fish. Increase in heat can be a bad form of pollution as factories and power plants discard water which has been used for cooling. The warmer the water, the less oxygen it can maintain for fish. Thermal pollution is particularly hazardous to fish populations during hot weather and when stream flow is sluggish.

Beneficial alterations of youthful streams for fishing include small dams which make cool pools above and plunge pools below for trout; deflectors to alter direction and rate of current; streamside management of vegetation to provide shade yet allow a fisherman to work along the bank without battling too much brush; some low-water monkeying around with a crowbar to reposition boulders for somewhat easier passage of fishermen in the stream; and clearing excessive vegetation which clogs the stream and snarls fishlines. Unfortunately, the most obvious improvement needed by many streams is the removal of human-deposited trash. *(385)*

Mature streams are usually less susceptible to modification for fishing. Small piers or anchored floats permit us to do dangle-leg fishing. Narrow and clean fishermen's trails, not too close to the bank but with spur trails here and there to bankside fishing spots, add convenience and pleasure.

Accessibility—If people never get to a stream to see and hear and feel it, its beauty lies in natural storage unappreciated. That is not necessarily wrong. Some parts of nature should be kept distant, wild, barely attainable; their wilderness beauty is worth saving for those moments when it is deeply felt by those who have labored hard to savor it. Conversely, though, some of those with very limited ability to get to streams should be able to enjoy them. At certain places there should be streamside trails smooth enough for wheelchairs, perhaps reserved for them and their escorts so that they can experience bankside stream-watching and, if they wish, fishing. Stream conservation should plan carefully the degree of accessibility for various portions along each watercourse so as to provide opportunities for a variety of experiences.

Simplification—The complexity of nature is often wonderful, its bafflingness being part of its beauty—as with a young lady who confuses an admirer by subtly concealing and withholding some of her charms. Few people would enjoy nature if it were always so open as to be obvious. So here in stream management the conservationist again faces the eternal problem of maintaining balance. Many people will not appreciate a stream unless its features are made somewhat obvious by simplification. Removing some trees and bushes along the bank can help, giving a little larger view to attract an admirer, perhaps just enough to partially reveal or suggest the next curve. Laying the bank too bare would not be wise; too many men might throng there to pursue its pleasures and leave the stream spoiled.

If there is a dense clump of willows where a sandbar juts out into the current, some careful pruning can simplify the tangle of stems and expose the old willow trunk from which so many sprouts have sprung. Cutting trees along a portion of the bank can let the sun in to stimulate a solid bank of dense shrubbery, its very solidity making a more simplified, readily appreciable pattern in the landscape picture. Relocating stones in the bed of a riffled stream can form a little pool which, like the rest sign in a bar of complicated music may be the interval of simple quietness which is its most beautiful passage.

Education—Much can be learned from a natural brook. But man's mind is often restless in the presence of nature unless he can experiment with it. Streams are wonderful laboratories for the inquirer who wants to know what will happen *if*. . . Suppose we put a dam here. . . Suppose we restrict flooding here. . . What will happen if we divert some water into a canal. . . Can we design a lock to lift and lower boats over a rapid. . . Can we build a bridge whose piers can withstand the ice floes of spring. . . As knowledge is built from trials and errors, nature's laws begin to be understood and written down and tested with new experiments, whose results inevitably raise new questions. New experiences help frame new laws. Growing understanding of how nature works gives people a growing ability to work with nature. Primitive men looked at rivers for thousands of years before a scientific spirit led them to design a raft that was more than accident. Now, thousands more years later, our foremost scientists are still learning about flow mechanics, and our children, all born ignorant, have to learn that water is wet and wants to run downhill and that if they build a suitable craft they can float down the river.

Yet how many schools have a brook? Every school should. Water is a natural motivator of curiosity, especially when it is moving. It stimulates the urge to find out. Water in a basin is good for learning; water in a bathtub is better; water in a brook is best.

CONSTRUCTED STREAMS

A constructed stream exists where Man makes water run where it would not naturally flow. He may just supply the water and let it find its own downhill course, but usually he will also design and construct the course it is to take to please him. Constructed streams flow through tubes, hoses, siphons, pipes, gutters, aquaducts, ditches, tunnels, canals, and occasionally through a new brook or river, in which case they appear more natural than streams flowing through the above devices.

Values of constructed streams. The ability to direct water is like the control of fire, one of those early civilizing discoveries that helped distinguish man from all other animals. Developing water resources gave man power over his natural environment by enabling him to irrigate his primitive agriculture. And with the power came the responsibilities, so that instead of continuing as a wandering hunter he had to stay settled and tend his irrigation ditches. History has shown that when various cultures failed to maintain their water resources, they perished. Today our technologically advanced cultures consume enormous supplies of water; our technological as well as biological dependence on water increases. To get the water, powerful efforts are made to pipe it or flow it in surface channels, sometimes from far-distant sources.

The water must be directed to the right place and be of suitable quality. So, even as man alters the environment of the water by moving it about, he must safeguard it, protecting it from contamination. With the growing intricacies of our culture, this responsibility has become very complex, so that the human intelligence used today in caring for water will not only determine the fate of modern man but will also make or break the many plant and animal populations whose lives have become so inextricably geared with his. Nature's value to man has become man's value to nature.

Uses of constructed streams. Sometimes a constructed stream will lead to a reservoir from which the water is drawn as needed. The most significant thing about the new channel is that it is moving water to where it is needed. But with ultimate irrigation ditches, the water is used as it flows along, by dissipating either into the soil for the plants' roots or into the air by sprinklers for increasing the humidity of leaves and stems and for watering the soil from above. By the time water reaches the end of the channels it may have been mostly or entirely used up. In dry lands, water allocation does not often permit any excess to decorate the landscape as surface water.

In some cases, however, recreation has high priority, and not just in a reservoir to which a stream is made to flow but along the course of the stream itself, as the following paragraphs suggest.

Canals. Some parts of the world have had canals for centuries. Venice, on the low east coast of Italy, Holland and other low countries of northwestern Europe, and coastal areas of southern Asia come to mind. Their canals were not built for fun; they have been major and minor arteries of daily business. But certainly these colorful waterways have been a major source of pleasure too. Nowadays technologically advanced countries tend to "ship" more by air, highway, and rail than by water. While many canals in Europe, Southeast Asia, and elsewhere are still carrying an increasing traffic, in the United States many canals built in the eighteenth and nineteenth centuries have been abandoned. Whenever possible, these canals should be revitalized for recreation, including boating, fishing, swimming, and bringing nature's water and water life into areas of congested artificiality. Motorized boats should be allowed only on the largest canals, and then with rigorous regulations. In many cases old tow paths can make beautifully graded bicycle paths. Hiking and horseback trails also can follow the canals; but because good grading is particularly important to bicycles, they should often be given priority on tow paths. Making new canals should be considered too.

Constructed cascades.   The delightful sounds of youthful streams have been recognized for centuries. The most artificial effort to capture them is probably a fountain; but somewhere between a fountain and a wild stream is the miniature rock garden cascade tumbling down in the back yard, nursing-home courtyard, or wherever else it can bring pleasure. It is usually turned on and off by a sillcock for a hose or by a valve in the cellar to a pipe. (In the north, the pipe should be buried below frost level or drained at its lowest point before freezing weather). At other times a diversion from a natural stream can supply the cascade. Or it can be run by a pump from a well. Sometimes the water can be recycled from the plunge pool back to the top by a suitable pump. If not, the water must be given a proper channel to a storm sewer or surface stream or be permitted to soak into the ground, if the ground is sufficiently porous. The placing of the rocks determines the cascade's flow and sounds.

Educational ministreams.   Mention has been made above of the value of streams for learning at home and at school—if there *is* a stream. Too often there is not, except those which run unseen through pipes. Given a supply of water, it is easy to make a stream almost anywhere, but not so easy that mistakes will not be made. From mistakes made and mistakes anticipated and avoided comes much learning. A spilled glass of milk makes a temporary stream, usually with distributaries. Use it. Perhaps, though, you can help a school make a more permanent but still flexible ministream for education.

(See also *10, 16, 36, 48, 73, 87, 98, 109, 115, 125, 129, 132, 145, 154, 161, 201, 219, 232, 241, 297, 320, 333, 376, 402, 411, 487, 517, 569, 574.*)

8   Shores

The Water's Edge
Stability of Shores
Shores as Boundaries
Ownership of Shores
Public Access
   Behavior of the public
Uses of Shores
Rocky Shores
Non-Tidal Rocky Shores
   Occurrence
   Facilities for boats
      Breakwaters
      Docks
      Launching facilities
      Navigational aids
      Artificial islands
      Causeways
      Boathouses
   Lookouts
   Trails
   Hides
Tidal Rocky Shores
   Hazards of tidal shores
   Docks and floats
   Tide pools
   Trails
   Management above high tide
   Birds and mammals

Contents

THE WATER'S EDGE

Water is a distinctive feature of our planet. The size and temperature range of Earth enables it to hold hydrogen and oxygen in that wonderful combination, H_2O. It exists in its gaseous form, vapor; in its solid form, ice; and in its liquid form, which is what we usually think of as water. Downhill it flows into the hollows of Earth's crust, the basins of oceans, seas, lakes, ponds, and puddles. And wherever the surface water meets the land, it forms a shore, be it at the edge of puddle or ocean.

The edge of anything is its most intriguing part. It is at the edge that any object enters into action with its environment, more or less modifying its surroundings and to some degree being modified by them. Dramatic examples can be seen at the water's edge. There we can come to a clearer understanding of how geologic processes over long periods of time can make alps out of sea mud and sea mud out of alps.

The forces of water molecules revolving in the long cylindrical waves grind the shallow shores; twice daily the scouring tides make channels; the steady alongshore currents transport sediments which form sand spits; and storm waves undercut sea cliffs and level off rock benches. These are examples of the dynamics of water at the shore (38). But another edge is involved: the land and sea both have a top edge, against the atmosphere. That edge also is dynamic. The winds rub along the top of the water generating waves, sometimes ripples, sometimes long-troughed rollers, and sometimes oceanic monsters. And winds blow sands from the beach into dunes. The sands reflect their heat back into the atmosphere. The warmed air rising may make air currents so tall that they expand cooling to form the fluffy clouds often seen over shores of bare sand or rock; these clouds are made of water vapor molecules which the air picked up from the water.

Then there is the biology of the shore adapted to the dynamic physical environment, the many forms of plants and animals which live in spite of and because of the waves: the special organisms which can survive in the sand and like it; those which cling to rocks and reproduce their kind for millenia; and the ones which make mole-hill mountains in a world of shore mud. *(271, 296)*

STABILITY OF SHORES

A basic problem of shore management is stability. Water levels fluctuate. Erosion gnaws away the land. Sediments accumulate at certain places in varying amounts. Thus shores may move, sometimes a negligible distance but sometimes a very significant one. A person wishing to use a shoreline intelligently must know all he can about any movements resulting from changes in the land or water. In cold climates the effects of ice must be assessed, as well as those of liquid water.

SHORES AS BOUNDARIES

Historically shores have been used as boundaries. The United States stretches from coast to coast; states are often bounded in part by rivers, such as the Ohio, the Mississippi, the Snake, and the Columbia. National governments often specify in the oceans, seas, and great lakes legal boundaries a number of miles from the edge of dry land. States and smaller political units often own to midstream rather than to the bank of a river. Private ownership may be to midstream or to the water's edge. In some coastal states, private ownership runs to a high-tide line, the state owning the inter-tidal zone. While shores of lakes and oceans have made helpful boundaries, streams have often been poor ones because they may change their courses, and also because their watersheds, when divided by a boundary stream, cannot be conveniently managed as one political unit. Shifty streams can cause shifty land management.

OWNERSHIP OF SHORES

The more or less visible line which marks the edge of a body of water doesn't belong to anybody, but the land flanking it is almost always owned; the water itself may be owned; the ground under the water may be owned; and each of these may be owned by a different party! Often the ownership of shore rights is a complicated matter that baffles the best lawyers, as when states and the federal government contest ownership of offshore rights to oil on the continental shelf.

A party (individual or group) owning *land* along shore in one sense controls the shore, by permitting or refusing access to it by land and by determining how the land and its resources shall be used, for instance for a park, for rental cottages, or for a quarry. In another way, a party with *water* rights controls the shore, as when a power company withholds water behind a dam with the result that the downstream shores recede, perhaps even leaving somebody's dock high and dry. Thoughtfulness can often avoid legal problems.

PUBLIC ACCESS

At times the public has rights, such as boating and fishing, to certain bodies of water whose shores are entirely in private ownership cutting off access from public ways. The resulting problems are gradually being worked out, so that certain right-of-ways are negotiated for by the government in order that the public can go from public roads to the water without trespassing. Sometimes to do this a government has to use the right of eminent domain, by which it can legally take and pay for private land by court action, even though the owner is unwilling to sell. Whenever possible it is wise to try to foresee such problems and arrange for legal public access before any intensive shoreland management develops and before land costs escalate.

Behavior of the public. Sometimes private owners want privacy —naturally enough. Sometimes they enjoy having the public use the water in front of their cottages, much as one enjoys sitting on the veranda watching the comings and goings on a village street.

But too often private owners fear the public because of sad experiences with thoughtless and careless people. It is one thing to catch fish in front of a man's house, but quite another to land in his back yard, light a fire, and cook them; or to throw a beach party until two in the morning with loud canned music; or to leave broken bottles or other dangerous or unsightly trash, or a smoldering beach fire!

So many shores, like many other environments, are spoiled for so many people by those who are ignorant, stupid, or careless—or all three. To make best use of shores, each conservationist must set a good example, must somehow maintain a great faith in human nature, and must help in the massive efforts needed to educate the public in regard to the country code of good outdoor manners.

USES OF SHORES

The best way to avoid inappropriate use of beaches or anything else is to provide plenty of opportunities for uses which are fitting—and to let people know about them. This book outlines constructive opportunities which help develop attitudes based on knowledge, intelligence, and a sense of caring for natural resources and one's fellow man.

Major uses of shores include: embarking on boats and landing from them, whether canoe or ocean liner, and loading and unloading their cargoes; direct enjoyment of the water and the immediate land which looks over it; benefiting from the sands, breezes, and wide skies supplied by a stretch of water; recreation based on the shore plants and those in the water—scraggly trees, beach peas, and seaweeds, to mention just a few; watching, photographing, or harvesting the fish, waterfowl, and other animals which frequent the shore. These uses are discussed in the following sections according to the type of shore.

ROCKY SHORES

There is a rhythm to the earth's crust. It slowly heaves and subsides. Where a mountain range stands high, the lower levels of rock feel a tremendous weight; then as the mountains slowly diminish from the erosive forces of air, ice, and water, the load becomes less where the mountains stood but becomes greater under the piedmont plains built up from the eroded sediments. The underlying layers of rock adjust to these changing loads, heaving up when released from mountains of pressure, subsiding when piled progressively with sediment. So sometimes the land stands tall and sometimes it lies low.

Over geologic time the shores do not stay at the same places. As land rises and falls, the edge of water finds itself at one time washing far inland across low coastal plains, at another time battering rampart cliffs rising from ocean depths at the outer edge of a continent. Geologists speak of the stages of youth, maturity, and old age for shorelines, depending upon how much the forces of erosion have accomplished in smoothing them (221).

Rocky shores are geologically youthful. The water has much work still to do to transform rugged headlands into a smooth sweep of beach or extent of mudflat. The environment is tough. The conservationist who wants to work with nature on a rocky shore must also be tough.

NON-TIDAL ROCKY SHORES

Occurrence.   Along streams, ponds, lakes, and certain seas with minimal tide, some land has withstood erosion, so that rock outcrops stand solidly at the water's edge. Occasionally there are cliffs dropping precipitously into the water; at other times broken rock at their foot, more or less ground up, forms a terrace at or just below water level. Here and there flat or gently sloping ledges or rounded boulders may give the shore a different aspect. Interspersed may be coves with sand or gravel beaches flanking them or with a bar across them, possibly with marshes and an entering stream. Wherever rocky shores occur there are geological reasons for them which can be profitably investigated. Knowing why a shore has a rocky, youthful topography adds interest and understanding of the forces of nature with which man has to deal.

Facilities for boats.   Approached from the water, even non-tidal rocky shores can look forbidding. Sailors know that sharp rocks may lie hidden under the water and that to run ashore accidentally may mean broken timbers. But where the shoreline has resulted from submergence of the land, irregularities of the coast may provide sheltered coves in the lee of islands or protected harbors in drowned valleys (such as fiords). Safe anchorages may also occur where rivers flow down from the hinterland into bays between rocky headlands, if the streams have enough current to maintain a channel through the bars which the waves and alongshore currents form across them (p. 243).

In the later stages of shoreline development, where rocky headlands have been eroded back until they form a continuous cliff with a very narrow, shelving foreshore, boats should not be encouraged. But on less hostile coasts the shore can be made accessible to boats of appropriate sizes by using breakwaters, docks, and navigational aids such as beacons and buoys *(432)*. These can be engineered by amateurs on a small scale for little boats, right down to toy boats, which have many of the same problems as large boats on rocky shores.

Breakwaters—These are usually made of rocks, especially along rocky shores. Huge blocks of quarried stone are best, since their flat edges enable them to be fitted close together so that the waves have difficulty wedging between them and forcing them apart. Their weight is important. Any object weighs much less in water than in air; this partially accounts for the ability of large waves to toss huge rocks around. For small breakwaters on not-too-exposed shores, whatever rocks are at hand can be piled with as little space as possible between them. If the stones are too small to withstand by themselves the strength of waves, they can be held together by a crib of logs spiked together. On relatively straight rocky shores, a breakwater is usually L-shaped; but on a shore with coves it may stick straight out into a cove.

Docks—For convenient and safe loading and unloading of passengers and goods, make a flat area to which a boat can be tied, at about the same height as the boat's deck. For a raft or canoe, this may be only a foot above water level. If made of local rocks, such a structure blends with the surroundings. If solidly made it can serve also as a breakwater, when built at right angles to the direction from which storm waves are most apt to approach. Concrete holding the stones together adds durability; and a flat capping layer of concrete, just slightly roughened so as not to be slippery, makes for safety. Eyebolts can be set into the concrete for fastening mooring ropes; or holes for eyebolts can be made in the rock with a star-drill. Docks can also be made from rocks plus wood, or just wood.

Launching facilities—Getting a boat into and out of the water can be a problem on a rugged rock coast. When possible, look for a gravelly or sandy place. If none is available, a launching way can sometimes be made of long timbers and cross-ties ("marine railway") sloping from high ground down across (but well above) the rocks and out into the water. The top end is securely fastened to trees or ledges, while the lower end is well ballasted (weighted down) with rocks at the sides.

A rather extreme method for forbidding, steep slopes is to swing a small boat sideways into the water from a sheer rock by using davitts (pivoting hoisting apparatus).

Navigational aids—Channel markers for recreational boating in small bodies of water can be of various sorts, ranging from plastic bottles on weighted strings to elaborate stone towers. On sizable lakes and seas, setting out buoys, spars, or other markers is a serious responsibility regulated by law. A marker poorly placed or which does not stay in the correct place may mislead a boat and cause it to go aground. The U.S. Coast Guard has special standard designs for markers for navigable waters. But on a small lake or stream it is quite feasible for campers, for instance, to make a "light house" that can boast a signal fire on top (with the fire warden's permission) on special nights such as when the canoe trippers are due back in camp.

Artificial islands—No island? Too bad. Well, why not make one! Remember that stones are much lighter in the water than in air; so you can move a lot of them relatively easily, even quite big ones, if you can roll them into the water or gather them from shallows and find some way to move them while keeping them submerged. Choose a shallow site and don't plan too big an island. A ring-shaped one like a coral atoll gives a miniature harbor in the middle and requires less fill than a solid one. Possibly you will find that you underestimate the strength of waves; by another summer the top of the island may need to be rebuilt. *(432, 364)*

Causeways—A long pile of rock can give foot-passage to a near island if the water is not too deep. To control access to the island (for instance to keep hoodlums, younger brothers, or even parents off), leave a gap in the causeway and make a drawbridge, perhaps a simple one-plank affair. A causeway can also serve as a breakwater to improve a harbor.

Boathouses—A good boat, even a toy boat, is worthy of protection from the elements during any season that it is not in the water. A boathouse should be close to the water but above storm waves, if possible in a hollow sheltered from winter winds. It should have a large door and, except for the smallest boats, launching ways running down to the water. Perhaps a little boathouse can be framed from small trees cut locally, roofed and sided with driftwood boards so that it blends with the scenery. If more routinely made of two-by-four dimension stock or larger sizes and covered with freshly sawn boards or plywood, it can be stained or painted with colors blending with the native rock and vegetation, or even be camouflaged with appropriate colors and patterns. Really patient people who know the joys of working with stone may build the boathouse walls of native stone.

Lookouts. The open space provided by a body of water lets the eyes roam. That is one of the delights of the shore. You do not have to see a distant blue horizon, nice as that is; just a little view across a pond may be special in thickly wooded country, or in a city where the horizon is mostly overhead.

The higher you are above the water, the farther you can see. Vantage points can be invitingly developed along a rocky shore; pick them with care. Consider the best views and the safest places, and how they can be reached by safe trails. Development may be minimal, perhaps just a flat stone unobtrusively moved to a good place for sitting; or maybe a weatherbeaten plank set athwart two flat stones. The length of the plank may be related to how many people are to sit on it and how close they like to sit. A really rugged low stone wall may give protection at a steep place and also provide a footrest if close enough to the bench. Use local rock. Lookouts should be located on little branch trails, rather than directly on a trail paralleling the shore. Then people walking along high land above the shore can bypass the lookout if it is already in use and thus not disturb those enjoying it. Avoid fireplaces at lookouts; locate them in less exposed, less windy, and less distracting places. If there is heavy public use, provide trash containers; build a stone wall around them or at least paint them so they will be inconspicuous.

Trails. Usually trail construction is difficult and hazardous on a slope of rocks, so pathways are kept back a little way from the top. In that case spur trails come out to lookouts as near the edge as is feasible and safe. If woody vegetation obscures the view all along the main trail, some cutting and chemical planticiding can open narrow vistas or broad panoramas looking out to the water.

Occasionally it may be worth the challenge to bring a branch trail down onto the rocky slopes, for instance to give access to a little beach or sea cave or other interesting or particularly beautiful spot. Then you must learn the art of handling the local stone to provide a tread for safe footing. Or when necessary, concrete can be used to secure rocks which cannot be made firm by wedging and weighting; and concrete or asphalt can be used to give a non-skid tread. Grinding some of the local rock to mix or embed in concrete prevents it from looking out-of-place. Iron stanchions with an eye on top for a guard rope or cable can be set into holes drilled in the rock or set into concrete at dangerous spots.

Hides. In appropriate sites, stone walls with peepholes and camera-ports can be made for photographing whatever wildlife frequents the rocky shore or adjacent habitats. Made of native stone, these should be almost invisible when seen from below or from the same level. If deemed useful, a roof of driftwood and/or boughs or thatch can complete the hide to make it inconspicuous from above.

TIDAL ROCKY SHORES

Life and landscape are much influenced by the moon on shores where its gravitational pull markedly affects the height of the water. The tides rise for about six hours to flood level, then subside for about six hours to low ebb. These phases are about 50 minutes later each day. At full moon each month, the smaller gravitational pull of the sun works with that of the moon to give the extra high and extra low "spring tides"; and two weeks later at new moon the not-quite-so-high and not-quite-so-low "neap tides." Strong winds can augment or lessen the heights of the tide locally, and can hasten or delay them. *(116, 441)*

Hazards of tidal shores. In most places tides are slight and innocuous, but coastal irregularities can accentuate them. The large volumes of water involved can build up great velocity when forced through constricted channels and can rise to great heights when forced into narrowing embayments. The world's most extreme case is the Bay of Fundy, but similar effects on a smaller though still dangerous scale occur on many other rocky coasts. Always when boating along or clambering on rocky tidal shores, you should have all your senses alert to keep in touch with what nature is doing. In new territory, inquire about local currents and rise and fall of the tide. It can be dangerous to row until exhausted against a too-strong seaward tide. And while it is an adventure to be marooned on coastal rocks by an incoming tide, it is more than exciting if those rocks are totally submerged at flood tide! And do not get caught on a crescentic beach beneath cliffs too steep to climb when the tide comes in.

Docks and floats. Where tides of four or five feet or more occur,

Even in coves sheltered from storms, well-made piers can suffer damage by ice. Harborside, Maine.

boats tied at the top of a dock with a painter (bow rope) short enough to keep them out of mischief at high tide may hang with their bows out of water at low tide. Or even with the painter adjusted properly, they may be awkward to load and unload at low tide. These problems can sometimes be avoided by having a supplementary platform at a lower level on one side of the dock, with steps down to it, which can be used at low tide but which may be covered by the highest tides. With such an arrangement, be careful about slippery seaweed on the lower level and steps.

With tides of five feet or more it is best to have a floating platform which adjusts its height to that of the tide. Access to it is by sturdy planks leading down from the shore or from a fixed pierhead. This gangway is almost level at high tide and steep downward at low tide; crosswise cleats make for safer footing when it is steep and wet. The float is held in place by ropes to shore or pier on its inward end and ropes or chains to pilings, anchors, or mooring blocks at its outer end. Chains are better because their weight sinks them so that they are less in the way of boats and swimmers. Full use of a tidal rocky shore requires some such landing facilities. *(365–432)*

Tide pools.   A pool of salt water left by the receding tide is one of the most intriguing of biotic communities. Many marvelous organisms, including starfish, mussels, barnacles, minnows, and seaweeds of many shapes and colors are able to live their lives and be on ready exhibit in hollows in the rocks between the tides. *(244, 586)* Where tide pools are absent or too small, it is sometimes possible to pile rocks together in a suitable place and cement them to form one. To give the maximum amount of working time between tides, the dam should be near the high-tide level. In other cases it may be possible to chip a hollow in the shore rocks if they are not too hard. (Always protect the eyes with goggles or plastic shield when chipping rock.) After the pool is made, see what marine plants and animals can be made happy there. If the water is shallow, it will get too warm on sunny days while the tide is out for keeping creatures like sea-anemones and sea-cucumbers, which are adapted to deeper water. Minnows will probably be comfortable until the next high tide re-unites their minni-world with the great ocean—unless a gull catches them. *(84)*

Trails.   Trails along the rocky shore between high and low tide
(intertidal trails) can be fashioned in a manner similar to that for
non-tidal shores, but closer attention must be paid to safety because
of the slippery coating, sometimes almost invisible, made by some
seaweeds. Users must be warned also about lacerations caused by
rubbing against barnacles.

Management above high tide.   Conservation practices described
above for above waterline on non-tidal rocky shores (p. 232) apply
equally well for rocky shores above high tide.

Birds and mammals.   Sea cliffs and rocky islets sometimes support colonies of highly specialized fishing birds, including gulls,
terns, cormorants, and gannets. The best conservation for these
areas is to leave the birds alone, except for well-planned educational
visits and nondisruptive research. Similarly the solitary nests of
eagles and ospreys should be enjoyed and studied from a distance
that cannot cause disturbance. Such wild creatures have enough
problems already in the increasingly populous and artificial world
of man. Aquatic mammals such as seals need similar consideration.
Let them live as symbols of the grandeur of the lonely shore.

GRAVEL AND COBBLE SHORES

These shores are composed predominantly of rock particles coarser
than coarse sand but smaller than boulders. Cobbles can be thought
of generally as from hen's-egg to fist size. The grinding and transporting power of waves and currents removes the finer particles and
leaves the coarser ones. Sometimes winter storms may make a cobble
beach where it has been sandy during the summer; but at another
time one summer storm may convert what has been a beautifully
sandy beach for years into a relatively useless gravelly or cobbly one.
On many such stony beaches the pebbles are nearly spherical; but
often they are disk-shaped or flatly oval, forming a "shingle beach."

Uses.   Gravel beaches can be used for landing small boats when
the waves are not prohibitively large; but they are often subject to
strong wave action, so they do not usually afford well-protected
landing places. Shelter for a small boat on a lake or protected bay
of the sea can be created with an L-shaped jetty made of logs. When

spiked or lashed together, these form a crib which can be filled with gravel as ballast to hold the logs in place.

Because of their coarseness, gravels and larger stones do not make good swimming beaches for sunny sprawling and for wading. But the water is sometimes beautifully clear because of a minimum of fine mineral matter in suspension. Frog-footed skin-divers can get out to deep water across such areas without letting the pebbles bother them. Children of light weight and older people with tough feet or old shoes can seek out pebbles to pick up and admire for their smooth feel, odd or beautiful shapes, and bright colors. Wetness brings out the pebble colors and helps one decide which ones are worth taking back for pebble crafts and which to plop back into the water. Where the energy of waves has ground the larger pebbles to a flat shape, they are excellent for "skipping" across the surface of the water.

Use of shore gravel for construction is sometimes considerable. Beach gravels can be screened into piles of different sizes. The coarsest are used for filling in low spots in roadbeds and the like, or are passed through a rock-crushing machine. Smaller sizes are mixed according to job specifications. Many a tar roof has a topping of gravel to lessen fire hazard and/or to give it better wearing qualities. Such use today is negligible, compared to what is used for constructing roadbeds and concrete for road surfaces, dams, buildings, and other structures. Particularly in the western United States gravels are excavated from the shores, bars, and beds of streams which are so handy to the valley roads and dams to be constructed. Unfortunately engineers have often been insensitive to other values of the streams. Gravel shallows are needed for spawning of salmon and trout. Careless digging in gravel bars and riffles can upset the delicate breeding cycles of these and other fish; and sediments stirred up can make ecological problems for other forms of wildlife as well. Carefully planned digging can sometimes provide some gravel without disrupting the entire stream, but be sure to take a broad view of the valley's resources before installing a mechanized placer operation.

SANDY SHORES

Perhaps the most astounding characteristic of a sand grain is how many brothers it has. Many sands are silica, which is hard and in-

soluble compared to other materials which have been pulverized by the grinding of wave action or dissolved and washed away. Some beaches are composed of other relatively hard minerals, or even of quite soft ones, where these are abundant and harder ones are absent. Some beaches are made primarily of shell fragments. *(246, 488)*

Sand grains are of a size class which erodes very easily. Finer particles (silt and clay) pack together more readily, and coarse ones (gravel and cobbles) are much heavier and therefore not so easily moved. But wind and water have a relatively easy time moving sand, and they do so century after century, and thus form and reform dunes, beaches, and offshore bars. Where currents flow fast enough, they tend to pick up and carry along sand; where they slow down below that rate, they deposit it. *Tidal currents* wash in and out; *stream currents* come down into lakes and oceans bringing sediments and the energy to move them; *littoral currents*, sometimes called alongshore currents, flow more or less parallel to the shore; and *currents within waves* distribute sand, leaving ripple marks on the beach *(273)*.

Waves have energy, gained mostly from the wind, which moves the molecules of water around and around within the waves. In a normally oscillating wave, the water stays in approximately the same place, forming a revolving cylinder. The up-and-down motion forms a series of crests and troughs in the same place, while energy transmitted to the adjacent water makes the wavy surface of the water appear to move forward. Indeed the form of the water progresses even though the water itself does not. Confused? Drop a stick into currentless, wavy water and watch it go up and down while moving forward very little if at all, compared to the rate of the waves. A surfer dashing toward shore on his board at about the same rate as a great wave, continually sliding downhill, is using the force of gravity to provide enough velocity to keep with the wave. And a sailboat towing a dinghy will often have the tow-rope adjusted so that the little boat will keep sliding down the near side of the second or third wave astern, using gravity to make it easier to tow. Waves can cause such problems in this complicated world that it is extra fun to study them and occasionally be able to put them to work *(38)*.

When a wave coming in to shore begins to feel the shore underneath, the water particles lose some of their energy by friction with the bottom, but they may still have enough energy left to pick up sand. On reaching shore the wave loses its cylindrical form as friction delays the bottom while the top keeps going shoreward. If the wave is large enough, it becomes a breaker, its top curling over beyond the lingering bottom, excitingly crashing down in a bubbling froth. At this moment the water seems all confusion, but it is not. Each bit of water is operating according to all the proper laws of physics. If it has enough energy, it picks up sand grains; if not, it either leaves them on the bottom or, if carrying them, it drops them. Thus waves shape shores.

Beaches are one of the safest of outdoor environments so long as one avoids sunburn and sand blown or kicked into one's eyes. But a word of warning is in order about those very rare occurrences called "quicksands." Usually an inland phenomenon, they are found where fine sand is held in suspension by upwelling springs of water, creating treacherous places where one can get stuck or even drowned.

Controlling erosion. A beach will usually stay where it is. The sand grains may not all be the same ones which were there last year or which will be there next year—but why worry about that if the wind, streams, tides, littoral currents, and waves replace promptly what they remove? Storms, however, can make sudden and drastic changes with their fantastically energetic waves. On occasions a beautiful sandy beach is storm-scoured down to stony cobbles and gravel; the sand is removed and carried up or down the coast, where it forms new beaches or offshore bars *(364)*.

Sand as an energy-absorber—When a wave picks up and jostles sand grains, it uses up some of its energy. For this reason engineers combatting storm waves find sand more useful than huge granite blocks to exhaust the waves. Great stone seawalls may be tossed around by waves coming in over rocky bottom; but if enough sand can be dumped in front of the seawall, the water exhausts its energy in shuffling sand grains and does little if any harm to the large rocks.

Getting sand for erosion control—Depending on the scale of the operation, sand can be procured elsewhere and brought in, by spoon, basket, wheelbarrow, or truck. For larger-scale maneuvers, sand can be dredged out of channels where it is not wanted and dumped where needed for erosion control. Modern hydraulic dredges can suck sand in great quantities from a channel and sluice it through pipes laid to where it is to be dumped.

A subtler method of getting sand is to let nature bring it and deposit it. In many cases littoral currents are moving sand along sandy shores, gradually but somewhat continuously. Slowing these currents makes them deposit some of their load of sand. A *groin* will often do the job. It is a short jetty of stone or wood pilings projecting out from shore, more or less at right angles. Gradually a deposit of sand fills in the corners where the groin meets the shore and makes calmer water. A series of groins properly spaced can considerably widen a long beach and safeguard the shore above it from storm waves. This subtle way to trap sand grains involves the not-so-subtle problems of building groins from large rocks or pilings. On a small scale, that is fun. On a large scale, it is expensive. But leaving shore property unprotected from storms can be expensive too!

Uses of sandy shores. The recreational uses of beaches are so well known that they need not be described here. But many people are not conscious enough of why beaches are so enjoyable. While sometimes the analysis of beauty may destroy its charm, nevertheless those people responsible for developing and maintaining that beauty must give it much thought.

The size range of sand grains is a happy one for relaxed postures. The particles are fine enough so that no one piece pokes the skin severely; the weight of one's anatomy is sustained over a large surface by innumerable grains. Yet the particles are large enough so that they brush off one's skin and clothing readily, at least when dry; finer silt and clay cling tenaciously, whether dry or wet.

The infertility of sand is also significant to recreation. The particles are the least soluble ones of the region, having survived the abrasion and dissolving of the centuries; as such they have little left in the way of nutritious chemicals for plant growth. Therefore vegetation is often sparse or even entirely absent, especially where winds and waves keep reworking the sand so that organic matter does not accumulate. While plants in themselves are beautiful, respite from them in a well-watered region can give special charm to a landscape. An expanse of sand helps one's mind get down to the basics of one's environment—soil, rocks, and water and lets one's perception lift to a larger expanse of sky. Like a little chapel a block or two off a busy main street, a strand can bring the peaceful beauty of a place apart. *(212)*

In hot weather few experiences are more enjoyable than the stimulus of cool water on one's body, alternating with relaxation on warm sand—especially in congenial company; or an active game with other people, perhaps occasionally having to retrieve a ball from the surf; or a campfire, stories, and singing after the sun has set. But along with these social satisfactions there should be opportunities for the recreation of solitude, harder and harder to come by in our increasingly hive-like society. We must plan for such delightfully lonely recreation. But how?

Zoning of shore is a partial solution. Good landscape design can help funnel those seeking a gregarious experience to congested parking lots near safe swimming beaches. There people can enjoy the music of the other fellow's portable radio and make a new friend when a beach ball knocks down a beach umbrella. Good planning can provide picnic sites where one can cook a hamburger while enjoying the smell of a neighbor's hot dogs. In such areas of social concentration, special efforts can be made to provide water, sanitary facilities, proper disposal of litter, and restriction of campfires.

With many people thus concentrated in heavy-use zones, other areas should be reserved for recreational solitude. More people these days are going to the shore in cool or even frigid weather, seeking a lonely sweep of beach; for in warm seasons on many sandy shores it is next to impossible to have such an experience. *(394)* On the smaller beaches and on larger ones near cities where parking lots are close together, it is difficult to provide space-zoning for even a modicum of solitude. In these cases some time-zoning may help, for instance restricting ball games, radios, and picnicking to certain times of day or to certain days of the week. So far as possible, both time-zoning and space-zoning should be partially attained by education of the local community at sites away from the shore: at schools, churches, clubs, and homes. The community should learn the various ways of enjoying the shore. Then a minimum of restrictive devices such as reminding signs, fences, and patrols can help people on the site to a thoughtful sharing of the shore for a variety of experiences.

Most conservationists become somewhat specialized as they mature. Some have devoted a major part of their life-energies to promoting wise use of beaches, and have thus made awe-inspiring contributions to their communities—and, in some cases, through our National Seashores, to our country as a whole and to foreign visitors as well. We need many more beach-specialists, not so titled nor paid for just that job, but dedicated to searching out the special things which make a sandy shore a place apart; learning the many facets of this special gem of a natural environment; and sharing their discoveries and understandings with others. Can you help a child learn about water tables while digging a moat around a sand-castle? Can you increase the environmental sensitivities of artists by helping them to see and portray the interlocking arcs left by the waves of a receding tide? Can you help photographers build a sand-colored hide where they can use their cameras to record the reflections of sand-pipers running on wet sand? These are but a few of the innumerable conservation jobs needed to help a variety of people make the best uses of beaches.

MUDDY SHORES

Mud is usually a mixture of those fine particles of mineral matter known as silt and clay. (Occasionally mud is made entirely or in part of decomposing organic matter.) These particles accumulate where very slow-moving or stagnant water gradually deposits fine sediments. Any old mud-puddle has good lessons in deposition for those with some ability to observe carefully. Why are the finest particles usually deposited nearest the middle of the puddle, just as with ponds and lakes? Why is "mud-puddle" such a common term yet "sand-puddle" almost unheard-of?

Muddy shores are not popular. The fine particles adhere tenaciously to skin and clothing. The silt and clay stick to each other too, thus having a suction-like effect which makes it difficult to extricate stuck tires and boats; and many a loose shoe or rubber has been left behind in mud's grip.

But at an early age of exploring the feel of things, children like mud. It smears beautifully. It is cool on a hot day. If not too wet, it molds satisfactorily so that it is easy to make cakes and pies that look just like mummy's. The small child who has not had a chance to work with mud has really missed a chance to investigate an intriguing part of his environment.

Some adults have learned to make the most of mud. Pioneers in many places have stuffed chinks of their log cabins with mud, often in mixture with peat moss (sphagnum). In arid areas, mud is the basis of adobe for masonry. Country folk know the soothing effect of mud on painful insect stings and bites. But most important has been the use of mud in ceramics, the art and industry of making items like pottery, tiles, bricks, and writing tablets from baked clay. How eagerly early man must have sought for a clay bank from which to fashion dishes and jars. Today most clay for bricks and other ceramics comes from deposits in lake beds of earlier geologic times, but some is derived from along today's muddy shores.

Fertility of muddy shores.   A few muddy shores have clean clay of quality suitable for ceramics; but much more often they will have to lie unharvested, useful for just what they are, muddy shores, a fertile edge between land and water. The fertility comes from the fineness of the particles; they present a great deal of surface from which nutrients can diffuse into the soil solution. It has been estimated that a pound of clay may contain more than an acre of surface!

Use in arid regions.   The potential fertility of muddy shores in arid regions is often useless or even harmful to plants and animals because of the strong evaporation of what water there may be. This causes an upward leaching of salts from the soil. They concentrate

(Top) Two fishermen on a coral-rock jetty. (Bottom) When everyone else has gone fishing, you can sit alone on the shore and feel—and think, if you want. Plantation Key, Florida.

at the surface, sometimes forming an alkaline crust in quantities which only a very few highly specialized plants and animals can tolerate. About the only use for an alkaline muddy shore may be to mine the alkali, if by some rare chance there is enough to make its handling economic.

Use in humid regions.   In wetter climates, muddy shores often support lush vegetation such as cattails, reeds, rushes, bulrush, and tule, along with many other species. This plant life is the basis for the life of many animals. Therefore one of the most significant contributions of a muddy shore may be its wildlife.

Wildlife of muddy shores.   Many invertebrate animals live in mud, feeding on the accumulated organic matter or microorganisms therein. Noteworthy are shellfish such as various kinds of clams, some adapted to fresh water and some to salt. Extensive scientific management of shellfish is beyond the scope of this book and should be undertaken with the aid of books and leaflets and extension agents. But for a small stretch of shore, common sense coupled with good powers of observation can indicate how many clams can be harvested at what seasons of the year within legal limits without depleting the breeding stock—perhaps enough for an occasional family clambake or at least a thin chowder. Where low tides expose wide flats, edible mussels may also be available for food in those few remaining sites which are still unpolluted; and it is fun to hunt for little pearls in the biggest mussels. Indirect food may come from digging clam worms and using them as bait for fishing.

Many other little animals live in the mud and are hungrily sought by shorebirds. These mostly have spreading or even partly webbed toes and rather long bare legs; their bills are mostly long too, well adapted to a muddy dinner table. To watch sandpipers, plovers, herons, and the like is one of the joys of the outdoorsman. Many a birdwatcher and sportsman remembers vividly his first view of an avocet or the first time he heard the wild piping of a yellowlegs. These are experiences which are worth a before-dawn rising or patient waitings in a hide as the sunset pales to an afterglow. Perhaps as the full moon comes up one will have the good fortune to watch a raccoon patter along the water's edge, leaving his tracks in the mud. (488)

Preservation of mud.   The conservationist realizes as he watches the lives of the mud-folk that they are completely at the mercy of man. His modern living threatens them daily. One industrial or municipal sewer, one leaky pipe or oil tank, or one big dredge can bring disaster to an estuary, inlet, or pond. Most of the people who lay pipes do not understand or appreciate the intricate life-relations of mud. They think it a simple material! The conservationist is therefore challenged to help give adults as well as children meaningful experiences with the muddy shore. Ask a friend to help you find and photograph a sandpiper. Actually he may make the immediate task more difficult; but later he may help swing community opinion toward protection rather than destruction of the muddy shore. Your willingness to share such experiences can be most rewarding.

(See also *56, 98, 158, 228, 356, 363, 380.*)

9   Trails and Roads

TRAILS

A trail is a track repeatedly used because it is better for travel than areas on either side. *Designing a trail* challenges you to lay out the best possible route for your purposes. *Making the trail* requires that you make its superiority clearly recognizable to potential users— even if sometimes subtly, to preserve its natural look. And *maintaining the trail* involves keeping it in good condition even when nature and people may seem to be conspiring to ruin it.

PURPOSES

A primary purpose of a trail is to get people, and sometimes their goods, from one point to another. But for many trails the main purpose is less getting somewhere and more having a worthwhile experience along the way.

Often people need help in profiting from a trail. The popular so-called nature trail usually has signs to tell people what to notice

A spur trail off the main cliff-top trail leads to a bench where a person can be alone with the Atlantic Ocean. Passamaquoddy Head State Park, Washington County, Maine.

A stone cairn marks a trail in a treeless part of the Northwest Highlands. Beinn Eighe Nature Reserve, Wester Ross, Scotland.

and appreciate. In reality every trail is a nature trail, if only one's eyes and other senses are alert to natural things and artifacts made from natural things. A concrete sidewalk is made of formerly natural limestone and gravel, with cracks where windblown dust is creating more or less soil, niches for weeds and insects to try to colonize. Maybe the day will come when a well-educated public will no longer need interpretive signs telling them what to notice and enjoy. They will be aware of nature everywhere they go. In the meantime, we often need unobtrusive, helpful signs.

ROUTES

The shortest way for a trail is sometimes the best, but usually not. Even the important trail from cabin to outhouse should usually not be the straight line which is the shortest distance between two points but should have at least one curve around a dense evergreen shrub or closely pruned tree to give privacy. Also, the shortest way is often an invitation to erosion because it goes up and down hill; so it should run more nearly on the contour (Chapter 13) even though that route is longer. But a long trail need not go far; for example, the maze paths in a formal garden wind for a long way between tight hedges within a quarter acre or less. What fun children have in them!

Most people like a route which has a reliable tread under foot, one which frees their minds to savor delightful experiences along the way. Who knows what you may discover on *your* land as bases for experiences which your trails can provide, special places which help determine where your paths should lead. You may lay out your trails to go by the most venerable tree in your woodlot, or along the edge of a field of goldenrod, or past an old cellar hole, or to a lookout whence you can see the church steeple, or near cattails where red-winged blackbirds nest, or where a log invites you to sit in the early spring sunshine on a south-facing slope. Never design a dull trail; life is too short for that. Yet balance heightened interest at some points with more low-key experiences at others, as with a passage through a relatively uniform stand of pines after leaving the cliff, or a straight run after a series of zig-zags. Of course what may at first appear a uniform stand of pines may reveal a great deal of diversity when approached with a curious mind. When desired, signs can help people see that every tree is an individual, its form revealing its life experiences.

A combination of short and long loop trails gives choices to people

Elements of TOPOGRAPHIC TRAIL LAYOUT

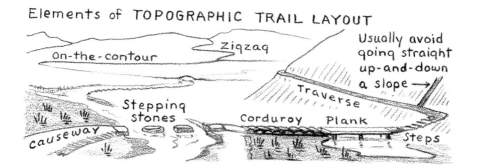

A boardwalk slightly elevated enables thousands of visitors to walk through boggy heath without damaging the delicate environment. Occasional signs interpret the ecology. Landmark Visitor Centre, Carrbridge, Scotland.

who wish to return to a parked car or other point of beginning. Simple signs, sometimes including maps, can indicate distances. Similarly, through trails to other destinations can be described. Diversity of interest is important. Grandfather may wish to saunter around the lily pond and rest on a bench, while mother and dad check out the wildflower trail and the children dash to the top of the mountain.

Do not assume that trails are for natural areas only. An urban trail can be mapped to explore alleys, public buildings, patches of exotic weeds around railroad yards, and others of the many intriguing places cities offer the observant. Suburban trails can also be of many types, including historic ones leading past houses built in different years or decades, with different styles of architecture and landscaping, and others exploring variations in topography and microclimate. Where utilities run on poles, you can use their serial numbers to identify points of interest, indicating them on a map or list for trail users. Any route can be interesting to you if you see it that way, and intriguing to others if you interpret it to them effectively.

TYPES OF TRAIL USE

Walking and hiking trails are usually our first thought, but consider also cross-country skiing and snowshoeing trails, bicycle ways, bridle paths, and even underwater trails for skin divers. Bicycle trails need a firm surface, either well-packed earth or paving, and should avoid grades over about five per cent going uphill; steeper grades downhill on one-way trails add to the fun. Bridle trails should be separate from other trails whenever possible, because of manure and hoof holes; in woods they must be trimmed considerably higher than walking and cycling trails. Powered vehicles such as motor-cycles, trail bikes, and snowmobiles must be kept off trails for the above purposes but can have trails of their own wherever their noise and fumes can be isolated so that they are not objectionable to those who have both a need and a right to get away from today's prevalent mechanization.

Sometimes a path needs to be little more than an understanding about not walking unnecessarily on the lichens and mosses when picking lowbush blueberries between the spruces. Penobscot Bay, Maine.

TRAIL CONSTRUCTION

How you make a trail depends on innumerable factors, including your purpose, your time and strength, and the kinds of environments through which it passes. Perhaps minimal changes will suffice to make the trail clear enough to follow; maybe just walking the same route a few times will compact herbs enough to suggest that this is the way. Once an attractive path is clearly defined, people and wild animals tend to use it, and, happily, wear and tear on adjacent areas are reduced. But of course concentrated usage requires that the trail be able to stand up under traffic. Where use is heavy, you may need to do much more than define the pathway. You must in such cases lay out the trail to minimize erosion and in some places literally build it, especially in wet places and on steep slopes.

Trails in wet places.   For most adults, route trails around wet areas rather than through them. Rocks, soil, or logs can be used to build up a *causeway* in low spots which are wet or mushy. To get and move rocks and soil, see page 325 and page 184. The surface of the tread is best made of coarse-textured soil which will not lift moisture by capillarity. *Corduroy trail* is well adapted to wet places in or near treelands where poles or logs can be cut. These should be a little longer than the width of the tread and laid side by side across it, then covered with soil to exclude air and give a compacted, even surface. The logs may last a long time because continuous wetness deters wood-rotting fungi when air is kept out by the soil.

Where water or mud are too deep for fill or corduroy, posts can be driven down to support a *plank walk*. One way to drive the piles in

cold climates is to chop a hole in the ice with axe or fisherman's ice auger where each post is to be set, especially when you would rather cope with cold than with mosquitos. Where posts are not feasible, plank walks can sometimes be floated on pontoons of some buoyant material. In treeswamps, supports for planks can sometimes be nailed across between pairs of suitably spaced trees. (Be sure to remove the nails if the walk is abandoned, so that the nails will not cause an accident for a band saw operator if the trees are ever taken to a saw-mill.) For a narrow plank walk used by the public, a railing of wood or rope may be advisable. Be sure to inspect wood railings regularly and maintain them in safe condition.

Stepping stones are both practical and fun across shallows and marshy places. They should be placed just so, and so, and so—to make the way easy or difficult as seems appropriate. Sometimes in Japanese gardens the first stones are set to challenge you to keep your balance, for instance so your right foot will want to cross over in front of your left foot to maintain your equilibrium; then the next stones seem to be logically arranged for normal walking and you look up more relaxed and see a beautiful vista in front of you. Stepping stones should be flat-topped and firmly set. If stones subside in time, they should be reset with gravel or other lasting support beneath.

Trails in steep places. Usually it is best to plan a gradual route slanting up a hill rather than straight, with such zig-zags as necessary to lead in the right direction. Except where agile people want a challenge or where there is no topographic alternative, avoid steep slopes. They erode easily unless made of stable rock, and they prevent access by the aged and the handicapped (see p. 259).

Zig-zag trails provide a gradual grade for ascending and descending steep slopes. The corners of such trails are called *switchbacks*, or when more rounded than angular, *hairpin turns*; and the straighter stretches between them are *legs*. They must be carefully constructed to prevent erosion. Where the upper leg is slanted inward to make water run in a gutter at the foot of the backslope, there must be a diversion at the corner to prevent this water from continuing down the next leg (see p. 260). Otherwise water accumulating from leg to leg is almost sure to cause bad erosion. These diversions pay homage

(Top) Sections of logs make rustic paving for a frequently used trail through subalpine meadow. Shoshone National Forest, Wyoming. (Bottom) Flat stepping stones provide intriguing access to a marshy pond margin and safeguard its wet frailty. Stockbridge, Massachusetts.

An improperly laid out trail can quickly disintegrate into a leg-breaker. If no good trail is provided, people make short cuts and start severe erosion. Cape Cod, Massachusetts.

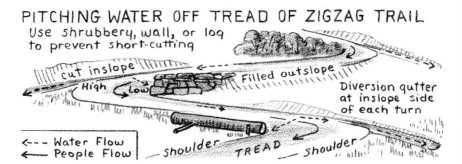

PITCHING WATER OFF TREAD OF ZIGZAG TRAIL

Use shrubbery, wall, or log to prevent short-cutting

cut inslope
High Low
Filled outslope
Diversion gutter at inslope side of each turn

‹--- Water Flow
‹—— People Flow

shoulder TREAD shoulder

to a cardinal rule: *never let people and water run downhill along the same course.* Where they do, the double wear makes maintenance difficult, if not impossible. Maintain a high crown on the trail's center to shunt the water off to the side. Because unskilled and thoughtless hikers tend to short-cut from one leg to the next without bothering to go around the corners, have as few switchbacks as you can while still making the trail seem to aim in the desired direction. People are less apt to cut corners if they have faith that the path is efficiently getting them to where they wish to be. Stone fencing and thickety vegetation maintained by pruning can be used on the downhill side of legs to prevent short-cutting, which should be avoided in every way possible. Shortcuts pack down the soil and make low spots which concentrate runoff water where people are short-cutting, thereby countering the above rule and causing bad erosion, which will often destroy both the trail and adjacent environments.

Stepped trails are sometimes necessary to prevent erosion on steep grades, either up the entire slope or in conjunction with zig-zag or traverse trails. (Traverse trails are long slanting legs.) When possible, use heavy, flat-topped stones to make well-stabilized *risers*, the vertical parts of stairs. Their tops form the *treads*, or part of them. If the stones are not wide enough for the complete treads, fill in behind them with well-tamped, compactable soil. Sometimes, instead of stones, pieces of old pavement can be sturdily embedded to make steps. At times it may be best to make a wooden form into which concrete can be poured to make a step.

Old railroad ties make good risers if they are not too disintegrated. Put the best side up to give a safe tread and tilt them up slightly at the outer edge, making sure they are firmly set into compact soil so that they retain their position; when in doubt, stake them on their downhill side with stakes whose tops are slightly lower than the tops of the ties. Telephone and electric poles, like railroad ties, have been treated with preservatives under high pressure and therefore may last a long time. The poles, however, will need to have the top side hewed flat to form the tread, an adz being the most efficient hand tool.

Logs used for steps should have their bark removed. This is most easily done to fresh-cut logs in spring and early summer, when tree growth is still active and the cambium tissue between wood and bark is moist and slippery. Bark left on logs retains moisture and promotes the growth of wood-rotting fungi. After removal of bark, treat the logs with wood preservative. Be sure to stabilize the logs, either by butting their ends into the backslope(s) in trenches or by driving preservative-treated stakes on their downhill sides. Wherever wood is used in trail-building, realize that at least yearly inspection and faithful maintenance are essential for safety. One rotted riser can break a leg of an unsuspecting hiker. While the veteran hiker is eternally alert to the condition of the trail, an inexperienced one will take for granted the quality of risers, if he thinks of them at all. Don't let him down.

A two-board cross-trail gutter diverts water from the steep trail to the right. Gardens of Inverewe, Wester Ross, Scotland.

Paving a trail.   Local stone can make a very durable and beautiful trail, perhaps the best (except for being hard on the feet for long distances, for which it is rarely used). Laying dry stone (that is, without mortar or other cementing material) is a great art. Usually we are in too much of a hurry these days to do it well, which is a pity. Seeing the enduring stonework of ancient Greece, Rome, Wales, or Peru raises deep questions about current values of how our time can be meaningfully spent. Making an esthetically pleasing path to ease the way for others is indeed a challenge. Blacktop and concrete should be last resorts for stabilizing steep trails where no less erodible route is possible. The best paths are those which unobtrusively seem to be a part of the natural scene.

ROADS

Roads are lands made suitable primarily for the travel of cars, trucks, and, much more rarely now, vehicles drawn by draft animals. Roads are a very specialized type of land use, preventing almost all other use of the land. Because today our modern highways are taking up more and more of our land area, conservationists have mixed feelings or even strong antipathy when they hear the phrase "new road."

By facilitating access to certain areas, roads permit more people to reach more places faster and with less expenditure of energy. They can be tremendously important in helping conserve some of our resources, even natural areas, which they can help protect from wildfire by allowing more patrolling, by permitting ready access for fire suppression crews and their equipment, and by acting as fuelbreaks of non-combustible materials. When land is faced by wildfire, roads can mean survival to an environment, whether it be a forest, a field of dry grain, a rabbit's thicket, or a vacation resort. Also, increased access can mean better harvesting of lumber, pulpwood, or beauty. Roads can make the difference between wise use and waste, depending some on one's point of view.

More facility in reaching an environment means also that more people can get to it for scientific study and for recreation. Also, the same people can reach it more often.

But roads are like the hole in the barn cut for the cat but used by the rat. The fire access road for the forester lures in the parker who carelessly flips a burning cigarette out into the brush. The logger's road may be used by a short-sighted timber operator interested in immediate profit rather than in sustained productivity of the land, which he therefore lays naked. The ruts leading to the scientist's trailer tempt the inexperienced camper who does not understand campfires, and invite that large segment of the public which recreates by emptying beer cans and pop bottles, leaving them as a mocking mulch on nature's floor.

In weighing the good against the bad, the conservationist realizes that the new speedways offer disaster to those tempted to stop to enjoy the countryside. Also they cut off access by secondary roads into adjacent environments. While that is a hindrance, the highways do have a beneficial insulating effect from population pressures, until roads enter the adjacent lands from the far side. Where separated highways leave sizable islands of land, there are opportunities for preservation of relatively natural environments—except for noise, fumes, de-icing salt, and other pollutants. Much of our thinking about highways can also apply to byways, even to a twisty little road to a nature center.

Roads influence environments in ways other than access and insulation, notably in their effects on water penetration and drainage. Hard-surfaced ones especially shed water fast. This runoff flows down the center or ruts if the road is poorly constructed or ill-maintained, but on a well-built road it flows across the road to its side. Along a road which is not elevated above the adjacent environment, a ditch may be formed which carries the water to any lower spot. If this low spot is on the uphill side of the road, there is a ponding effect which must usually be counteracted by running a culvert under the road to conduct the water to the downhill side. The result is an increased concentration of runoff water at the lower end of the culvert.

The many consequences of such changes in drainage are too varied to discuss here, but the conservationist must consider as many as possible. One advantage, for instance, is the possibility of creating

at the uphill end of the culvert a water impoundment for fire protection, wildlife, and beauty. Disadvantages, however, arise because
anything like a road which decreases insoak of water promotes runoff, creating higher floods and more severe droughts downstream.
The aggregate of such drainage changes over a large area such as a
city can devastate environments downstream, unless the city wisely
refrains from "reclaiming" all its bogs and marshes and uses them
instead as holding basins for water from road storm drains. Of course
a narrow road through a wide forest would usually have a negligible
effect (unless a beaver dams a culvert). But even one motorcycle
track across a sloping grassland may create enough of a drainage
change to initiate severe gully erosion.

Roads also affect local climates along their length. Especially where
a road necessitates clearing through shading vegetation, the changes
in microclimates are pronounced. For instance, heat reflected by
light-colored roads and absorbed by dark-colored ones influences
the temperature of the soil and air in the immediate vicinity. Populations of insects and other forms of wildlife often react to these environmental changes.

Clearing for a road may permit high winds to enter a forest so that
a whole stand of trees may be windthrown like a card house. A new
road bulldozed through dunes stabilized by vegetation may so alter
the wind currents as to reactivate the dunes, with dire consequences
from drifting sand.

Wherever woods are cleared for a right-of-way, increased solar
energy reaches the lower levels of the forest, with a resulting aug-
mentation in growth of sun-loving plants along the borders and with
changes in growth form of the bordering trees. Populations of insects,
birds, and other animals adjust to the changing vegetation. Thus
the forest community is drastically altered all along the course of the
road.

ROAD CONSTRUCTION

You will need more help than this book can give in order to build
any but the simplest roads, but the simplest roads are often best.
The preceding discussion of trails can help you build simple roads.

For more elaborate ones, professionals can help you better if you have first considered the fundamentals presented here.

Don't make hasty plans for roads. Building roads well can be wonderful fun, opening up new territory, creating new vistas of beauty, making something well enough to have it admired, something which will outlive you and serve people. But don't build unnecessary roads.

Purposes of roads. *Service roads:* primarily for routine business, such as pickup and delivery and patrolling. *Scenic roads:* mostly for slow recreational driving. They may have many or few parking pull-offs, or none at all. *Special roads:* include temporary logging roads, roads for scientific research, and roads for access in case of wildfire. Sometimes a major function of a road is to mark a boundary, or to be a fuelbreak. *Multiple-purpose roads:* the largest group, combining any or all of the above. A road designated as a fire-access road, for instance, may be kept open as a scenic road and also serve for patrolling in weather with high fire danger. It may also be a service road to a fire tower, trailside museum, or campground. *Extraneous roads:* include highways along external boundaries and those passing through environments being conserved but not administered by those managing the environments. These roads may be highly significant ecologically to a conserved area and therefore must be taken into account.

Season of use. Year-round use in many climates requires a paved or a well-maintained all-weather surface. A good gravel surface on a solid roadbed may do, but a hard-surfaced road will usually require less maintenance in hilly country and prove less dusty in dry weather and less muddy in wet. Though many of our best areas for outdoor recreation are now used during the summer season only, they will find increasing year-round service. Roads should usually be planned for winter use and maintenance.

Volume of traffic. The number of cars at one time should be considered along with the number per year or season, to plan for traffic and for wear. It is hard to plan with certainty for the future. Cars still wind through Boston following some of the old cow-paths around Beacon Hill.

Types of vehicles. Think not only of the day-to-day traffic of trucks on a service road but also of the exceptional vehicles such as fire trucks. Turnouts (lay-bys) on roads used for logging must be able to accommodate long-bedded logging trucks and trailers. Bridges must be rated for a maximum load.

Width of road.   The amount of traffic and its speed influence road width, but so do other factors. For instance a roadcut for a road where snow must be plowed should allow for room on uphill shoulders to deposit snow. Where a road must pass through a small but precious habitat, it is tempting to sacrifice safety by making the road narrow; try to restrict it to one-way traffic and slow vehicles down by embedding a four-by-eight-inch timber or a log in the road, with suitable warning signs. A stately tree loses some of its charm when it has been the scene of a bad accident.

One-way roads.   These have advantages. While the total area occupied by the roads is larger than with two-way roads, the area sacrificed to road construction at any one spot is narrower, thus causing less disturbance to the environment. For instance, less opening up of a stand of evergreens will reduce the chances of blowdown. Recreationally, a one-way road has less distraction by approaching cars, so that a person can better appreciate the environments on both sides of the road. When a one-way road is primarily for scenic purposes, the direction of traffic should be correlated with the time of day of heaviest use so as to minimize sun in travelers' eyes.

Length of road.   A road's length should be kept to the minimum to achieve its purpose, conserving time, energy, land, and materials. Gravel for road-building is getting seriously scarce in many areas, and in many places where it is greedily sought it can ill be spared, as in the gravel-bar spawning beds of fish. Increasingly, too, such materials will be needed for good maintenance of already existing roads.

Professional engineering help should be secured for deciding whether to lengthen a proposed road by winding it around a wetland or whether to take a shorter, more direct route through it. However, civil engineers and contractors may know nothing of the relative value of the environments involved, even though they may be able to compute the costs of cuts and fills. Don't settle for the "least expensive" road site unless non-dollar values have been well considered in the estimate; and environmental impact is no easy thing to compute!

Straightaways. These will usually be located where topography permits a road to follow a boundary or to join two points directly, according to the rule that roads be as short as possible. At times, however, a slight deviation from a direct route may permit a straight-away to run a course true north and south or east and west and thus assist in mapping an area where a grid of coordinate lines can facilitate research. A road so oriented can also help in recreational and educational areas to enable newcomers to get their bearings and better appreciate the lay of the land, the position of sun and stars, and the directions of prevailing winds and of storms.

Straight roads have a beauty all their own, which must often be developed by suitable planning, pruning, and other landscaping methods. Sometimes instead of orienting it with the cold rationality of connecting two points or of following magnetic lines of the earth, it is good to locate a straight road so that it points to some beautiful spot providing a vista or panorama as one travels. A great tree may be the focus, but because the road will usually be planned to outlive an old tree, it is perhaps wiser to aim at some geological feature expected to endure while the forests around it may come and go. If, however, the focus of a vista is on vegetation, careful landscaping can perpetuate the beauty of the scene, as by nursing along a young tree to replace an old one.

Curves. Topography usually dictates curves. At times, however, scenic roads should be curved to take advantage of landscape values such as noteworthy stands of trees, pleasant views across open spaces, and other features. Sometimes a road should curve in order to avoid marring a view from some other place or spoiling some choice environment. At other times a road may have to curve to by-pass some unsightly and unremovable object such as a hot-dog stand or gasoline station whose architecture was not designed to fit natural surroundings.

Curves in roads should be landscaped quite differently from those in trails, where a corner can often bring a surprise. The greater hazard of wheeled traffic requires that curves allow ample visibility, even on one-way roads, where there might be an obstacle such as a broken-down car just around a corner. It is therefore advisable to utilize the areas on the inside of curves for environments which do not impair visibility. In treelands this may require drastic pruning to

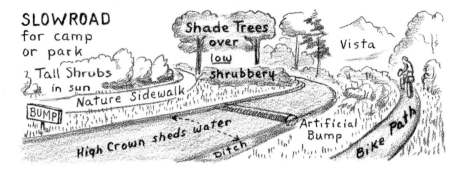

SLOWROAD for camp or park

Tall Shrubs in sun

Nature Sidewalk

BUMP

High Crown sheds water

Ditch

Shade Trees over low shrubbery

Artificial Bump

Vista

Bike Path

modify the natural habitat—removal of lower branches plus stem-wise thinning from below (p. 409) to remove the smaller trunks while leaving the older trees to maintain a canopy shading the ground. The shade inhibits growth of plants on the forest floor, making it easier to maintain the visibility across the curve than if the trees were all cut down. In other cases, all taller vegetation may be re-moved so as to keep only plants that hug the ground, like lowbush blueberries and flowering herbs. Planticides may be carefully em-ployed to permit only low-growing vegetation. When planning, consideration of vegetation management should make it possible to locate roads for minimum encroachment on natural environments and for minimum sacrifice to the safety laws of hurrying humanity.

Intersections. These present some of the same problems as curves, in terms of visibility. In addition, they should occur, as far as possible, only at level places. Triangles, cloverleaves, and the like take up much more area than simple right-angle intersections. How-ever, they may create relatively safe islands of vegetation to use as recreation areas and, to a degree, sanctuaries. Where vehicular traf-fic is heavy, underpasses should permit at least pedestrian access to these islands for recreational and educational use and for main-tenance. An eight-foot-diameter dry culvert may suffice as an under-pass.

Grades. Like curves, grades will largely be determined by topo-graphy. Season of use may help dictate maximum allowable per cent of grade (rise in feet per hundred feet, or other unit). Hard-sur-faced roads can be better maintained at a steeper grade than gravel ones. Other things being equal, the less grade the better.

Cuts and fills.   Cutting down high places and filling low ones is an everyday road-building practice (p. 260). It is important to grade the exposed new slopes to a slant less than the natural angle of repose of the materials of which they are composed, to prevent erosion and landsliding. Protect the exposed soil as soon as possible by mulching, planting, or both. Cuts and fills give opportunities for experimenting with environmental management starting with bare soil. Possibilities include rock riprapping with crannies holding rock-garden-type plants; moss gardens; ferneries; turf; and shrubbery of various kinds. There is a challenge to make the slopes beautiful, useful, and in harmony with their surroundings at the same time that they contribute to the safety of the road and minimize maintenance. We should be able to do better than just plant five rows of six yew bushes!

Shoulders.   Road shoulders extend from the paved or traveled portion down to the ditches of a cut and down to the adjacent environment in a fill. Even though there is no cutting and filling, there should be shoulder-and-ditch construction to pitch water off to the side of the road.

Especially where there are cuts and fills, there has been a regrettable neglect of proper provision for pedestrians and bicycle traffic along roads. Whenever possible, try to provide paths roughly parallel to a road. Often these will have to be along the shoulders, at least in places.

Ditches.   Ditches perform two important hydrologic functions along roads. First, they implement the rule that *no water should run onto a road from an adjacent area.* A ditch on the uphill side of a road prevents water from running down onto it. The depth of the ditch must relate to the size of the area shedding water into it and to the condition of that watershed. Where a forest soil deep with duff allows water to soak in or run off gradually, or where sandy soil lets most of the water sink in instead of run off, the ditch need not be so large as where shallow soils or paving speed the runoff. Ditches must be made adequate to carry abnormal rains and sometimes snowmelt, and they must be maintained so that they will not clog with autumn leaves or other debris. If not, roads may wash out unmercifully.

The second hydrologic function of ditches is to catch the water which drains off the road itself, implementing the rule that *water must not be allowed to run along in the road but must be pitched off to the side as soon as possible,* usually by crowning the center of the traveled portion of the road or by raising the outer side of a curve. Water thus drained down toward the uphill side of a road traversing a slope follows the ditch to a culvert or bridge by which it is allowed to pass to the downhill side. A ditch may or may not be necessary along the downhill side, depending upon the drainage conditions in the adjacent environment.

A broad, shallow ditch is usually to be preferred to a deep, narrow one for utility, safety, and maintenance (p. 312). However, it requires a wider strip of land for its construction. Where acquisition of adjacent land is not an insurmountable problem, habitats which are both useful and beautiful can well be developed as carefully vegetated drainageways wider than the traditional ditch. The resulting strips of wetlands, temporary or permanent as the case may be, will enrich both the flora and the fauna of the area and will help maintain a higher water table. Unfortunately it may also increase that horrible landmark, the beer-bottle zone.

A wide ditch deep enough to keep water much of the time can form a barrier to access from the road and give excellent protection to roadside environments, preventing both fire and trespass. Such moats often occur naturally around northern bogs and have preserved many which would otherwise have been destroyed. When power equipment is available for road construction, it can well be used to create such moats artificially.

Borrow ponds. Where gravel and other materials are excavated for road construction, there are excellent opportunities for digging deeper than the water table to create wetlands and water areas bringing diversity to the visual landscape and providing habitats for different plants and animals.

Culverts. These are large pipes or other conduits passing under a road to take water from its higher side to its lower side. They may be installed where there is a natural drainageway, such as a small stream which would otherwise be blocked by the road fill, or they may be required on the uphill side of a road at a low spot without natural surface drainage where concentration of water by the ditch would create unnatural ponding and overflow across the road. Commercially available culverts are made of corrugated metal, tile, or concrete pipe. Stone culverts are usually much more beautiful. Stone headwalls can be built at the ends of synthetic culverts to make them blend better with natural environments along the road. Some old country roads have impressive culverts made from local flat or quarried stones. These can be emulated by people with a leader who can show them the joys of using levers, hoists, stone-boats, brains, muscles, and patience to do what our forebears did. Country roads can also have less permanent culverts made from four planks of suitable width spiked together to make a square pipe.

Curbs. These are raised edges of roads which run slightly below surrounding grades, especially where there is a sidewalk. The curb is of hard material such as stone or concrete. Because the road is low it has no ditch, and water therefore runs along the edge of the road itself; the curb must be hard enough to resist its erosive power.

Berms. A berm is like a curb in that it is a hard edging for a road and must resist water flowing along the side of the road against it. But the land on the outside of a berm is not higher than the road, as it is with a curb. The berm must be continuous to keep water from flowing across it and eroding the shoulder. Berms can be made of concrete, tightly fitted stones, blacktop, or logs tightly butted against each other. They are an example of the many details which go to make an ecologically sound road.

(See also *20, 21, 41, 96, 105, 197, 204, 231, 286, 318, 339, 344, 350, 386, 387, 393, 425, 483.*)

II Environmental Components

10 *Air Management*

Slowing the Wind
  Structural windbreaks
  Location of snow fence
  Graded windbreaks
  Living windbreaks
  Location of living windbreaks
Speeding Up the Wind
  Adding energy to the air
  Freeing the wind
  Pruning to increase air circulation
  Cutting out trees and shrubs to increase air circulation
Heating the Air
  Warming by baring the ground
  Warming by felling
  Warming by pruning
  Warming by shearing
  Holding warm air
Cooling the Air
  Constructing a shady shelter
  Shade trees
  Water for cooling
Moistening the Air
Drying the Air
Adding Oxygen to the Air
Removing Carbon Dioxide from the Air
Filtering Dust from the Air
Reducing Noise
Making Air Fragrant

275

The gases which surround us and penetrate our tissues have too often been taken for granted—"free air," we used to say. Today we understand the threat of air pollution and work against contamination. But there are other ways to manage air besides cleaning it. It can be slowed down, sped up, heated, cooled, moistened, and dried. These practices can contribute to the enjoyability of the human habitat. In past centuries some cultures have suffered and even disappeared because they did not comprehend the effects of their actions on the air-water-land unity of which they should have been a working part. Today we give much more thought to developing and maintaining favorable *microclimates*, not only for local comfort and safety but also for their collective contribution to the climate of larger areas. The city-deserts created by our industrial society leave much to be desired. Planning for better air can make better environments. *(524)*

SLOWING THE WIND

We may slow the wind in order to:
1. Prevent damage from high winds which might harm buildings, overthrow trees and utility lines, flatten crops, or blow soil.
2. Make the wind drop its load of suspended sand, silt, or clay, which at the worst can sandblast glass, cut down utility poles, clog engines, dirty homes, and ruin vegetation.
3. Diminish the drifting of snow across roads, trails, or yards, or make snow accumulate on watershed slopes and croplands to provide water on melting.
4. Reduce desiccation by drying winds, which snatch invisible water molecules from anything moist, thus stunting trees, searing crops, singeing lawns, and parching skin.
5. Lessen the chill of cold winds, which remove heat from warm surfaces such as house, patio, and skin.

Moor grasses and thick wool are responses to Scottish mists. Wester Ross, Scotland.

Structural windbreaks. *Snow fences* or *drift fences* are made with intermittent openings so that the wind is not entirely obstructed and deflected; they are thus less apt to be blown over or to shift the wind problem to a neighboring location. Also they are less expensive than solid fence.

Vertical laths or poles held by interwoven wire or plastic cord can be laid out seasonally against suitably spaced posts, then rolled up and stored in the off season.

Discarded Christmas trees or other brush can be placed in a row to slow the wind. They can be supported by wires or ropes between posts; by their butts, placed in crowbar holes in packed soil or buried in loose soil; or by being leaned against each other and tied in tripod-like arrangements. Planting with vines adapted to the location increases and prolongs the effectiveness of a brush drift fence.

A wall, solid or with openings, of stone, brick, cinder block,

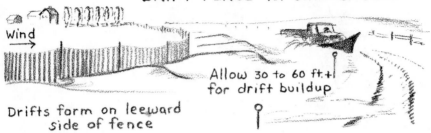

DRIFT FENCE for snow or sand

Wind →

Drifts form on leeward side of fence

Allow 30 to 60 ft.+ for drift buildup

cement block, or other masonry can make a small area truly snug from the wind but is usually too expensive for larger areas.

Stakes with burlap sacking tacked or tied on are useful for local protection of wind-sensitive plants, as around two or more sides of a newly planted specimen tree (p. 387). Or add burlap or other inexpensive fabric to an existing fence well located as a windbreak.

Almost anything not too expensive which will not blow away may be arrayed as an obstacle to slow the wind, but consider landscape esthetics. If you must use old autos, camouflage them with paints and plantings inside and out.

Like all structures, drift fences should be removed when no longer needed, unless in their aging they contribute beauty or a sense of history.

Location of snow fence. Snow settles out of the air on the lee side of a drift fence, where the wind is slowed down. Standard snow fence four feet tall should be erected at least thirty to fifty feet upwind of a road or other area to be protected, to allow room for the deposited snow. Where winds are severe across wide-open areas, use two or three ranks of fence. Living snow fence in the form of hedges is sometimes preferable to lath or pole fence, with a saving in labor by not erecting and taking it down each year, and in replacement cost. But the plants occupy more space in a field, a loss which may be offset in dry regions by the increase in moisture in the soil resulting from wind protection during the growing season. Hedges should be laid out not only to slow the wind but also, on farms, to follow contours conducive to efficient farm operations.

Graded windbreaks. When extensive grading is needed to develop a site, a windbreak can be formed by piling earth to make a protecting ridge, which can also reduce noise (p. 290) and provide visual privacy as a screen (p. 122). In a cold climate such a ridge can substantially reduce fuel bills. The soil to make it may come from excavation for a building, pond, or other modeling of the landscape. A graded windbreak should be covered with plants to maintain the slopes, add beauty, and attract wildlife (p. 373).

Living windbreaks. A living fence of shrubs or trees has advantages over constructed ones, looking more congruous in a rural scene or adding a natural touch to an urban yard. Living plants provide seasonal change of foliage, flowers, and fruits, and they help wildlife. In many sites they require only minimum maintenance, although in a small yard they may need shearing (p. 443) to keep them dense and within bounds. On a small property, they require more lateral space than a constructed fence.

Location of living windbreaks. Unlike a lath or pole drift fence, a living windbreak cannot be moved around, so it should be very carefully located. On a new site where you are unfamiliar with prevailing winds and storm winds at different seasons, inquire of well-informed local people. But note that in hilly terrain and among buildings and/or clusters of trees or tall shrubs, air currents may be

A sheepdog enjoys a sheltered microclimate on the southeast side of a rock outcrop. Boulders hold his roof on. Sheltering woods have long since been lost. Llyn Ogwen, Caernarvonshire, Wales.

SNOW STORAGE by felling selected trees

Closed Canopy   Opened Canopy

More snow evaporates   More snow settles
back into the air   to the ground

Deep snowbanks between trees

deflected so that they are not the typical ones of the region. In such cases, use lath fence experimentally for a year or two and then plant the living windbreak on its lee side after the best location has been determined by trial and error. Leave the fence a year or more after planting to protect the young plants until they are well established.

Right-angle orientation to the objectionable wind is best for straight, extended windbreaks such as those protecting crops in large fields, but land contours or property lines may require modification. (155, 581)

SPEEDING UP THE WIND

We may hasten air flow in order to:

1. Keep it from depositing a load of soil, dried leaves, or snow. (The faster any current moves the more it can carry, according to the V^6 Principle, p. 211).
2. Increase drying—helping the wind pick up moisture from damp ground, crops susceptible to fungal diseases, clotheslines, or tents and other camping gear.
3. Promote cooling. Evaporation is a cooling process, whether from skin, clothing, vegetation, ground, or other surface.

Adding energy to the air. Only rarely can a land manager add energy to the wind to make it move faster. A campfire to dry out clothes is a small, temporary measure. On a larger scale, smudge pots and electric fans are used by orchardists on nights which threaten frost, to make turbulence which mixes cold air settling near the ground with warmer air overlying it. In outdoor recreation areas, removing vegetation so the sun can strike in on bare soil will create local updrafts on sunny days; the warmed, rising air will draw cooler air from the sides, providing a slight but appreciable flow in air which might otherwise be stagnant.

Freeing the wind. Air movement is increased by removing obstacles to the wind. For instance a board fence, wall, or tight hedge may run across the lower end of a sloping garden. In summer, cool air (heavier than warm air) is impounded there as it flows downhill in the evening, making a cool place to sit at the end of a hot day. But this fence or wall should have a gate which can be opened in cooler seasons to let unwanted cold air flow out of the garden rather than form a frost pocket. At other times, native vegetation or plantings should be removed because they obstruct the wind (p. 421).

Pruning to increase air circulation. In damp climates, buildings suffer from excessive moisture where trees or shrubs have been planted or have grown too close to them. Careful pruning (p. 439) lets drier air move between buildings and plants.

Fruit trees such as apples benefit from central pruning, which admits fresh air to the middle of the canopy, reducing fungal growth and making easier distribution of pesticide sprays in the interior of the foliage, if you must use sprays.

At campsites and picnic places, judicious pruning adds enjoyment by improving the microclimate, admitting a little breeze or deflecting air currents as desired. Trimming to create a funneling effect can provide a jet of air at a precise spot such as a barbecue fireplace, from which excess heat and smoke can thus be removed in a suitable direction. Such pruning should be combined with the creation and main-

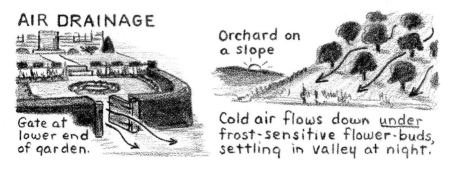

AIR DRAINAGE

Gate at lower end of garden.

Orchard on a slope

Cold air flows down under frost-sensitive flower-buds, settling in valley at night.

tenance of vistas (pp. 267, 235); and it should leave part of the site sheltered for use in cooler weather.

Cutting out trees and shrubs to increase air circulation.   Where pruning alone does not suffice, remove woody plants to create a breeze. Particularly where trees are involved, plans should be well thought out, for many species of large trees cannot be replaced in a human lifetime even in a favorable site; and where growth is slow, as in exposed places on coasts and mountains or on infertile soil, it takes a long time to regrow even small trees and shrubs. But excess trees should be cut without compunction (p. 411). Many a house and camp in a forested region suffers from a poor microclimate because it is buried in dense woods which cause humid air to stagnate. However, keep plenty of trees for shade, visual beauty, wildlife, and their many other values.

An elongated clearing to admit breeze should be oriented with an end towards the approach of the prevailing wind in fair weather, and this opening can be relatively wide to give a funneling effect. But in coastal and mountainous areas liable to strong winds, particularly if the soil is shallow or the trees shallow-rooted for other reasons, avoid opening up the forest so much that the trees may be windthrown. In such cases a narrow clearing open at both ends is better than a wider one with no egress for the wind at ground level. (For methods of clearing, see p. 421.)

HEATING THE AIR

The homeowner, gardener, and recreationist especially will benefit by making some microclimates warmer. Building a fire has only very local and temporary effects on temperature, useful when picnicking or camping or, rarely, in an icestorm to make a warm updraft under a valuable specimen tree. For larger-scale heating in more usual circumstances, we must use the warmth of the sun, somewhat managed by manipulating soil and vegetation.

Warming by baring the ground.   Air is heated to some extent by the sun's rays as they penetrate it, but much of the energy goes through to be absorbed or reflected by the vegetative cover or the ground. Bare soil absorbs heat from solar radiation; the darker its color the more it takes in and the longer it holds it, other things such as soil moisture being equal. Whenever the soil becomes warmer than the air above it, some heat will pass back into the air. Therefore local heating can be achieved by maintaining a dark ground unvegetated, as by black-topping with asphalt preparations; keeping weeds removed from loam, peat, or other dark soil; sterilizing dark soil with chemicals toxic to plant growth, or even spreading coal dust on snow. The effect may or may not be significant, depending upon many other factors; but it is sometimes worth considering. For instance a three-foot-wide asphalt path just south of a veranda will, if unshaded, warm the air above it more than will flagstones set as stepping stones in lawn. The warmth may be undesirable in midsummer but a real asset for a grandfather sitting on the veranda in spring and autumn when there is chill in the air; and even in winter quite far north, the heating effect may prove beneficial. Keeping light-colored soil free of plants will also provide warmth to the air above, but with more fluctuation of temperature between night and day and between sunny and cloudy weather.

Warming by felling. Trees and tall shrubs with foliage intercept much of the sun's energy before it descends to the six-foot layer of air next to the ground where most of our gardening and outdoor recreation takes place. Removal of this shade is our major way of heating air. Cutting down trees has a pronounced effect, especially when they are large and wide-spreading. Study the situation carefully to foresee as many as possible of the ecological results of felling. An opening cut to admit warm sun rays will also increase air movement; so give thought to leaving or developing windbreaks (p. 279). An evergreen tree on the south side of a site cut to provide winter warmth should perhaps be replaced with a deciduous tree for summer shade. When clearing for warmth, consider doing only part of the job at a time, experimentally, to prevent overclearing.

Warming by pruning. Cutting off branches can often let in adequate additional sunshine without necessitating removal of whole trees (p. 439). Study the area carefully to note where shade is cast at different times of day and at different seasons by individual branches. Making shadow-maps is intriguing and sometimes helpful. Remember that living plants change their own shapes in addition to being altered by you, so allow for growth between cuttings. Assessing the vitality of the plants being pruned helps gauging the rate of growth. Where seasonal growth occurs, in regions with pronounced winters and summers or with wet and dry seasons, note the length of stem growth between the scars left by the terminal buds of the immediately preceding years; these give clues to the growth rate which may replace pruned branches.

Warming by shearing. Densely textured hedges or other forms of plant growth shaped by shearing (p. 443) can be designed to deflect cooling winds and create pockets of warm air. This technique is good around barbecue areas, bird feeding stations, and other places where people or wildlife gather.

Holding warm air. Keeping air in one place long enough to be heated is important but often difficult. As a volume of air is warmed it becomes less dense and thus lighter and tends to rise while cooler air moves in from the sides replacing it. The relative rates of heating and of air movement determine the amount of warming achievable. Windbreaks can be used to give some control of the air mass. They can be structural, of graded earth, or of living plants (p. 276). Where ground slopes, a barrier across the slope above the area being heated helps retain warmed air, with a gate in this wall or hedge kept closed to capture warm air or opened on hot days to provide a cooling upslope breeze.

Because water retains heat longer than most substances, a pool or marsh will hold some of the daytime heat and give it back to the atmosphere at night, and will hold summer heat into the autumn, thus tending to stabilize temperature. This beneficial effect, however, is often counteracted by a downslope flow of cooler air which starts after sunset on a clear night when heat radiates back into space from the airshed above the pond or marsh. Early autumn frosts will form around the water and mists will condense over it as the water-warmed air immediately above it is cooled.

COOLING THE AIR

Methods are mostly the reverse of those noted above for heating the air. Shading of an area with trees or tall shrubs keeps out the sun's rays and evaporates moisture into the air from their leaves,

RAMADAS

Thatch

Stone + Poles

Poles + Adobe

cooling them and subsequently the air. Sometimes an artificial structure is needed to keep out the sun's energy.

Constructing a shady shelter. Where trees will not grow or have not yet grown large enough for shade, a structure, variously called a summer house, gazebo, tea house, or ramada depending in part on the section of the country, can provide a shaded spot for outdoor relaxing. A light-colored roof (reflective) will prove cooler than a dark-colored one (absorptive). More natural-looking are arbors or pergolas constructed of open frames covered with vines. These have the advantage at times of flowers and fruits as well as of the evaporative leaves, but they do not provide so much shelter from heavy showers as does a roofed summer house. Some nooks can best be shaded by a shelter partly enclosed and partly vine-covered.

Shade trees. Where the climate is moist enough and not too cold, trees are appreciated for their cooling shade. Their air-conditioning effect has too often been taken for granted, except in the hotter and drier climates, where their beneficence is more obvious—and harder to come by. In many of our middle-latitude cities, which have become deserts, great effort is needed to increase the number and size of trees along streets, in parks and other public places, and around stores, factories, and homes. For greatest cooling effect in summer, shade trees should be on the southwest side of the building or area to be shaded, so that their shadows fall across it in the early afternoon when the sun's rays are hottest. In middle and northern latitudes where winters are cool or cold, the shade trees to the south of a house should be deciduous so that when their leaves have fallen they admit the warmth of the sun at seasons when it is most appreciated (p. 374).

A special effort should be made in parking lots to sacrifice a few parking places in order to have growing space for shade trees (p. 000).

Water for cooling.   Even a small body of water can have a local cooling effect for comfort in hot weather. This is greater on the side which is downwind in fair weather (the east side in the zone of prevailing westerlies for instance). Such cooling is one of the many benefits of artificial ponds and marshes (p. 205) as well as natural ones (p. 197).

On a very local scale, air can be cooled by fountains or sprays of water forced into the air by gravity or pumps; but the results are usually diminutive compared to the air conditioning more naturally supplied by broad-leaved trees and shrubs. The cooling effect may be much less noteworthy, though, than the humidification discussed below.

MOISTENING THE AIR

Humidity is an important factor for both plants and animals. While the overall climate is the major determiner of atmospheric moisture, modification of microclimates by man can markedly change the humidity, mostly through manipulation of vegetation (p. 368). Plants have tremendous importance in the water cycle (p. 297). As a rule the thicker the vegetation of an area the more humid will be its atmosphere. Reclaiming deserts is primarily a matter of establishing dense vegetation to develop sufficient humidity for it to maintain itself, or to be maintained artificially by irrigation.

When an area is too dry to support the desired plants and animals, it may be possible by planting gradually to increase the vegetation and thereby the moisture. While the most desirable plants may not be feasible at first, select ones which have a fair chance of surviving under the dry conditions. Then care for them by protecting them from wind, by giving supplemental water if possible, and by mulching to help conserve soil moisture (p. 340). In time, less drought-resistant plants may be grown.

Mulching even without planting can increase the humidity a little, perhaps enough to make life possible for some volunteer plants and little animals. Even an old board or cloth left on bare sand may invite a colony of sowbugs and their associates, increasing the vitality of the site as the soil atmosphere is humidified *(67)*.

Directly moistening the air with a fine spray is usually prohibitive except for commercial crops, but it can be a lifesaver for new plantings in dry sites or for establishing plants in time of drought. Crops can be pressure-irrigated in mountainous areas where water is plentiful and a head of pressure can be developed by running a pipe down from a reservoir. A small *mist garden* can be similarly created for mosses, ferns, and other plants dependent on high humidity. The efficiency of direct application of water to the air depends mostly on the amount of air movement which might remove the moisture and on the degree of heating of the air, which makes it take up the moisture. So when watering, consider matters discussed in earlier parts of this chapter.

Watering the soil and plants in a dry site, of course, also increases the humidity of the air, as some of the water evaporates and some is transpired into the air by the plants.

Establishing surface bodies of water increases the humidity. Vast areas of the semi-arid and arid West have improved microclimates because of reservoirs and irrigation. However, in our eagerness to get water onto the land in a dry downstream area, which always increases the value of the land, we must not forget that making upstream reservoirs may require flooding land which should not be flooded according to the set of values of the people in the upper watershed. This problem of conflicting interests relative to water supply is a grave one, which our society must face squarely.

DRYING THE AIR

One reason for drying the air is greater comfort in hot weather; lower humidity means that the body can better get rid of its excess heat by the cooling evaporation of perspiration. Another reason is to inhibit the growth of fungal parasites of man, other animals, plants, and of fungi living on plant and animal products such as foods and fabrics. Fungi are lovers of moisture; so one of the best ways to curb them is to make the environment drier.

Excess humidity can be removed by increasing the flow of drier

MORNING SUN dries out a campsite facing east

air from a drier adjacent area (p. 281) and/or by augmenting the amount of radiant heat from the sun on the area (p. 282).

ADDING OXYGEN TO THE AIR

The gaseous composition of air normally includes about one-fifth oxygen, for which we have too seldom given thanks. During biological evolution and the attendant chemical evolution of the environment of living organisms, the oxygen content of the air has changed. Evidence suggests that there used to be none or almost none. What we are privileged to breathe today has presumably been supplied by the activity of green plants. Modern man's technology is making awful changes in the atmosphere's gases, not just locally but worldwide. Scientists cannot tell us for sure what will be the long-term effects of burning vast quantities of fossil fuels as we do, but we know burning involves taking oxygen from the air. The oxygen content of air is less readily measured than humidity and temperature. But those who raise fish in aquaria know how important it is to have green plants to supply oxygen unless it is continually added with an air pump to maintain vitality. So it may well be with our bottled-up life in great cities. If fresh air does not blow in from the country we must depend upon local green plants to help maintain our supply of oxygen. We may not be suffering from inadequate oxygen in our cities. Data are lacking. But it will do no harm and may well do good for us to add more of this life-giving gas by growing more green plants in our cities where they are so lacking. (See also next paragraph.)

REMOVING CARBON DIOXIDE FROM THE AIR

By the same token (and it may be only a token), plants remove carbon dioxide from the air. The burning of fossil fuels seems to be contributing a small but threatening increase of carbon dioxide to the planet's atmosphere, which tends to make the world a little warmer. Remains of the lush green plants of the ancient Carboniferous Era in the form of coal, oil, and natural gas are seemingly being burned faster than today's green plants can use up the resulting carbon dioxide in their photosynthetic processes. One major challenge of conservationists is to help industrialists and economists prevent the wholesale unbalancing of atmospheric gases. On a token scale we can increase the green vegetation in the cities where unthinking land development has removed too much plant life. Some plants, such as most lichens and some lilacs, are city-sensitive and refuse to grow where man has contaminated the air. But urban stalwarts like tree-ofheaven, ginkgo, and london plane are still able to do their part in cycling oxygen and carbon dioxide to make our cities more livable. *(13)*

SOME CITY TREES which help balance urban gases

Ailanthus

Maple

Ginkgo

Elm

Sycamore

FILTERING DUST FROM THE AIR

Fine particles of mineral soil, soot, and pollen often contaminate the air and cause irritation. When possible such materials should be kept from entering the air, as by good soil conservation. Where prevention is impossible, screens of plants can often filter out significant amounts. Plantings should be across the prevailing wind in dry weather, and of course upwind from the area where dust relief is sought. The broader and denser the band of vegetation (p. 279), the more effective. But even a single row of small evergreens can help restrain dust blowing from a dry dirt road (p. 382).

Filter plantings act in two ways. Serving as windbreaks, they slow the air and make it deposit some of its load of suspended matter.

This affects the coarsest particles primarily, such as fly ash and soot and the heaviest mineral particles. Such plantings also trap dust on the surfaces of leaves and stems.

The taller the vegetation, the farther it casts its *dust shadow*. A small yard may benefit from a six-foot hedge of dense evergreens, sheared at least once a year (p. 443), while a larger property may profit from a row of tall trees allowed to grow to their natural sizes and shapes. When the filtering is needed only in the leafy seasons, as at a summer home, the plants can be deciduous, and therefore less expensive to buy and easier to transplant (p. 381) than evergreens.

When clearing land (p. 421), keep dust in mind and leave a good amount of existing vegetation as a screen and filter. Developers, lacking training in ecology, rarely leave enough.

REDUCING NOISE

Air carries vibrations which we recognize as sound. When these are unpleasant we call them noise. *Quietness* is a natural resource which is becoming increasingly precious as our society gets more crowded and mechanized. At times there is enough racket actually to make people ill, even permanently disabled. At other times the noise is a slow corroder of the nervous system, or at least a nuisance interfering with communication. The most effective anti-noise practices are those which stop noise before it starts, like better design and maintenance of machines, or which outlaw noise, like legislation forbidding airplanes over wilderness areas. At other times one can only struggle to keep out the racket. *(53, 130)*

Plants are seldom effective barriers to loud sounds. *Screen plantings* probably help only to the extent that by visually hiding the source of noise they may keep our minds off the irritation. Solid walls of masonry or wood do help. Even more effective are *ridges of earth*. These cast a good *sound shadow*, diking out noise and forming a pleasant pool of quiet from sounds arising at ground level. They are no protection, however, from a neighbor's loud radio in an upstairs window or from aircraft. The taller the ridge the broader its base must be; so earthen barriers are not feasible in small yards.

For a moderately large yard, a combination *wall-and-ridge barrier* will shut out more noise than a wall alone and require less space than a ridge with its outslopings. Whenever a ridge slopes down toward a building nearby, make sure that a trough prevents water from draining all the way to the building; land should always slope away from a building enough to keep its foundations dry (p. 352).

Psychological counteraction of irritating noises like trraffficccccc by providing pleasanter sounds such as the plashing of a fountain is recommended by some people; but the total result is an increase in air vibrations *(236)*.

MAKING AIR FRAGRANT

Just as our noses warn us of danger, for instance by the acrid scent of wood smoke in dry weather or by poisonous sulfur fumes, so can they bring delight, perhaps drawing us to a blossoming swamp azalea when we are penetrating a moist tangle in search of highbush blueberries. Knowledge of fragrant native plants enables you to favor them in naturalistic landscaping. In the Northeast, let sweetfern spread in the sun by removing taller plants whose shade would kill it. Let hayscented fern extend from around the boulders in the old pasture. Plant pines on the south slope, where the warm sun's rays will distill their fragrance into the air. Dig a hollow for a marshy spot where the moist air of evening can carry the scent of algae. Favor the sweetpepperbush when clearing at the edge of the sandy swamp to make the lane redolent with its perfume.

The gardener has a special legacy of fragrant plants, inherited from many generations of his odor-conscious predecessors. The mint family and the composite family particularly have many members recommended for the herb garden; and a host of other flowering plants can embellish the air currents at the appropriate place and season *(133)*. All the world cannot smell so delicious as an orange grove or a forest of balsam fir or a shrubland of sagebrush. But many a lawn could smell better with more white clover blooming in it. Many a yard would be more fragrant with a grape arbor. Improving the qualities of the air can create new zest for living.

(See also *62, 211, 248, 340, 352, 382, 396.*)

11   Water Management

Water in and around living things is indispensable to life; it enters into the living materials and processes of every cell, providing strength, building elements, a medium for internal transport, lubrication, and temperature control, among other things. Plants must have water available to their roots or other absorptive organs, and animals must be able to drink or take water in through their food.

Many organisms require water outside as well as inside; that is, they live immersed in it. It buoys them, supports them on all sides, holds food suspended while they swim to it and engulf it, or brings food on currents to where they wait with open mouths. Water removes waste products which if allowed to accumulate would poison them. It maintains a relatively constant temperature for its inhabitants. Currents, vertical and horizontal, distribute both plants and animals and disperse reproductive cells of many kinds. Water gives protection from hunters in the air above and from drying out, so aquatic organisms do not need the elaborate water-conserving mechanisms required by terrestrial plants and animals.

Water poses problems, though. Since it is denser than air, more effort is required to move through it, unless there are compensations such as streamlining, lubrication, and current-catchers of one sort or another. Water makes it difficult to obtain large amounts of oxygen for respiration, even from cold water, which holds more dissolved oxygen than warm. And water sometimes becomes contaminated because of what occurs on watersheds when people do not care what happens to the water and aquatic organisms.

Many aquatic habitats are introduced in Chapters 6, 7, and 8. This chapter should help you manage the water in such habitats. (73, 297, 534, 558)

294

A thunderstorm up on the Ramshorn (background) can rapidly change this dry wash into a tumultuous and dangerous river, even though the sun continues to shine overhead. Don't camp or build along a dry wash! Dubois, Wyoming.

WATER AS A GEOLOGIC AGENT

Liquid water performs many of nature's grandest jobs. Pulled by gravity, it forever tries to run downhill, scratching and snatching as it flows, wearing mountains down to sea level and dumping them into the sea itself until the continents lie low and far extended, sometimes to the very edges of the ocean deeps. Arriving at base level, the water keeps on working, gnawing at the shore with a sideways appetite whose relentlessness can turn a headland cliff into a far-stretching beach of finest sand. Erosion by water is a common story. Less often we hear of its lubricating effect, causing landslides, or its weight, causing earth to fall down, or its support of soil, keeping it from collapsing. *(154, 201, 509)*

Solid water, ice, forms a permanent mineral cover on Antarctica and Greenland and on the highest mountains. Elsewhere in cool climates, water has pronounced seasonal effects as ice and snow.

The weight of glaciers sculptures mountains; they slide down slowly holding embedded boulders as engraving tools. Continental ice sheets have bulldozed down hills, formed new ones, and created lakes and bogs. Melting ice and snow unleash liquid water to do its work. Melting and freezing repeatedly in a rock crack, ice expands with enough force to keep widening the crevice and chipping off rock fragments in enough quantity to create talus slopes and piedmont plains. And all that is only a beginning of the story of the work of ice. *(167, 310, 312)*

WATER AS A CLIMATIC FACTOR

Water contributes to the uneven distribution of solar heat around the world. Water heats and cools more slowly than land, so climates of islands and coasts are more uniform than those in mid-continent, and shores have later springs and later falls. Prevailing winds across waters make downwind shores cooler in spring and summer and warmer in autumn and winter. Warm air rising over land on summer days makes onshore breezes bringing in the coolness of the water; and at night a reverse air flow wafts warm air from the land out over the water, unless some larger air mass exerts an influence. Similarly, in autumn and winter a cooling continental air mass with high pressure pours outward toward a warmer low-pressure air mass over the ocean. Where cooler, heavier air fronts on warmer, moister air, heat exchange precipitates the moisture which forms clouds and maybe rain or snow.

A cloud cover may insulate land from cold air above so that heat does not radiate out to space so fast as in clear weather, so that the land stays warmer; or precipitation may cool the land. As ocean currents like the Gulf Stream bring warm waters of equatorial seas to higher latitudes, they warm the climates there; and cold currents like the Japan Current and Labrador Current influence the air above them too, often precipitating the fog so common off Maine, maritime Canada, and the Pacific Northwest. Chapter 10, *Air Management*, discusses some ways in which water in the atmosphere influences local climates. *(366)*

THE HYDROLOGIC CYCLE

Water is remarkably mobile. A molecule from a distant ocean, invisible yet important, may at this moment be entering our lungs. And the moisture we are exhaling may some day help build the ice on which a penguin will sit. The hydrologic cycle is based on universal orderliness; water molecules always conform to nature's laws, as when water runs downhill or evaporates or is absorbed by plants and transpired into the air as vapor, or freezes to make a skim of ice on a pond. But water is very much subject to the whims of man these days. With a pump and a twist of pipe he can make it go this way or that way. With a little heat he can make it disappear into the air. With a little cooling by expansion, he can click an ice cube into his glass or air-condition a great office building. In many ways man seems to have mastered water; he can do so much to modify its wanderings. Yet still we are plagued by floods and droughts and suffer increasingly from pollution of once-clean waters. We have much to learn even as we try to apply what we think we already understand. Our place in the water cycle is not altogether clear. *(115,287)*

WATER AT THE AIR-GROUND INTERFACE

Clouds of droplets or drops of water are formed by condensation whenever the air cools to its *dewpoint*, a temperature determined by humidity and other factors. When precipitation reaches the ground, it has four major possibilities. (1) Some may stay on top of the ground, vegetation, or buildings as *surface water*. (2) Some may sink into the ground as *insoak*. (3) Some may flow downhill as *runoff*. And (4) some may return directly to its gaseous condition in the air as *evaporate*. Much of your success in environmental management will depend on how sensitively you help determine the proportions of water taking these four courses when it reaches your land.

WATER MANAGEMENT AND ESTHETICS

Managing water is of great practical importance, life depending as it does on good quantity and quality of water. One important quality of water can be called its beauty, however defined. If you do not think water beautiful, look closely at one drop, or the ocean; or drink a cool cup of unchlorinated springwater. In management, its beauty is worth more than a passing afterthought. Plan to maximize it.

MANAGING WATER BY MANIPULATING VEGETATION

Normally the native vegetation of an area is adapted to the natural cycling of water in that locality. The plants permit a maximum of water to soak into the ground for storage and slow release. Any excess will stand on the surface, run off, or evaporate. Destroying considerable native vegetation, as Technological Man almost always does when he colonizes virgin territory, dislocates the water cycle, decreasing the amount and rate of insoak and increasing the amount and rate of runoff. Therefore, when native vegetation must be destroyed, whether for cropland, roads, house lots, or whatever, an effort must be made to assess the kind and amount of change being made in the water regimen and to attempt some compensations facilitating insoak and holding back runoff. To date, most "developers" have not learned this lesson.

Because the managing of vegetation and of soil holds most of the clues for watershed management, Chapters 13 and 14, dealing with those subjects, should be helpful. The following paragraphs call attention to appropriate sections in those chapters and elsewhere in this book. (129, 411, 505)

Preserving native vegetation. To maintain the most natural water regimen, keep intact as much as possible of the native vegetation. That may be difficult but is well worth the effort; it will reduce the need for expensive ditching, damming, and other water control measures downstream. Map on paper and mark out on the ground areas to be left undisturbed during development. Permanent walls or fences are excellent, but should not look too artificial. Temporary fencing of stakes, drift fence, or rope between trees is good. Red or orange plastic flagging or strips of white cloth tied to trees and bushes help delineate an area. Try to get people to understand the reasons behind such restrictions (p. 158).

Increasing water yield by altering native vegetation. At times native vegetation competes with man for water from a watershed. While detailed, proven techniques are still lacking for most areas, it may be possible with cautious experimentation to reduce native vegetation on some watersheds while still maintaining a cover adequate for protecting soil and wildlife. Because runoff will be less uniform than under completely natural conditions, reservoirs will be needed to impound the extra runoff during times of high flow for use during times of lesser runoff. The amount of water gained for man's use will be roughly what is no longer transpired and evaporated from the removed vegetation, less the amount lost from the surface of the reservoir, though other factors are of course involved. Removing large trees and making deep reservoirs will afford the greatest harvest of water. The safest place to store water is underground, in the natural pores of soil and rock or in excavated reservoirs. Wholesale removal of vegetation is *not* recommended. In semi-arid country some shrubs, called *phreatophytes* (well plants), draw heavily on groundwater. Short-term benefits from removing all these water-depleting shrubs often may not warrant the long-term ecological dislocations of soil, atmosphere, vegetation, and wildlife that result from such tampering with the hydrologic cycle.

Drying wet ground by removing native vegetation. Occasionally native vegetation makes an area too wet, say for a permanent campsite or homesite. Whenever possible avoid using wet areas for purposes unsuited to them, for they are usually needed as they are to maintain a balanced water cycle. If no drier site is available, partial clearing of trees and/or shrubs will admit drying sun and ventilating air and hasten runoff of rain, and, at some sites in cold regions, snowmelt (p. 287).

Drying the ground by planting. In some situations a pioneer trick may still be applicable. Where the ground became muddy around the dooryard pump, pioneers would plant sunflowers, noted for their strong transpiration, to dry out the soil. Today the water from a downspout may cause puddling in a low spot of lawn which can well be planted to tall herbs such as sunflowers or goldenrod, or shrubs or a tree or two. These have greater transpiring ability than lawn grasses.

Moistening the ground by planting.   Where sun bakes in on bare soil, it removes soil moisture by evaporation, and its ally the wind removes the moist air. Even a little vegetation will ameliorate the environment by providing some shade and wind protection and contributing mulch of old leaves and stems which conserve soil moisture. Nature usually uses annual plants (p. 397) to colonize bare soil. Many weeds such as foxtail grass and ragweed can be pests, but are often important for making bare soil livable for less hardy plants. The colonizers are termed *pioneer plants*. Nature also uses many specialized, drought-resistant perennials where soil moisture is low on bare rocks or bare soil, for instance lichens, perennial bunch-grasses, shrubs like sand cherry and creosote bush, and fleshy plants (succulents) like cactus and sedum. Study nature's local vegetation development and use her plants, but try to speed up the succession of stages in one or more of the following ways.

Mulching—Straw, small stones, or other mulching material (p. 340) protects the ground from excessive radiant energy from the sun and reduces evaporation by the wind. It still, however, permits access of some water to the soil and thus tends to hold water. The amount of mulch that vegetational development might take years to accumulate you may be able to bring in and spread in a few minutes on a small area.

Planting native pioneers—Sometimes nature does not have a good supply of seed handy to sow on newly bared ground; so bringing in and distributing seeds, rooted cuttings (p. 391), or transplants (p. 374) will speed the covering of the soil by vegetation.

Planting foreign pioneers—Occasionally plants not native to an area will be available and suitable, such as commercially obtainable grasses, legumes, mustards, and buckwheat, widely used to stabilize new road cuts and shoulders. They will hasten the natural seeding-in of some native plants of later stages of vegetational development.

Direct planting of later stages of vegetation—Entirely skipping one or more stages of development is possible when precautions are taken to provide a suitable environment for the plantings (p. 374).

For instance, direct seeding of pelletized seeds gives each little embryonic plant a better chance of surviving. The pellet may include
around the seed a coat of soil with fungicide, rodenticide, and fertilizer to help it get a start on hostile bare soil. Another technique is
extra-dense planting of sizeable transplants, which support each
other by shading the soil and slowing the wind (p. 276). Mulching
and watering of course help.

   Supplemental watering—If water can be made temporarily available, by irrigation, spraying, or even watering with can or bucket,
during the early growth of plants—which is when dryness causes
the greatest mortality—then their more rapid growth and better
survival will the sooner create conditions of humidity in which they
can grow without supplemental watering. It is a difficult question as
to how much care to give plants in their new home. The more the
better, depending upon what else has to be done.

MANAGING WATER ON BARE GROUND

Water on bare ground can be a blessing or a curse. A manager of
land must study the land, determine its best use, and then make what
adjustments he can in the water regimen to further his good purposes.
Primitive man found that a roof of hides, bark, or thatch would
create a dry house by making the rain run off to the sides. Modern
man, extending this water-shedding principle to paved yards and
streets, has made great cities into a new type of desert by hastening
rainfall into downspouts, gutters, and storm sewers. By the time rain
clouds have cleared, most of the precipitation may be well on its
way downstream—and contributing to a flood. The basic idea here is
an important one in conservation: A local advantage from fast run-

Stream Flow: Rate & Load Relationships I

FAST CURRENTS
can carry big loads
of coarse particles
—or lots of "fines",
   or both.

SLOWED-DOWN CURRENTS,
having lost energy,
must deposit some of
their loads, the coarse
particles first.

Stream Flow:. Rate & Load Relationships II

Source	LONG PROFILE (along course)	Mouth	Puddle, Lake, or Ocean

Most erosion where gradient steepest and flow fastest.

Most sedimentation where gradient flattest and flow slowest.

Friction with water slows a stream, causing deposit of a delta at the mouth.

off may contribute to a large-scale disadvantage; or it may benefit everybody if a subsequent slowing up of water prevents harm or waste.

Compensating for hastening runoff. With demand for water growing fast, we should not waste rapid runoff but should slow it down, helping it sink into the ground where it can be stored as groundwater, or catching it in a reservoir. In areas deficient in fresh water, rain from the roof may be shunted by eaves-troughs and downspouts into a rain barrel or underground cistern for storage (p. 206). Cities can impound their runoff from storm sewers, using the reservoirs for fire protection, irrigation, recreation, or other appropriate purposes. *(201)*

Hastening runoff by compacting the ground. In many climates, natural processes tend to loosen soil. Clay swells when wet, then shrinks, forming cracks as it dries. Frost action in heavy soils (p. 334) fluffs up the soil. Earthworms, ants, sprouting seeds, growing seedlings, and dying roots also loosen soil, promoting insoak and reducing runoff. Tamping or rolling earth counteracts these processes (p. 358). The fine particles are forced into the pores of the soil and partially or completely seal them, preventing insoak.

Stream Flow: Rate & Load Relationships III

Youthful Stream   SHORT PROFILE (across course)   Mature Stream

erodes downwards in V-shaped valley. Deposits mostly only during low flow.

erodes sidewards in flat valley forming a flood plain. Depositing and eroding usually beautifully balanced.

Stream Flow : Rate & Load Relationships IV

Mature Stream meanders (wiggles)

as it cuts
sideways

erodes outside of curves
(nipped bank)
where current
flows fastest.

deposits on
inside of curves (slip-off slope)
where current is slowest.

Hastening runoff by paving. In most cases paving is intended primarily to create a hard surface to prevent ruts; but secondarily, it almost always makes a non-absorptive surface. Care is taken to slope the surface enough to avoid puddles. The result is rapid runoff and quick drying. Earliest paving was of stone, baked clay, or blocks of wood set on end. Now concrete and asphalt are the major materials hastening runoff, applied daily to get rid of water and make smooth, hard surfaces for our wheels. If you must pave, do so with maximum restraint, considering possible downhill results of the hastened runoff.

Hastening runoff with flexible coverings. Various cloth or plastic sheetings and sprays are increasingly being used as temporary measures when there is no need to harden the ground. One example is the covering of professional ball fields threatened by too much rain.

Hastening runoff by increasing the slope. The steeper a slope, the faster water will run off it. Excavated soil from cellars of old New England houses was often banked steeply to shed water away from the house and keep the cellar dry in that humid region. Fortunately the climate was such that it was easy to prevent erosion by grassing the resulting bank. Because steepening a slope requires grading which

Stream Flow : Rate & Load Relationships V

Mature Stream loses energy
with friction at
banks and bottom,   Levee   Levee
where it therefore
must deposit some
of its load as it
slows down.

Flood Plain,
where sediments
are deposited also
during flooding

Stream Flow : Rate & Load Relationships VI

A youthful stream
descending to a plain
and losing energy
may dump its load
forming an
ALLUVIAL FAN
("a delta on land") . . . even close to home

destroys existing protective vegetation, special efforts must be made to reestablish plant growth as soon as possible or to use paving or other techniques to hold the soil in place (p. 338).

Hastening runoff by ditching. In some very humid climates such as in Wales and Scotland, ditches are run directly downhill, at right angles to the contours, to create drier conditions on the moors prior to afforestation. This exceptional technique must be used only when gentle precipitation and dense groundcover, such as grasses and heaths, prevent erosion. In most situations, overly wet environments can be safely drained by ditches carefully laid at an an angle only slightly divergent from the contours, so that water runs in them only slowly and therefore without eroding (p. 353).

Slowing runoff over the ground. In many situations water is too precious to waste by hastening it away unused. Also, we cannot afford the attendant damage caused by erosion and sedimentation. On bare ground, sheet erosion can occur on very slight slopes, removing valuable topsoil and leading to formation of gullies which cut destructively into the subsoil. On steeper slopes the damage can be much worse; trickling rills lead to far more harm than their initial small size might lead one to suspect. Slowing down the flow of water curbs erosion by reducing the current's carrying power according to the V^6 Rule (p. 211). Even a little slowing can help a lot.

Preventing flow of water onto bare ground. Do not let water flow onto bare ground from adjacent areas. This warning applies particularly to roads, trails, and heavily used recreation areas (p. 341).

Slowing runoff by increasing insoak. Several methods, often working together under natural conditions, increase insoak. The texture and structure of the soil are to be considered (p. 335) because they determine the number and size of the pores into which water can seep. Breaking up caked soil by plowing, disking, harrowing, spading, forking, raking, or some other type of cultivation (p. 396) increases insoak. Such operations should follow closely the contours of the land, especially where long slopes are involved, so that furrows will serve as along-slope ditches to retain the surface water rather than act as up-and-down gullies to speed runoff and accelerate erosion.

You can increase the porosity of a small area of clayey soil by mixing in sand to change the texture; but large quantities may be needed, and sand is heavy to move and hard to mix with clay. Adding organic matter such as peat, humus, straw, leaves, or manure will also increase the sponginess of soil. In time these will disintegrate, but by then living plants should be well established and will themselves fluff up the soil.

Retarding runoff with obstacles.   Any obstacles to flow on a slope make temporary pondings. Tiny obstacles like bits of mulch create innumerable little ponds, perhaps only a drop in size. Sticks laid across a slope make slightly larger delaying pools. Little ridges of soil created by plowing or harrowing on the contour make elongated puddles. Small crescentic pondings are formed when trees or shrubs are planted on a slope with little rims on the downhill side of each planting depression. "Thinking on the contour" helps devise obstacles to make water walk rather than run downhill (p. 342).

Slowing runoff by encouraging vegetation.   The above methods should be considered preludes to establishing plants, the most important technique to protect the soil and make it porous. (See Chapter 14, *Planting.*) Soil-dwelling animals are significant too in maintaining an absorptive soil, but it is seldom if ever practical to introduce them to increase insoak; they will come by themselves when, through planting, you have made the soil habitable for them.

MANAGING WATER IN SMALL STREAMS

Thoughtful planning (Ch. 7) may indicate that a stream should be left in its natural condition as a free-flowing watercourse. But occasionally parts of a stream should be slowed down, sped up, deepened, made more shallow, cooled, heated, aerated, or cleaned. Any one practice affects other stream characteristics. Deepening the channel will probably cool the water, increase its oxygen content, and speed the current, while making it shallower will have the opposite effects. The smallest streams, including those that do not flow all the time, are best for experimenting. River management in the United States went through a phase of too much management of big rivers downstream, with too little attention to small streams, where erosion and flooding were starting. The U.S. Soil Conservation Service has promoted upstream management. However, hands-off management (p. 180) must be kept in mind. *(125, 370, 569)*

Dams.   Constructing small dams can be one of the most productive and enjoyable of conservation practices. Many more very small dams are needed. Most of the basic principles of dam construction are involved in little dams, to which the following discussion is limited. Larger dams are occasionally valuable, but should be planned by teams of trained ecologists and engineers according to government safety specifications, built by competent contractors, and inspected periodically by county inspectors or others responsible (p. 209; *232, 320)*

Dam sites—Select a site which will require the minimum amount of dam to back up the amount of water required for your purposes (p. 205), usually at a narrows if a deep, cool pond is wanted. A longer, lower dam is desirable for shallow, warm impoundments (p. 190). Often a series of dams is better than one tall one. Study the configuration of the valley and mark out a contour line indicating the extent of backed-up water when the pond is full and overflowing (pp. 203, 204).

Strength of dams—The volume and weight of water to be held back should determine the strength. Each cubic foot of water weighs 62.4 pounds, so the total volume creates a push seriously to be reckoned with! Not only must the possible loss of the dam be faced, but also the potential damage downstream should the dam suddenly let go. The size, materials, and manner of construction should be precisely planned and carried out, except with the smallest for-fun dams. Because a small break in a dam may suddenly become a large one as the water tears through it, a dam is often no stronger than its "winkest leak" (523).

Dam materials—Choice of materials is important. Consider the size, strength, and permanence desired, availability of local materials, cost of bringing in materials if local ones are inadequate, and your ability to handle them.

Making a "whimsy pool" in a very small brook may take only a few minutes or an hour or so using materials at hand. You can create a quiet spot for reflection where there had been continuous running. Select a suitable narrows and start throwing in rocks or sticks, first bigger ones and then smaller ones on the upstream side. Plug the holes with wads of grass and mud. Mix generous quantities of sweat and mosquito-slapping with equal parts of cool wading and current-watching. Garnish with ferns and mosses.

Short-lived dams for small streams can be made from vegetable material only. In grasslands of the West, ranchers used to create temporary irrigation dams by dumping loads of hay across a small river after the danger of meltwater freshets had passed. Today a few well-placed bales of hay may greatly improve a swimming hole or wading pool at less cost than a plastic backyard pool.

Dams of logs laid across a stream can be relatively long-lasting, especially if the logs are large and carefully placed above a narrows or with their ends dug into the banks. (Kept wet, wood rots very slowly.) Sticks laid pointing up and down the stream seem very improbable for holding back water, but that is the beaver's way of building dams. Of course the beaver adds a generous application of mud on the upstream side to fill the pores, a good technique for treating any dam of grass or wood.

Rock-core dams have the stability of weight greater than wood, but because submergence in water gives rocks considerable buoyance, a swift stream can easily move stones a man can barely struggle with in air. When moving stones, do not lift them out of the water unnecessarily or let them strain you or throw you off balance if you do hoist them into the air. Use angular rocks and interlock them as much as possible, or use smooth faces fitted tightly against each

DAMS, DIKES, & LEVEES

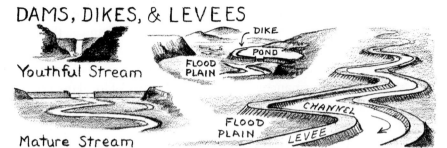

Youthful Stream

Mature Stream

other. Smaller stones and gravel should fill the chinks, with finer material plugging at least the upstream side to give maximum solidity and impermeability.

Earth dams with a thoroughly compacted clay core have minimum permeability. Surface the outer earth with erosion-resistant material, usually a rock facing of riprap on the upstream side where it is subject to wave action by the impounded water (p. 313). In a little brook, sod will work well as a facing material. Earthen dams must also be protected from erosion above the water level, sometimes with a rock or gravel veneer but more often by planted grass. Avoid trees because they are apt to blow over when they get large, disrupting the dam as their roots are torn out.

Concrete, usually with larger stones, makes rugged little dams for the amateur as well as gigantic dams for power and "reclamation" projects. Cement is heavy to lug into backwoods projects, but the satisfaction of building an enduring structure may make it worth moving by handbarrow, backpack, or canoe. Hopefully, sand to mix with the cement to make concrete can be found near the dam site. Wash any silt and clay out of sand before mixing three parts of it to one of cement. Adding wet gravel and some coarser stones gives strength and reduces the amount of cement needed, but make sure the cement is thick enough between them to give a strong bond. Wet large stones before forcing them into wet concrete. Where the artificial appearance of cement is inappropriate, use local stone for facings. Also, irregular pockets for holding soil can be used as planters for mosses, ferns, and other native herbs. If the dam is also to be used as a footbridge, you can set into the fresh cement fittings for pipe posts for a rope railing.

Abutments and bed—A strong dam poorly joined to the land on either side or beneath may be no better than a weak dam. Clean bedrock to build against is most desirable, though other solid material may suffice for small dams. A loose, porous material which has remained in place for centuries may yield rapidly to the pressure of impounded water or a permeating trickle. Whenever possible, wedge the dam into the upstream side of a narrows.

Spillways and overflow channels—Dams on streams must allow the normal flow of water to continue after a new pool has filled. The water can be immediately returned to its original channel just below the dam by passing over or through it; or the water can be let into a new channel if that seems more appropriate, perhaps to turn a little mill wheel, form a canal with locks, or irrigate a garden. But if you do not wish to return the water to its original course in the same quantity and quality as it had before building the dam, study your responsibilities to people downstream. In the eastern United States *riparian law* (law of the streambank) stipulates that water must be returned to its original channel before reaching the property of the next owner downstream, or a legal agreement must be made. In the West, *water appropriation law* has established systems for allocating water from streams, and legal rights for diverting water are often very complicated.

The spillway must be of erosion-resistant materials such as solid rock, separate stones of a size which cannot be moved by the current of a maximum flood, concrete, metal pipe, clay pipe or tile, wood, or dense turf. It is important to seal carefully the joint where the spillway meets the upstream face of the dam so that water will not leak around it into the more erodible part of the dam.

In addition to the spillway made to take care of normal flow, a supplementary overflow to carry off floodwaters safely can be built. Its outlet should be set at such a height that it will begin to function only when the pond is full. It also must be of erosion-resistant materials. If it can lead to a low spot other than the normal channel, one where it can safely impound floodwaters, it will decrease flooding downstream.

Apron, cut-off, and wing walls—The disposal of water from the lower end of a spillway or gate is important. Unless made of unerodible material, the lip may wear back. Any vertical drop from the lip will make a waterfall which will dig out the channel at that spot, forming a *plunge pool*. This pool will have relatively cool and well-oxygenated water favorable for fish in warm weather but care must be taken that the waterfall does not cut back into the dam. Design a lip with strong overhang or vertical *cut-off wall* of unerodible material. The *apron* across which the water runs beneath the waterfall should also be unerodible and be flanked by a *wing wall* on each side to contain the overflowing water.

The water falling from a dam can be esthetically important. The height of the stream has been increased by the dam, so the water has more potential energy than it originally did there. This is converted into kinetic energy, the energy of motion, as the water falls. Creative design can make swirls, sprays, and bubbles as well as smooth curtains of falling water; and the music made by the tumbling water can to some extent be composed by the designer.

Water-control structures in dams — A spillway of fixed size and height permits the same amount of water to flow out of a full pond that is flowing in. An *adjustable gate* gives control of both pond level and stream flow. The simplest gate has a vertical slot on each side to hold the ends of *flashboards* extending across the opening. The flow is controlled by slipping in or removing boards to establish the desired height of water, which pours over the top board through the gate. There are a number of commercially available control gates, for instance those opened and closed by a wheel geared to a valve in a metal culvert running through the dam. Your county agricultural agent or U.S. soil conservationist can tell you of sources.

Power dams — Compared to commercial hydroelectric dams, any water-power installations resulting from this paragraph will be almost invisible. Yet it is a good lesson in conservation and history to build a mill, even though it is only a mini- or micro-mill. A little sluiceway with an undershot waterwheel or a flume of wood from the top of a dam to an overshot waterwheel adds interest to a dam even though its contribution of power is not needed to grind corn, saw lumber, or light a city. Perhaps it can pump a little irrigation water for a garden or generate enough electricity for a streamside tent, or run a Tibetan-type prayer wheel.

Locks. If a stream is navigable, even if only for toy boats, a dam presents an obstacle. It can be surmounted if a canal can be built and fitted with a box whose ends can be opened and closed to give access to boats and raise and lower the water level. The end gates can be equipped with flashboards, or, for toy boats, with just one board pulled up and pushed down between slots. Double doors hinged at the side and opening upstream require more complicated engineering. *(521)*

Fish passageways.   Dams can be obstacles to fish in their passage up and down stream to complete their life cycles. Fish stairs are a series of little artificial pools constructed at one end of the dam, with little waterfalls between them no higher than the fish can jump. Find out from your state's fish and game agency proper specifications. Large dams may have elaborate fish ladders and elevators which have proved more or less successful.

Canals.   A canal is a constructed waterway for boats, usually connecting with a stream and/or lakes. Even a little ditch-like canal dug in perhaps only a couple of boatlengths from a stream can be handy to keep a canoe or other small boat safe from currents, waves, and the view of people. On a larger scale, whenever a navigable stream is dammed, a canal with a lock or locks should be made unless it is prohibitively expensive and a good portage can be made instead. In the state of Maine, a navigable stream is legally defined as one which will float a log.

Dig a canal almost on the contour, with just enough flow to keep it from stagnating, with enough draft for the boats which will use it. It may be just wide enough for one boat, with wider places here and there for boats to pass or to turn around. In flat recreational land such as marshes, canals can be made one-way to enhance the feeling of isolation and cause minimal ecological change. *(237)*

Excavated material can be piled as a spoilbank on one or both sides, with a gentle enough slope to revegetate fast and keep soil from washing back into the water. Often it is best to stabilize the banks with appropriate plantings (p. 315), or at least by mulching (p. 340). Sometimes excavated soil can be piled higher on one side only for a well-graded foot trail or bicycle path or an old-fashioned tow path (p. 256). It can also provide a windbreak and lookouts for boaters who wish to land and climb it. The side of the canal without a spoilbank can be left untouched to provide a natural environment. Landing places here and there, either a beach or dock, will be appreciated on long canals. If water weeds become a problem, see Chapters 6 and 14. *(237)*

Portages.   When a dam thwarts small boats going up and down a stream, a *portage* (carrying place) should be provided. It consists of one convenient landing place above the dam and one below, connected by a trail or road as short and smooth as possible. When trailered boats are used, paved launching ramps are appreciated.

Trails and roads across dams.   A dam can serve as a bridge. All but the smallest can carry at least a foot trail. One sturdy top log, flattened, can suffice for the nimble-footed. A tightly strung rope can make a handrail for the timorous or wobbly. A slightly wider dam can carry a bike path or saddle-horse trail. Compaction by use will be good for the dam so long as the level is kept up adequately.

Fords.   Sometimes a dam alters the water in the channel below it, making a good place for a ford, a shallow with even footing such as fine gravel where one can wade or horseback across, at least at times of low water. Off-the-road vehicles may also use such a ford but should take care not to make ruts or cause siltation of water flowing down from it. In the arid Southwest of the United States, many roads dip down across the dry bed of an intermittent stream. The dip may be paved or unpaved. The traveler must beware of flash floods or soft roadbed from sediment at such fords. In Britain, paved roads sometimes ford small streams.

Bridges.   An impoundment may increase the need for a bridge at its upper end in addition to passage across the dam. However, the upper end of an artificial lake is often its most natural part, so a road and bridge there may best be omitted to keep the area wild.

Ditches.   Ditches can be very useful small streams. Because of their intimate relation to soil erosion, they are dealt with in Chapter 13 *(28, 135, 227, 275, 291, 527)*

New channels for streams.   After reviewing various purposes for modifying streams (p. 218), you may decide to experiment with some cautious changes. If you shorten a segment of meandering stream, you increase its energy at the point where it returns to the original channel (p. 212). The resulting extra velocity and cutting power may cause a severe problem at that point or, more subtly, at places farther downstream, possibly eroding a neighbor's pasture or chewing at a bridge abutment. Conversely, making a stream more winding will decrease its ability to carry sediment, causing it to dump a gravel bar where it is not wanted or creating some other sedimentation problem. As a rule, try to make any new channel the same length as the old one, remembering the V^6 Rule (p. 211).

You can sometimes use nature's cutting power to make a small mature stream cut its own new channel once you get it started. A slight notch in the natural levee at a desired low point and perhaps a little damming of the original channel may do the trick. Natural hydraulic excavation will do the rest more or less as you wish. But be cautious!

Sometimes a channel should maintain its course but be deeper— for better boating, hastening the drainage of an upstream area, getting gravel for highways or fill or making concrete, or for dredging for placer gold or other valuable minerals. But a price must be paid for anything taken from nature's storehouse. Natural scenic beauty may be an early victim of dredging. So too may be fish such as salmon who spawn in shallows over gravel bars. Another problem may be increased siltation downstream. Sometimes undesirable consequences of channeling can be mitigated. A temporary sedimentation pool may keep water clear farther downstream. Perhaps riprapping or deflectors can reduce accelerated bank erosion. We usually have to make more than one change when working with nature, to maintain her balances. *(370)*

Riprapping streambanks. Riprapping is protecting a bank from erosion by surfacing it with some resistant material, usually rock. It is sometimes used on youthful streams when they are dammed or when they are eroding valuable property, and on mature streams when they nip at the outside of a meander (p. 212). Riprapping usually looks artificial and may be ineffective unless you have closely studied the stream's energy (p. 211); so do not use it unnecessarily.

Flat rocks or pieces of broken pavement, when locally available, are probably most efficient, giving maximum hard surface for the weight of stone to be moved (p. 233). First grade the bank to a slope on which the rocks can rest smoothly. Then spread over it a *filter blanket* of gravel to keep bank particles from washing out between the riprap stones and causing their collapse. Start riprapping below

low-water level and extend it up above expected flood level. Place the stones carefully, edge to edge as much as possible, to cover and protect the soil beneath.

Riprap reduces the tendency of a stream to erode at that site, but if the stones are too smoothly placed the resulting reduction of friction at the bank will add to the velocity of the current, which will therefore tend to erode more farther downstream. *Dumped-stone riprap* therefore often serves better than hand-placed stone, especially if angular stones or concrete fragments are used. More stone is needed, but it creates more bank friction.

Moving riprap is often best done overland, but at times it can be rafted downstream or, more laboriously, brought up against the current.

Gabions.   Gabions are wire baskets used to hold loose stones in place while leaving interstices through which the water can run, an advantage when you want to make minimum changes in stream energetics. Gabions can be constructed from wire fencing laced together with galvanized wire or plastic cordage. Usually they are about four- or five-foot cubes, each staked down in its middle and then lashed to those next to it.

Stream deflectors.   One way to prevent erosion of a stream bank is to slow down the current hitting it, thus reducing the water's cutting power. A deflector is built upstream as a projection from the bank at a downstream angle to divert the current from the injured spot. It may be of piled rock, either dumped or in gabions, or of driven posts (called piles or pilings) supporting a fence-like structure of boards, stakes, or brush. Watch results carefully to see what the deflected current may do downstream! Skillful placement of deflectors may be able to create currents which bump into each other and expend their energy against each other rather than against a bank.

Bulkheads and retaining walls.   Valuable land is sometimes protected at the edge of a stream by vertical walls of wood, stone, or concrete. In some sites they may also serve as a dock for boats and a place to sit—and maybe fish.

Old auto bodies.   Old cars and similar junk are seldom satisfactory except in emergencies; they are usually sad symptoms of sick watersheds and sloppy stream management. They may save a little soil, but they waste metal which should be recycled, and visually they disrupt the landscape. However, where poor people are fighting a local battle against a stream, we should recognize their plight and take a watershed-wide approach to solving their problems rather than blaming them for doing their best with an old car body.

Woven mats.   Mats can be made from lithe boughs of willow cut from vigorously growing trees or shrubs in spring. Interweave them and stake the mats to the bank or weight them down on it with stones. In intimate contact with the soil, they may sprout innumerable shoots to slow flood waters and send down multitudes of roots to hold the bank together. Mats of saplings cut at other seasons are less apt to sprout but may do so, and will be of some help even if they do not grow.

Sandbags.   In an emergency, sacks of burlap or other material can be filled with sand to bolster natural or artificial levees or to be dropped in front of an eroding bank as a temporary measure. Stack the bags tightly against each other. Emergencies there will be until many more people better understand the natural dynamics of streams (p. 211). Each time anybody dumps fill on the edge of a floodplain or in any other way constricts a stream channel, we can expect the stream to react by flooding, eroding, and sedimenting. We must practice good upstream management and let streams for the most part work out their own balances downstream; working with nature often requires more self-control than nature-control.

Cooling a stream.   Water heats and cools slowly compared to most substances, so cooling a stream is difficult but occasionally worth while, to help cool-water organisms such as trout or to make water cooler for a summer camp. Encouraging shading trees along the bank keeps off some heat from the sun. Deepening the stream with a series of small dams stores cooler water at the deeper depths. Introducing irregularities to make riffles may at least theoretically cause some cooling by promoting evaporation, a cooling process. Deep reservoirs to store meltwater from winter snows or water from higher altitudes can be used to augment stream flow in warm weather, cooling it.

Attention should be given less to making a stream cool than to keeping it cool by maintaining groundwater, which is insulated by soil and vegetation. That means maintaining porous soils for maximum insoak and keeping them well vegetated. Also we should try to minimize the heating of streams by utilities, industries, and municipalities. Thermal pollution must be of continuing concern; it will sometimes require, in addition to watershed management on the streams themselves, political action where influential people gather.

Heating a stream. Where warmer water is desired for swimming or possibly other purposes, removal of shading vegetation may be in order. Spreading water out in a shallow basin above a swimming hole can increase its heating by the sun. Major devegetation of a watershed to warm it would be advisable only in the coldest climates. Discussions with water-using industries may turn up some factory-warmed water available for heating a swimming pool or for fish culture, without undesirable ecological effects downstream.

Weeding a stream. Aquatic vegetation may interfere with fishing, boating, and swimming and require ecological consideration. If the weeds are native plants present in normal numbers, the question arises as to how many can be removed without upsetting important ecological balances; you must weigh the values of introducing human activities such as swimming against the values of the stream in its naturally vegetated condition. If weeding seems desirable, proceed slowly and experimentally with mechanical or chemical weeding (p. 400). If the aquatic weeds are native plants which are markedly increasing beyond previously tolerable numbers, try to find out what has stimulated their overgrowth. Has some formerly competing plant suffered from an introduced disease? Has chemical pollution from heavy application of nitrates or phosphates to farms or lawns in the watershed caused the overgrowth? Is thermal pollution a possible factor? Has the flow of water increased or decreased, or the amount of sediment? If you can identify one or more such factors, try to control these rather than make a direct attack on the weeds, though sometimes both approaches will be necessary.

If the undesired plants are of an introduced species, a direct attack is usually best; cut off photosynthetic and reproductive parts and, if possible, pull up roots. In any case, be sure a plant is truly undesirable before removing it. Sometimes plants have hidden values.

For instance, some floating "weeds" of Florida's irrigation ditches under the subtropical sun prevent water loss from the surface and do not unduly retard flow beneath the canopy of their floating leaves. The farmers like these "weeds". *(427)*

Changing the sounds of a brook. While a mature stream may flow in almost total silence, a youthful stream (p. 211), like a child, seems to have energy to spare for making noise. A waterfall of a large river can be thunderous. A rill may trill. Every stream should be listened to as one does to a symphony—which it literally is. The rhythm, pitch, and timbre of many instruments are there, though at first hearing only a constant rushing may be perceived.

Why should anybody want to change the sound of a brook, which is so naturally enjoyable? You may have fine artistic reasons, or maybe you just have the all-too-human curse of wanting to tinker with nature and you realize that changing the sounds of a brook may be the least harmful mischief you can perform. First listen to the overall song, and maybe catch part of it on a tape recorder. Then try to analyze the symphony, separating the sounds and pinpointing their sources. Decide which sounds you wish to keep and which you may want to change. Probe experimentally with a narrow board or stick to alter the flow at appropriate spots. Then, and only then, alter the position of a stone or add or remove a stone or stick to change the song. Do not make so many changes in any one day that you do not have time to sit and listen to the new song. You may want also to tape-record it to compare with the original, even if not to share it in a concert hall or preserve it for posterity.

Cleaning streams. In their natural condition streams carry water, dissolved minerals and gases, sediment of more or less finely ground rock, organic acids and other chemicals from organisms, organic remains such as leaves, twigs, and dead fish, and living organisms. Streams are normally busy. Now man comes along with his increasing population and hyperactivity and adds innumerable wastes from his own body and from his technological culture. But streams can take only so much.

What constitutes "dirt" in a stream? We can all agree with the old definition that "dirt is matter out of place," but because of diverse viewpoints may have trouble reaching accord as to what belongs in a particular stream. City kids think old or not-so-old shopping carriages turned on their sides make excellent stepping stones. Many adults throw an old tire or refrigerator into a brook, not seeing the value of spending their time and energy to dispose of it in any more complicated manner. *(376)*

A conservationist must always be asking himself what belongs where. There are some easy answers, but also innumerable difficult ones. We say, for instance, that some streams should be kept "natural," that is unpolluted and free-running without dams or other works of man. But what about canoes on our natural river? They are works of man. Will we compromise by saying that a quiet, green canoe is not "dirt," even though the doe drinking from the bank may think so? Perhaps it is not enough to reach agreement with our fellow men about how natural is "natural." Perhaps we must also reach accord with nature and see things from the doe's point of view.

Removing rubbish—Man-made junk does not belong in streams. Remove it alone if you can, but getting others involved gives them too a chance to work with nature. Inventory the kinds of junk to be removed. Get strong bags for small items, burlap ones for broken glass and sharp metal. For heavy items, you may need a volunteer garage tow truck, farm tractor, or contractor's equipment. Keep safety in mind. Even in shallow water sharp objects are dangerous. Wear boots or strong sneakers. Canvas work gloves are good insurance. Watch out for deep holes, strong currents, sunburn, and overexertion. Insects and, in some places, poisonous snakes may have to be reckoned with. But carefully faced risks are minimal and far less dangerous than a stream on which responsible citizens have turned their backs.

Removing natural materials—Most of us have an urge to simplify landscapes (p. 222). A dead tree fallen into a stream looks out of place. Large stones do not seem suitable on a sandy beach. So we trim and rake and tidy up after careless Mother Nature. But we can overdo our prettifying. Turtles like to sun themselves on a partly immersed tree trunk; small fish escape from big fish among its brushy branches; and children play unnamed and untrademarked balancing games as they venture out from shore on the bole and larger limbs. A fisherman's lost hook and leader may indicate differing feelings about dead trees in streams. So strive for variety and tolerance of other viewpoints when managing streams. If a fisherman disagrees with you, a doe may be on your side.

MANAGING WATER IN PONDS AND LAKES

Ponds and lakes are a source not only of water but also of energy. Impounded water loses much of its kinetic energy (energy of motion), but gains potential energy to do work when allowed to run out; and it stores heat energy. When we deal with a water body, we must consider the probable effects of any proposed management on both the liquid and the energy. The effects may be far-reaching, influencing not just the pond but also the water table of the surrounding area, the local microclimates, geologic and hydraulic processes downstream, and a host of living organisms closely or distantly related to the ecology of the pond. *(10, 48)*

Making ponds deeper or shallower. Depth has varying values and effects, some of them discussed in Chapter 7 with suggestions for techniques involving damming or digging. Use the bibliography too, and your own imagination.

Heating and cooling ponds. See, in this chapter, *Cooling a Stream* and *Heating a Stream* for appropriate techniques.

Managing pond vegetation. We can let plants "just happen" in a pond and enjoy what we get, or we can be choosey about the species and what we consider their optimum numbers and vitality. All aquatic plants are fascinating to those who make the effort to study them, and some of them are remarkably beautiful. Some aquatics are highly beneficial to what may be our primary purpose for a pond, for instance pondweeds for a waterfowl pond. Others may be pernicious pests, such as waterhyacinth in a swimming and boating area.

Water levels, temperatures, and rates of flow will help determine the presence, health, and numbers of various species of plants, as will the chemical composition of the water (p. 215). The type of bottom material, for instance rock, gravel, sand, or mud, will make a difference in what can grow. To be an aquatic gardener, you will need to be inquisitive about the environmental requirements of the plants you want and those you consider weeds. While this does not pretend to be a gardening book, it does want to encourage you to be an aquatic gardener in order to get maximum joy from your water areas. But some of the most enjoyable ponds are those left completely natural, weeds and all; so do not cultivate everything. *(427)*

Managing wildlife in ponds.   The principles of wildlife management touched upon in Chapter 15 can be applied to aquatic environments discussed in Chapters 6 and 7. Perhaps you can create an environment for days and years of happy fishing, or a marshy spot where a heron comes to feed at sunset.

Preventing pollution in ponds.   Most of what is said above about pollution in streams applies also to ponds, but because water in impoundments or natural pools is less mobile, pollution in them poses some extra problems. Polluted water tends to linger; and in many ponds oxygen exchange at the surface is less than in most streams. An extra effort should be made to monitor the amounts of any foreign substances admitted to ponds, to watch for any hints of untoward effects, and to reduce pollutants and hold them to a minimum. Consult with public health officials and ask if you can cooperate with them. Procure help from science departments at secondary schools and colleges. Get to know officers and active members of groups such as the Izaak Walton League and ecological societies so that you can work with them in promoting clean waters.

(See also *98, 110, 129, 132, 219, 241, 272, 303, 338, 402, 487.*)

12   *Rock Management*

In large masses, rock stands seemingly immovable. But nature's greatest geologic forces shift whole continents around on the softer layers underneath them; heated rocks flow out onto the surface from volcanoes; the changing burdens of sediment force up new mountain ranges; earthquakes crack the surface, creating faults in the rock masses; and gravity plucks rockslides from mountainsides and piles them in valleys. On a smaller scale, nature moves rocks embedded in creeping glaciers, leaving them as boulder fields and scattered erratic boulders; swift streams tumble large rocks down their channels; and ocean waves toss around the boulders along the shore.

Well-laid cobblestones will long outlast blacktop of asphalt, and they have a visual quality all their own, especially in rain. Clovelly, Devon, England.

By comparison with nature, man's efforts to manage rock are puny. Locally, though, we can achieve significant results, by either *destructive* or *constructive* means, both useful. (Geologists speak of nature's forces as creating landforms either destructively or constructively.) Artists, for instance, either make a sculpture by carving into rock or build up *rock flour* (clay) into a bowl, statue, or other creation.

In destructive use, man chips away at natural rock masses to harvest stone or minerals from quarries and mines. He whittles away at a cliff and makes a cave, and bores through a mountain to make a tunnel. Useful materials are procured or useful space created.

Constructively, man piles up rocks and rock chippings to alter his environment amazingly. Thus were the Great Pyramids constructed. Thus was broken rock laid as ballast to hold the railroad ties carrying rails across continents. And thus modern highways are built of crushed stone and skyscrapers made of rock aggregate in the concrete. Constructive as these uses are, the results from another point of view are destructive. We see mountains blasted apart and great spoilbanks of quarry trash piled as useless scars on a beautiful countryside. We see cities and highways spread out with little thought of lost values as they destroy the rural landscape.

The question of balance again: how do we understand "constructive" as weighed against "destructive"? If more of us face such problems sensitively on a small scale by a little work with rock in its natural setting, perhaps we can train ourselves to make wiser decisions when dealing with our larger landscapes.

REMOVING ROCK FROM OUTCROPS

An *outcrop* is bedrock showing at the surface. Its type is determined by the geological history of the site. An *igneous rock* was fire-born, cooled from some ancient lava, internal or on the surface. A *sedimentary rock* accumulated from mineral particles laid down by water or wind. A *metamorphic rock* resulted from alterations long ago of igneous or sedimentary rocks. If you are lucky enough to have an outcrop, learn all you can about it, from books, museums, universities, or amateur or professional "rock hounds." A small

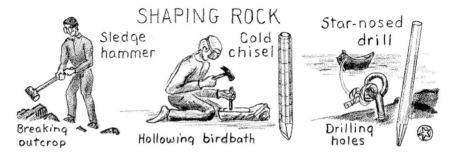

SHAPING ROCK

Sledge hammer

Cold chisel

Star-nosed drill

Breaking outcrop

Hollowing birdbath

Drilling holes

sample a couple of inches on a side can help a geologist enlighten you. *(161, 414, 579)*

Look repeatedly at your outcrop, from different angles. Come back to it other days and sit on it or lean against it. Get to know it. How does it feel to your hands when the sun has been on it? How does it look when shadows fall aslant it at sunrise and sunset? How does the rain trickle down it? Does it ever wear a cap of snow? Does it have a flecking of lichens, or graceful grasses growing in its crevices? You may enjoy your outcrop so much in its natural state that you refuse to crack or chip it; but you may decide to remove some of it to make a stone bench, a few steps, a niche for rock plants, a birdbath, or a small inscription.

BREAKING ROCK

A *cold chisel* and small hammer can exert a lot of force when applied at an appropriate spot on many kinds of rocks. The trick is to recognize the right spot, in relation to the grain of the rock determined by its mineral composition, cleavage, and bedding planes (if any), and to any zones of weakness such as those caused by frost-cracking, flaking from alternating heat and cold, physical stress, chemical disintegration, or root action. Patient trial and error bring either positive results or increasing contentedness wth the rock in its natural adamantine state. Some rocks are too hard to crack with hammer and chisel. *(Always* wear glasses or other eyeshield when hammering rock; one flying chip can cause blindness!)

A bigger hammer used directly (without chisel) can bring more force to bear, but lost is the accuracy of a chisel in applying pressure at a precise place. Experiment with points of attack. Sometimes a whack at right angles to the grain may produce better results than the more obvious striking along the grain. (As with chiseling, wear eye protection!)

Drilling a series of holes can give better control of the shape of the rock spilt off. Use a *star drill* held in one hand and hit it with a hammer, giving it a slight turn between blows. Budget a lot of time unless the rock is soft. Wedges driven into the row of holes and successively tapped may crack off the piece you want, at first luckily and later skillfully.

A pneumatic or electric drill can perform professional jobs that could not be done by hand in your lifetime. For a large job, explosives may be needed; but do not expect small-scale subtlety when working with dynamite, although a skilled, licensed operator may do very well some of the time *(315)*.

MOVING ROCKS

Most rocks are dense, so all but the smallest are heavy. (A very few, like frothy lavas, pumice, and tuff, are lighter than water.) Moving rocks without machine-power is hard work but lets you feel nature's laws intimately. Gravity is experienced a little differently than when you lift yourself out of bed, hoist a fork to your mouth, or pump blood from your feet to your lungs. You will have to both counteract gravity and use it thoughtfully.

When possible, quarry rock uphill from where you will use it. When rock removed is surplus at the site, use it as close to the site as possible, preferably downhill. But don't be tempted to fill a low spot which should be kept as a hollow (p. 169). Even cart it uphill for a worthy purpose.

Lifting rocks. When lifting rock, bend your knees, not your back, to let your legs do the work. Keep your toes out from under; you can never predict when a rock may slip and drop accidentally. Do not let your fingers be pinched between your rock and another; one slip can in a second crush a finger or hand if a rock is heavy.

When a stone is too heavy or awkward to lift by yourself, get a helper. Roll or slide the stone onto a burlap bag or canvas which can

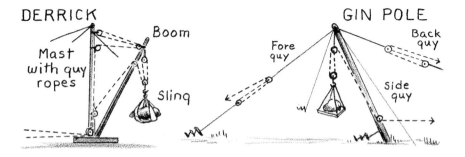

DERRICK

GIN POLE

Boom

Mast with quy ropes

Sling

Fore quy

Back quy

Side quy

form a sling between you, to distribute the weight and keep it farther from your feet in case it falls. Stones can be hoisted a bit at a time by using a *pry bar* at one corner. Slide small stones or sticks under the lifted edge to hold it up while you repeat the process at another corner. More help comes from using a *block-and-tackle* pulley system hung from a *tripod* for lifting straight up or from a *gin pole* for swinging stones sideways.

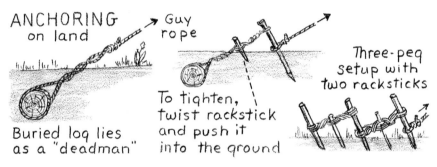

ANCHORING on land

Guy rope

Three-peg setup with two racksticks

Buried log lies as a "deadman"

To tighten, twist rackstick and push it into the ground

Rolling or sliding rocks. When possible, roll or slide a large stone rather than lift it. When rolling a large stone, do not get downhill from it. Roll stones at right angles to their short axis, except sometimes when rounding a corner; then be extra careful. When moving a large stone that does not roll easily, use a *following stone* to hold it up partially while you prepare for your next shove. Use a *nudging stick* to poke the following stone under, thus keeping your fingers out. Use a pry bar (crowbar, strong pole, or iron pipe) to lift a corner of a heavy stone or to slide it. Prepare the surface along which a stone is to be rolled or slid. Remove obstacles, grade the way, or provide a plank. Greasing a plank reduces friction for sliding. A rock rolled onto it can often best be moved not by sliding the rock

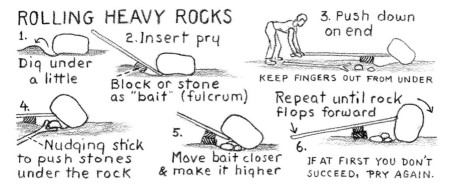

ROLLING HEAVY ROCKS

1. Dig under a little

2. Insert pry

Block or stone as "bait" (fulcrum)

3. Push down on end

KEEP FINGERS OUT FROM UNDER

Repeat until rock flops forward

4. Nudging stick to push stones under the rock

5. Move bait closer & make it higher

6. IF AT FIRST YOU DON'T SUCCEED, TRY AGAIN.

on the plank but by putting rollers such as short logs under it and moving the entire plank with the stone on it. (This is probably the most primitive wagon, forerunner of modern diesel trucks.) The larger the diameter of the rollers, the more easily they traverse the terrain, but the higher the stone must be hoisted to put it on the plank, or the higher the plank must be lifted with the stone to put it on the rollers.

If a stone is too large to lift, roll, or slide by manpower supplemented by simple machines like inclined planes, levers, and pulleys, you can perhaps solve your problem by breaking the stone into movable pieces; or give in and hire a bulldozer and truck. Or maybe you decide the rock belongs where it is "to hold the world together," so you work creatively around it, enjoying it.

BUILDING WITH STONE

Laying up stone has special pleasures. It does not conform to our wishes so readily as wood, but thought and experimentation develop skill. And the results are relatively permanent, subject to wind, rain, heat, and cold, of course, but not rotted by fungi or consumed by fire. Structures made of local stone blend with the landscape, giving a satisfying natural look. Dry-wall construction, that is without cementing mortar, is particularly challenging. If you can do one tenth as well as the ancient Incas, Egyptians, Welsh, and Scotsmen you are doing well indeed. *(391, 588)*

Stones for foundations. Four *cornerstones* will hold a log cabin or summer house off the ground, keeping the timbers up so they

Many wall-builders say that a one-stone-wide wall will soon topple; but intricately laid granite walls only one stone thick have stood for centuries on Dartmoor. Devon, England.

stay drier and do not rot so fast as they would on soil. A *continuous stone foundation* is better for winter warmth and may keep skunks from making a home under the floor. Use *footings* for foundations. Frost action can rapidly shake apart a well-built wall if it lacks a proper footing, made by digging a ditch below frost line and filling it with small stones whose coarse pores will not retain water and therefore will not heave and sink with freezing and thawing.

Stone walls. Various purposes and different materials lead to many kinds of stone walls, both wet (with mortar) and dry. Some old walls in Wales are of great slabs of slate set on end into the soil side by side. In Devon one finds walls only one stone wide and five feet tall built of quarried granite. New Englanders built walls of precariously balanced rounded glacial boulders. Any way, give your wall a good footing in a trench dug below frost level. Use stones as large as you can handle in the lower *courses* (layers). The wider your wall the stronger. Run some longish stones lengthwise of the wall as *stretchers* but be sure to put some long ones crosswise as *headers*. Where two stones meet in one course, bridge over the joint with a stone in the next course above. Use little stones, preferably somewhat wedge-shaped, for *chinking* (filling in cracks), and for leveling irregular stones so they will provide flat *bearing surfaces* for the

DRY WALL
H = Header S = Stretcher
F = Filler C = Chinker

WALL with MORTAR

RETAINING WALL

Batter

Bases of walls buried below frost

stones set on top of them, or to level the top of the wall. The more stones you can fit into a given volume of wall, the stronger it will be and the more windtight (p. 277) and noiseproof (p. 290).

A top course of sharp stones set on end helps keep people off your wall. They may not mean to knock a wall down but often do when climbing or sitting on it.

Your wall may be *single-faced*, with stones neatly aligned in one plane on one side but with the back irregular. Or if it is to be seen from both sides, with more labor and love you can make it *double-faced*.

Retaining walls. A wall to hold up soil at the edge of a terrace or bank is usually single-faced and made with a *batter*, an inward-upward slant to its face to help resist the outward thrust of the weight of the soil and its expansion with any freezing. The stones should slant downward and inward. When laid wet with mortar, a retaining wall in cold climates should have *weep holes* here and there, especially near the bottom, to drain the soil and thus minimize frost action.

Walls with plants. Plants growing in or on a wall can improve its looks immeasurably. Pockets of soil are best built in while the wall is being made. Where the wall is to restrict livestock or provide a screen (p. 122), it can have its effectiveness extended upward by plants growing on top, as is noteworthy in Devonshire and Cornwall. Such a wall can be a double row of stones slanted downward and inward, with the space between filled with soil. Hawthorn and nettles are planted as restrainers of cattle and trespassers—quite effectively. You can use whatever plants you please, adapted to the soil and site. Hawthorns like an alkaline soil. How about blueberries if you have an acid soil? A privet or barberry hedge atop a low double wall has advantages over a tall stone wall, especially when you ponder lifting ponderous stones to the top course.

STONE FURNITURE

Portable aluminum and plastic lawn chairs pop up all over the countryside to make comfortable resting places for those who enjoy nature. More harmonious with the natural scene are two stones with a weathered plank across them, or a rustic all-stone bench of local rock. If well made, it may delight people for several hundred years. Perhaps birds too will perch on it—and necessitate some cleaning off with a handful of grass and maybe a little rainwater from the nearby birdbath of chipped stone. What lime remains will encourage the colorful growth of lichens to decorate your bench; did you ever see lichens on an aluminum deck chair?

POSTCRIPT TO ROCK MANAGEMENT

You may never develop the skill to shape a flint arrowhead. You will never lay up stone to build a fourteenth-century Gothic cathedral. Such mastery came from a mingling of necessity and imagination, a mixing of the desire to survive with the wish to soar. Rock often seems commonplace, obdurate, and improbable. But take another look at it. Study it. Experiment with it. Maybe you can work with it and through it subtly shape your environment to make a better world for yourself and others. Perhaps while working with rock you can derive some of the joys of the shapers of arrowheads and the builders of cathedrals.

(See also *190, 280, 307, 449, 490, 584.*)

13   Soil Management

Productivity
Water-Holding Capacity
Thermal Effects of Soils
Changing the Grades of Soils
Keeping Soil in Place
    Maintaining vegetative cover
    Protecting vegetative cover
    Reestablishing vegetative cover
    Mulching
    Grading soil to prevent water erosion
    Grading soil to prevent landslides and slumps
    Controlling gully erosion
    Controlling wind erosion
    Grading soil to reduce wind velocity
    Structures to slow the wind
    Planting to control wind erosion
    Controlling shore erosion
    Controlling streambank erosion
Making Soils Drier
    Dry wells
    Ditches
    Gutters
    Drainpipes
Making Soils Moister
Using Soil to Grow Plants
Using Soils for Grading
    Saving topsoil
    Compacting soil

No simple thing, soil. It is a mysterious complex which should be considered sacred, in a sense, for from it springs all life. Some understanding comes from recognizing its five major components: mineral particles, soil atmosphere, soil solution, dead organic matter, and living organisms. The meaning of soil to humans depends on the complex interactions of these five constituents. What we are and what we do, day in and day out, depend on the soil. *(29)*

Unfortunately our highly urbanized populations have little first-hand opportunity to meet soil. Most people confuse it with dirt and prefer to steer clear of it. They may even be visibly shaken, insecure, if they have to step off pavement onto good growing soil with spongy structure. A major problem for conservationists is to provide more opportunities for more people to have intelligent contact with the soil which gives them life.

We have only limited soil on our planet. It is only a thin skin on the outside of the earth's crust, made only very slowly by geological processes and matured by the lengthy interactions of climates and living organisms. The earth has difficulties these days trying to feed and clothe the expanding human population in addition to supporting all other forms of life. Now we ask it also to absorb prodigious amounts of our body wastes and profligate dross from our industries. We mine it too, extracting gravels, sands, and clays for our vast constructive ventures. Soil conservation must not be thought of just as having farmers plow on the contour; it involves all of us appreciating and managing wisely the thin covering of soil which determines whether we live richly or poorly—or die. *(18, 186)*

It would seem old-fashioned to recommend that we bow to the ground, kiss the soil subserviently, or offer animal sacrifices to a god of the earth. But primitive peoples who may have done so presumably had keener appreciation of the values of soil than do most of our supposedly educated population today. We need to redevelop a strong sense of right and wrong about soil, so people will realize that we must only borrow and not steal from the soil, earth's treasurehouse. Farmers, suburbanites, and city dwellers alike, we must have at least mental contact with the soil and preferably meaningful physical contact too. While this chapter may be of special help in understanding soil, all the other chapters also involve soil while trying to help you manage the land with feelings of reverence for it. The more knowledge you gain, the greater will become your realization of the soil's mysteries. *(265, 486)*

PRODUCTIVITY

Whatever land you manage, if it has any green plants at all and any wildlife, these will be sustained by the soil. Most of the material needs of the process we call life are found in the soil. Especially important are nitrogen, phosphorus, potassium, iron, magnesium, and calcium. Many others are also important, although only a trace of them may be necessary. All our terrestrial food supplies, and indirectly much of our aquatic foods too, come from plants produced from the soil, and from animals which have fed on plants from the soil. From it also come our plant and animal fibers, medicines, and a host of raw materials which our industries synthesize into today's marvelous artifacts. *(90)*

Soil productivity depends on many factors, including its five major components listed above and the multitude of ways these interact. The minerals, for instance, make for fertility, especially when finely powdered, but without adequate soil moisture they will be unproductive. The minerals plus moisture, however, will not yield plant growth if the soil is too compacted and therefore lacking in pore spaces for soil atmosphere. Helping soil to produce on your land involves careful manipulation of many factors after careful observation of the soil and experimentation with it. *(88, 450)*

WATER-HOLDING CAPACITY

To be productive of vegetation and animal life, soil must hold water in its pores. This ability is of great significance also in storing water in times of plenty and releasing it slowly in times of need. Thus floods are averted or alleviated by underground storage of water, and droughts are minimized by slow seepage of water into the streams, springs, and wells which maintain the life of the land. The soil's capacity for holding water reduces erosion caused by runoff. Soil which washes downhill in every rain is of little use. Unstable soil is often worse than useless, causing innumerable problems of sedimentation as well as of erosion.

In managing the water-holding capacity of your land, notice first the *soil texture*, that is the relative amounts of the mineral particles of various size ranges. From coarsest to finest these are: *boulders, cobbles, gravel, sand, silt*, and *clay*—a simple list to know backwards and forwards. Other things being equal, the coarser the texture of a soil, the less its water-holding capacity. Gravels dry out faster than sands. Pure sands hold little water above the *water table* (top of saturated soil). Silts retain moisture much longer; and the very fine interstices of clay soil retain water strongly. Soils with a mixture of coarse and fine particles are called *loams;* they often have excellent water-holding capacity as well as fertility.

As you investigate the textures of the soils in your area, you will learn much about the distribution of different kinds of plants, for some of them grow best on the droughtier, sandy soils while others prefer the moister conditions of finer-textured soils *(55).* Because soil is heavy and difficult to mix, we usually do not increase the water-holding capacity of sandy soils by adding silt or clay, though in small areas it may be practical. More commonly we accept the texture as it is and use it for whatever plants are best adapted to it. (See Chapter 2, *Barelands.)*

Water-holding capacity is increased by *organic matter* in the soil. It helps maintain pores, which act like holes in a sponge and provide many surfaces to which a film of water can adhere even when the centers of the pores are penetrated by soil atmosphere.

Living organisms are also helpful in promoting water-holding capacity. Whether they are little animals or the tips of roots, they dig and push through the soil, making passageways through which water can penetrate. Encourage the life of the soil *(276, 457).*

Soil structure (not to be confused with soil texture) is a major influence on water-holding capacity. Structure refers not to the size but to the arrangement of particles. If they are all jammed together, the structure is described as *massive*. If they are loose and can move somewhat independently as in dry sand, the structure is *single-grained*. If the particles adhere forming large crumbs, it is *crumb structure*. The crumby soils have excellent water-holding capacity, and soils with this structure are said to have "good tilth." Pores within the crumbs retain water tenaciously while the larger spaces between crumbs admit soil atmosphere. Thus the soil retains moisture without being waterlogged. Soils with loamy texture are most apt to have crumb structure. Crumb structure in cultivated soils can be encouraged or destroyed by working it at the right or wrong time. Digging when the soil is too wet or too dry makes the crumbs disintegrate, but working it when moist tends to form crumbs. Getting *the feel of the soil* is most important. Pick it up and work it in your fingers, particularly rubbing it between your thumb and fingers to feel for the gritty particles of coarser textures and the more slippery "fines," the silt and clay. *(52)*

Soil compaction also has a strong influence on water-holding capacity. Fine soils deposited by wind or water so that they fit together with little pore space, as in lake-bed clays, may be very compact. When wet they may hold water a long time but their capacity will be low. Over-grazed pastures may be so strongly compacted by hooves that only specially adapted weeds can grow. Human feet also have a tamping effect on soil, as in picnic groves and trails and where thoughtless people cut corners from sidewalks across lawns. These areas often have poor insoak and maximum runoff, with attendant problems of erosion and sedimentation. Paving is an extreme case of soil compaction for special purposes. It is often very convenient for vehicles, but its spread is creating gigantic problems in soil and watershed management. Paving must be handled with much more restraint than it is at present. *(26)*

Water-holding capacity of soils has helped determine the climates of the world through influence on the vegetative cover, and vice versa. Similarly, soil management can influence microclimates on your land, as in a backyard garden or recreation spot in the forest. (See Chapters 5 and 10.)

THERMAL EFFECTS OF SOILS

Porous soils are excellent insulators against heat. Subsoils remain cooler than the surface during periods of atmospheric warming, as campers who dig an icebox to keep food cool know. During periods of atmospheric cooling, as in autumn, soil loses heat more slowly than does air. With moist soils, these heating and cooling effects are more pronounced, because water is slow to heat and cool compared to rock particles. That is why fine-textured soils holding much moisture are managed by farmers as "late soils," which cannot be cultivated until later in the spring than coarse, sandy soils, which are "early soils." Soil color too has some effect on temperature, darker soils tending to absorb heat faster than light-colored ones. Just how much man has contributed to the creation of the deserts of the world is not known, but scientists suspect that ignorance of soil management as it affects temperature and hence the water cycle and plant growth has been one contributing factor. Sometimes today we create mini-deserts by careless handling of soils.

CHANGING THE GRADES OF SOILS

Primitive man made little use of soil for changing the ups and downs of his world, for soil is heavy and he lacked powerful tools. A mound of soil to cover the dead, some earth scratched over offal to help keep off the flies, a little hill around the corn and beans—that was about it. In more advanced cultures, digging ditches for irrigation and diking of irrigated fields had a bigger effect in shaping the landscape.

Today we have mighty power that can move mountains and fill valleys, thus changing the grades of the land around us. Formerly Indian trails followed the lowlands, the "valley road," and the hilltops of long ranges, the "ridge road"; they forded streams at the narrows or shallows and visited the next valley through a pass, col, or notch. Our highways are still located with relation to the topography but with much less concern for minor features. If a bog stands in the way of a new highway, a dragline will scoop and haul out the peat or muck soil which would have given unfirm base for construction; great earthscrapers knock a hill into a hollow, or great trucks rumble to a hillside or gravel bar where a powerful shovel gouges out gravel to fill them. Thus a new beautifully graded highway takes the place of the old, dippy, twisty one—and a bog is filled and a hill leveled.

"Cut" and "fill" are small words but today they involve millions of acres for highways, reservoir dams, home sites, industrial sites, airfields, commercial sites, and many other alterations of the natural design of our surroundings. Somehow conservationists must help speed- and comfort-hungry populations achieve a better balance between what is gained and what is lost by changing the grades of the landscape. To lose a hill is often to lose an inspiring view and delightful microclimates. To lose a marsh is often to sacrifice an important flood-control basin supplied free by nature and to throw away its wealth of life and beauty.

Much of soil management does involve changing grades. A farmer's plow does just that; so does his harrow. These tools make little hills and valleys which bury seeds and kill weeds. Furrows either make horizontal, contour-following ditches which conserve water by making it stay back and soak in, or they run more or less up and down. In this case they hasten water off the land so that it cuts into the soil and carries it off leaving an arid subsoil exposed on the hill and, at the foot of the slope, an unwanted deposit of sediment. In the past few decades, soil scientists have added much to what the ancients knew about grading. If our culture is to survive, we shall need to heed and apply what science has learned.

KEEPING SOIL IN PLACE

Soil in motion is hard to manage. *Wind* picks up the finest clays, the slightly coarser silts, and even large sand grains. In deserts, wind can literally mow down utility poles by sand-blasting their bases. *Water* can pick up fine particles too, but in addition can move gravels, cobbles, and even boulders. *Gravity*, with or without the partnership of wind or water, moves soil downhill, either a grain at a time or as slumps and landslides. Moving soils are almost always non-productive, failing to support vegetation and animal life. Erosion literally gnaws away at our basic life-support system, the soil.

Maintaining vegetative cover. A first rule of soil management is to protect soil from currents of wind and water by maintaining as complete as possible a blanket of living plants. In deserts, a continuous cover is not possible, except locally by irrigation. In semi-arid areas, the best nature can do is usually a sparse spotting of native shrubs and bunchgrasses with perhaps a carpet of short-lived flowering annual herbs in moist seasons. In slightly moister regions, grasses make a continuous growth protecting the soil. In humid regions trees, shrubs, vines, and herbs together give dense cover sheltering the soil from heavy precipitation.

RUNOFF & INSOAK of various kinds of ground,

PAVING (and roofs) — Almost total runoff / Little insoak
HARD-PACKED DIRT
LAWNS and FIELDS — Little runoff
FOREST DUFF — Almost total insoak

In each region, climate is both a cause of erosion and a partner in growing suitable protective vegetation. In arid areas, a flash flood from a thunderstorm can in a few minutes erode more bare soil than could a century of tempests in a humid forest area. A cold climate may allow only a short season for growing protective vegetation yet it prevents erosion for months by freezing the ground hard as rock. *(129, 298)*

Protecting vegetative cover. Never remove or allow to be removed more vegetation than absolutely necessary to accomplish a desired new land use. Developers, engineers, and contractors have become used to doing things in a big way with big machines, because it is economical—for them. They are accustomed to removing native vegetation almost entirely, and then more or less replacing it— wherever the land is not built upon or paved—with a cover of introduced vegetation of only one kind or a mixture of a very few kinds, for instance a new turf of bluegrass and redtop grasses. Such plantings are better than none but often inferior to the destroyed native vegetation in terms of diversity for ecological balance. The introduced vegetation is almost always less economical to maintain in acceptable form than the natural flora would have been. Unfortunately the ecological complexities are beyond the training of many of the developers; so you will have to have patience and use tact as well as persistent firmness in trying to keep destruction to a minimum. You may also have to be firm with yourself in managing your own land.

Fire in dry seasons is a major threat to the vegetative cover of soil. Wildfire must be prevented wherever possible, and when it does start its rapid and complete suppression must be diligently carried out. *(67)*

Drainage lowering the water table may cause severe damage to certain kinds of vegetation, making it liable to destruction from fire or from normal sun and wind. Then, with the plants dying, the soil becomes exposed to the elements.

Grazing has been for centuries a major factor in destruction of protective vegetation, notably in Mediterranean-type climates around the world. The amount of grazing which amounts to over-grazing is often a subject of dispute. In all cases the long-term effects on the soil must be taken into account, not just the short-term economics of those persons currently grazing sheep, cattle, or other livestock.

Reestablishing vegetative cover. Whatever the climate you live in, watch the soil as the seasons turn and watch the growth of plants which can hold the soil in place. Plants introduced from other regions, especially commercially available grasses and legumes, may be excellent for rapidly stabilizing large areas of soil disturbed unduly by agriculture and construction—which can cause much destruction. Native plants, however, are usually best for covering small areas of bare soil. Often plants growing very close by can be transplanted easily, one from here and one from there so as not to denude the other locality, to start recolonization by local flora. *(129)*.

Natural vegetational development should be kept in mind as helpful when reestablishing vegetation.

Mulching. Soil unprotected by living vegetation can benefit by any one of a number of non-living *mulches* (coverings) to keep it from blowing or washing away. Mulches give other benefits too, such as minimizing temperature changes, reducing freezing and thawing, preventing evaporation of soil moisture, and encouraging many soil organisms.

Organic mulches are such materials as pulverized bark, wood chips, sawdust, old leaves, crop residues such as cornstalks and straw, waste products from processing crops such as peanuts and cotton, and animal manures. These shut out wind currents and encourage rain and snowmelt to soak in rather than run off erosively. As they rot during warm, moist seasons, they contribute organic matter to the soil. If not laid on too thickly, mulches tend to catch seeds produced nearby and promote their germination and establishment, thus hastening revegetation. Erosion netting is a commercially available mulch helpful in stabilizing soil while starting new vegetation, especially turf.

Inorganic mulches are mineral. *Stone riprapping* (p. 313) is a very coarse mulch of large stones laid side by side with only small cracks between. *Cobblestones*, which are coarse, water-rounded pebbles larger than gravel, make excellent mulch around isolated trees in recreation areas, protecting the soil yet allowing water to soak in while still letting children stand against the tree as a home base for games or as a secure spot from which to watch other children. *Gravel mulch* protects dirt trails by preventing washing, and it minimizes weeding. In the Orient, gravel is used extensively in garden design as a simple yet texturally interesting groundcover, a good base and background for beautiful boulders, potted trees, or other featured plants *(445)*. In arid areas, a repeatedly cultivated surface of some soils forms a *dust mulch* so fine that water cannot move upward through it by capillarity and be lost to the air in evaporation; thus during a year or more of fallowing, water can be conserved for a future crop.

Mulching has long been a favored garden practice. Special techniques can be learned from gardening books and horticultural magazines. Many of the methods apply to conservation beyond the garden, in places where soil has been exposed and must be protected.

Grading soil to prevent water erosion. The steeper a slope, the faster water will run down it; and the faster a current runs, the greater its power to carry away soil, according to the V^6 Principle (p. 211). So when grading a trail, cutting into a bank, or in any other way shaping the land, avoid making steep slopes unless you can protect them with vegetation, mulches, or retaining walls. It is often better to expose a longer slope by cutting back the top of a bank or extending its toe rather than to try to maintain a shorter but steeper slope.

Irregularities in graded soil make depressions which can hold back water or speed it downhill. Elongated patterns of ridges and grooves made by plows, harrows, or hand tools such as rakes and hoes are very helpful when made horizontally across a slope, that is, *on the contour*. In wet weather each ridge becomes a little dam preventing runoff and each furrow an elongated lake promoting insoak. Where moisture is excessive, you can slope the pattern very gently downhill to allow very slow flow off the land, at a rate which will not wash away the soil. Lead the water to an area of soil protected by vegetation, mulch, or paving, or to a water body.

on the contour   FURROWS   up and down
slow down erosion   accelerate erosion

Grassed waterways are used by farmers to gather the water from the ends of furrows and lead it slowly downhill at a rate which will not cause erosion. The same technique can be used on non-crop land which for any reason has been laid bare. For instance, a grassed waterway above a new road cut can prevent water from higher on the watershed running down across the fresh cut. It is important in all cases to allow plenty of growing time for the grass before furrows lead water onto it. To speed the development of a small grassed waterway, rectangles of sod neatly laid edge to edge can turf it.

Furrows and ditches too steeply pitched will promote rather than control erosion. For short trenches you can use your unaided eye to guess the appropriate layout, altering it if you find in the rain that water flows too fast or too slowly in it. But because slopes can be very deceptive even to a trained eye, be sure to keep a watch on your ditch to make sure it drains properly. For long furrows or ditches, avoid trouble by laying out the line along a contour sighted with a carpenter's level, line level, homemade T-level, inclinometer, or surveyor's transit, setting stakes to mark the contour.

Short irregularities also help promote insoak and decrease erosion-causing runoff. A bump-and-dimple surface can be made with a spading fork used so as to leave unbroken clods creating a coarse crumb structure. Because loosening soil can also make some of the more exposed particles more subject to erosion, it is best to mulch forked soil. A shovel or spade can be used rather than a spading fork, but extra strokes edgewise may be needed in heavy soil to break up too-large clods.

Terraces on a slope create level strips across it with minimal erosion. Terraces are a compromise with the slope. Having vertical or at least steep parts allows the intervening ones to be level, permitting insoak. The terrace edge must be of relatively nonerodible material such as wood or stone, or if of soil it must be well vegetated, mulched, or otherwise specially handled to prevent erosion. The flat terrace tops should be laid out on the contour in the manner described above for furrows.

Logs for terracing laid out on the contour will often need to be held in place by stakes on their downhill side. Removing the bark from both logs and stakes will make them last longer, because bark holds in moisture favorable to wood-rotting fungi (p. 418). Chemical wood preservatives such as pentachlorophenol deter rot but should not be used where sensitive plants are grown immediately beside the wood. Some woods are particularly resistant to rot, for instance locust and catalpa, so are good for terracing. Some trees, such as willow and cottonwood, will sprout if logs are cut from actively growing trees in spring or early summer and are bedded across the bank about two-thirds their diameter into the soil. Their continued life fends off rot and adds new shoots to help revegetate the terraced slope. (Don't remove the bark.)

Grading soil to prevent landslides and slumps. Land slippage occurs where grades are steeper than the natural angle of repose of the soil (see below); water or snow or other material adds abnormal weight; tilted bedrock or impervious soil gets lubricated by water making it a slippery surface on which soil can slide; the toe of a bank has been undercut by a stream or wave action, or by quarrying, ex-

cavating, or grading; people or other animals run up and down a
bank; or when earth tremors of quakes, explosions, or heavy machinery jar the soil. Avoid all these as much as possible. Give particular attention to the angle of repose of the soil, cutting back the
top of a bank or extending the toe to minimize chances of slumping.
Maintain a good surface cover of shrubs, vines, and/or herbs, especially deep-rooted ones. Trees also are very helpful, especially if kept
cut low in sites exposed to high winds. *(250, 469)*

The angle of repose of a soil is the angle with the horizontal of a
slope of maximum steepness beyond which a steepening causes particles to start tumbling or sliding down. The angle depends on the
size and shape of the particles. Good examples are the leeward slope
of sand dunes and the sides of gravel and sand piles in a gravel

Overgrazing by sheep has caused bad gullying. The better vegetated areas are least eroded. Strathcarron, Wester Ross, Scotland.

quarry. You can demonstrate angle of repose by pouring salt or sugar onto a plate and noting the constant angle of the conical pile no matter how tall the pile gets. Note that moist soil will have a steeper angle than dry; don't count on its staying steeper, for the angle will change as the material dries out. The angle of repose is an important consideration on exposed land; it is difficult to stabilize a soil at any steeper angle, although it can be done more or less successfully with plantings, mulches, retaining walls, or riprapping.

Mountainous areas may have deep accumulations of snow and névé (consolidated snow). These add weight to soil and may start avalanches which tear up vegetation and soil and promote landslides. Establishing thick forest cover is the best deterrence, though this is a difficult and slow process at high altitudes on steep, exposed slopes.

The older forest in the enclosure at the left has prevented erosion. Now young trees have been planted on the lower slope to the right of the fence to help cure the erosion caused by heavy grazing. Strathcarron, Wester Ross, Scotland.

While planted trees are becoming established, artificial structures called gabions (quite different from the ones in streams) can be built in areas of deep snow accumulation in an effort to keep the snow from starting to slide.

Steep sandy banks present special problems, making stabilization difficult. Minimize the weight of any retaining walls by using vertical boards rather than logs, and slats instead of round branches to stake them on their downhill side. Because the single-grain structure of sand makes it apt to sift underneath the boards, they will need to be stuffed with vegetative matter. After installing a board, carefully dig with a trowel a narrow trench immediately behind the board and a few inches deeper than its base. Working with moist or moistened sand makes the excavation easier because the sand has less tendency to run back into the trench. Stuff into the trench the lightest-weight absorbent material available, something to hold moisture to help establish rooted vegetation. Along shore bluffs, if possible, find giant reed, a widespread species of marsh grass, tall and plumose with hollow stems, which has proved especially valuable *(438)*. Cover the reeds or other material with well-packed sand. Then plant soil-stabilizing plants such as American beachgrass, European beachgrass or marram grass, peavine, or other sand-happy plants. *(425)*

Controlling gully erosion.   A good rule for controlling erosion is to "make water walk downhill instead of run downhill." That involves keeping the soil covered with vegetation or mulch and making any ridges, furrows, ruts, or other inequalities run along the contour of the land rather than up and down. Major causes of gullies include overgrazing of grasslands, overcutting of forests, overremoval of shrubs, farming off the contour, running roads and trails too steeply up and down, driving all-terrain vehicles on insufficiently protected slopes (even gentle ones), and grading soil improperly when developing land and failing to protect it immediately with new vegetation or mulch.

The *first step in healing a gully* is to note the source of the erosive water. Always look uphill. Study the watershed. Do all you can there to promote insoak and thereby minimize runoff. If you do not

Rubble dumped into this gully does not get at the cause of the erosion: improper management of the watershed above, including cultivated rows running downhill instead of along the horizontal contours of the land. Pennsylvania.

own the uphill land, try for cooperation with those who do control it. Note the quantity of water flowing at different seasons in the gully. It is formed either by a *permanent stream* or an *intermittent* one (p. 210). Sometimes by wise land management we can prevent all runoff down the gully, but at other times we have to allow some water to run there, slowing it enough to keep it from gnawing. Of course sometimes we may want water in the gully, so long as its erosive force can be controlled.

Slowing the flow by grading usually requires modifying both the *short profile* (across the gully) and the *long profile* (along the gully). The short profile is modified by cutting back the tops of the banks in any oversteep places and extending their toes to partially fill the gully. This makes a gentler grade for any water running down the sides into the middle. (Remember the V^6 Principle, p. 211.) In fields, small gullies can often be shaped gently enough for farm operations to be carried on across them, on the contour. To modify the long profile, make terraces across the gully. Their flat parts promote insoak behind step-like retaining walls or steep slopes made from such non-erodible materials as logs, brush, old hay, stones, or rubble. Where there is a stream, these materials form dams and pools, at least some of the time. After any grading, reestablish vegetation and/or mulch as soon as possible.

Slowing the flow without grading can sometimes be accomplished by proper watershed management above, encouraging vegetation already in the gully itself, planting, and making check dams of logs, boards, brush, stones, or rubble. However, never just carelessly throw junk into a gully to try to heal it. Do your uphill homework first and then make check dams of which you can be proud, which will pass the hardest test that heavy rainfall and maybe snowmelt also can give them. *(530)*

Controlling wind erosion. Complete vegetational cover gives soil good protection from wind. Wind erosion occurs where soils are too dry to support a continuous blanket of living plants, as in deserts or along sandy shores, or where farming or grading for development have left soil unprotected. Reestablishing native vegetation or planting suitable crops, cover crops, or other groundcovers are the best techniques, but often special methods will be needed to make life possible for the new plants (p. 374).

Grading soil to reduce wind velocity. In semi-arid regions and in droughty, coarse-textured soils in humid regions, level plowed fields should have their furrows running at right angles to prevailing dry winds to slow them. Planting seeds in deep furrows provides the seedlings with some critical protection from wind. Where extensive grading is being done, a considerable embankment can sometimes be built as a windbreak. (p. 278)

Structures to slow the wind. Fences, usually set at right angles to the wind, provide a shelter in which plants can be started (p. 277).

Planting to control wind erosion. Sometimes a whole expanse can be stablized or protected by planting it all at once with a suitable crop or seed mixture recommended by farmers, agricultural extension workers from the state university, or U.S. Soil Conservation Service technicians. Often, however, a severely eroding area will have to be healed a little at a time, starting at the upwind edge to form a windbreak in whose lee other plants can subsequently be started (p. 279). The hardiest species should be set out first across the prevailing wind, preferably themselves in the lee of a structural windbreak (p. 73). Windbreak plantings should not be neglected after planting; over the years they need care to keep them thick and effective. Pruning, shearing, and fertilizing add to their usefulness in keeping soil from blowing.

Controlling shore erosion. (See also *Streambank erosion*, below.) Erosion on shores may be caused by water running down a bank (see above), by wind whipping the bank away (see above), and by waves and currents at its base.

Waves have energy derived from winds (except for seismic waves accompanying earthquakes). Their ability to carve the land depends largely on the strength of the winds which generate them and the distance (called *fetch*) they have come before reaching the shore. The greater the expanse of water, the larger and more forceful the waves can be. When a wave approaches shore, friction with the bottom and with shore currents uses up some of its energy. Picking up and carrying sand grains and jostling them against each other may also absorb much of a wave's energy and leave it little to cause erosion. In storms, however, abnormal amounts of energy may enable waves to cause enormous amounts of damage, cutting into banks or leaving only coarse stone where there had been a fine sandy beach.

Currents too bring energy to shape shores. Alongshore currents (also called *littoral currents*) remove fine materials from one stretch of shore and deposit it elsewhere, perhaps as a straight *spit* or a curved *hook* projecting from the shore, or as a *tombolo* connecting an island to another shore. These sedimentations form where the currents slow down. Offshore currents, including deep ones called *undertows*, move particles outward. They may deposit offshore bars roughly parallel with the coast, often submerged yet evidenced by a line of breakers where incoming waves bump their stomachs on them and consequently topple forward frothing *(38)*.

Bulkheads or *seawalls* can sometimes be built to retain a bank of soil, the hard stone or timber front hopefully withstanding the energy of the waves. On a small scale, as along the shore of a pond, a little stone wall may be adequate, or some firmly set posts with boards nailed to them. On large lakes, bays, and oceans, however, great waves may laugh at even huge granite blocks unless they are placed and interlocked with great engineering skill.

Groins are often more successful than seawalls, though they may be best used in conjunction with them in areas particularly susceptible to erosion. They project outward from the shore, usually at right angles. Their major function is to slow down alongshore currents, which thus lose energy and have to deposit some of their load of sand, according to the V^6 Principle (p. 211). This sand absorbs energy from incoming waves, which therefore are less able to cause destruction. They are particularly damaging where storms tend to remove beach sand, or where man has short-sightedly dredged away energy-absorbing sands or gravels. Sometimes it helps to dredge back sand between new groins rather than to rely wholly on littoral currents to bring new deposits.

At ponds, small groins can be made with rocks loosely piled. Rocks can be moved in burlap slings carried between two or more waders; they can be floated into place with homemade rafts or barges; or they can be piled atop a bank in warm weather and slid out over the ice in winter. Another style of groin is made of driven stakes *(piles)* to which slats are nailed vertically on horizontal members. This type, however, is more susceptible to damage by waves and by shifting ice.

The term *jetty* is frequently used for any structure such as a groin protruding to help control currents and waves, but particularly where it is part of a harbor or navigational channel. The tops of jetties are often designed for foot traffic or vehicles related to port activity. *(520)*

Aquatic vegetation such as marsh grasses and eelgrass plays a significant role in the drama of the sea's edge and should almost always be left undisturbed to absorb the energies of storm waves. Untold erosive damage can result from its removal. Interesting experiments in Europe indicate that plastic strips can sometimes be used as energy-absorbers to lessen wave erosion, in imitation of beds of seaweed such as the brown kelps, which give good protection to some marine shores. Possible protection for a disappearing beach development in the wrong place—a last resort?

Artificial reefs can sometimes succeed in taking the place of a natural offshore bar to create friction causing waves to break farther out than they would otherwise. Such reefs are occasionally recommended to promote cover for fish, and stone ones can be helpful. Reefs from old auto bodies should be considered as relatively short-term ventures; they should not be indulged in merely as a convenient way to dispose of metal junk which would be more appropriately recycled to reclaim the metal.

Shore erosion control can be very disheartening. One must have great respect for the forces involved and not assume lightly that they can be managed. It is best to leave shores as natural as possible, keeping buildings well back from them, and conserving dunes, underwater sand and gravel deposits, marshes, and beds of submerged aquatic vegetation such as kelp and eelgrass which help maintain the subtle balances of shoreline erosion and sedimentation. But experimenting with shore processes on a humble scale can be enjoyable and educational. Laying bets on the results of minor manmade changes can be a game which the more nature-sensitive person is apt to win. For instance, try putting just ten similar pebbles or cobble stones on a sandy beach, five parallel to the waves and five at right angles. What new beach designs will result as the little waves ripple in around them and out again?

Controlling streambank erosion.   Erosion along brooks and rivers is determined largely by the rate of flow, often expressed as cfs (cubic feet per second) or gpm (gallons per minute). Water velocity depends on such factors as the gradient of the stream, stated for example in the number of inches or feet it drops per hundred feet (or meters per kilometer); the straightness of its course; the shape of the cross section of its channel; the amount of suspended load (sediment) it is carrying; and the amount of friction created by its bottom, bank, and vegetation thereon. If you can puzzle out a way to change predictably any one of these factors, you can achieve at least some control over bank erosion. The possibilities are almost endless. Do not expect easy answers, but Chapters 7 and 11 may help you to study your stream, learn its habits, and curb any which may seem to be bad habits from your point of view and those of others downstream who may be influenced (pp. 209, 305).

MAKING SOILS DRIER

Drainage is most used when native plants of wet soil seem less desirable than a planted crop. While water is good for plant growth, all most crops need is the moisture held by capillarity around the soil particles; additional water fills the pores and excludes the soil atmosphere so important to growth. Drainage is also invoked for building in too-wet places; unfortunately those who plan and lay the drains are often unconcerned about the increased amount of unruly water dumped downstream and care not at all about conserving wetlands for wildlife habitat, keeping the water table up for groundwater supplies, or decreasing fire hazards. Poor drainage schemes are pathetically commonplace in the United States.

Drainage makes sense in certain cases, but there are other ways to

RUNOFF FROM DOWNSPOUTS

SPLASH BLOCK of concrete or plastic absorbs some of water's energy.

Thick lawn

DRY WELL

50-gal. drum with holes whacked in it lets water run out underground

Filled with broken paving or coarse stone

Screening keeps out leaves

Fill around with gravel

make soils drier. Sometimes cutting away some trees or shrubs, to let more sun and wind reach the soil, or planting suitable plants in an open wet spot (as the pioneers planted sunflowers around their backyard pump) will give good results.

Dry wells. Sometimes temporary puddlings result from downspouts under eaves troughs or from natural seepage into an area of relatively impervious soil. If so, dig a hole through the surface soil into (hopefully) a layer with greater porosity which can drain away the excess water. This *dry well* is filled with coarse rock or pieces of concrete or old brick, with finer stones and then gravel near the top. An empty fifty-gallon drum with holes pickaxed into its bottom and lower sides can be used to contain the stones and prevent inwashing of soil from the sides. Maintenance involves occasional removal of dead leaves or other debris on top which might prevent insoak.

Ditches. Ditches can be used to drain off surface water or lower the water table where a groove in the ground is not objectionable; otherwise use buried pipe (p. 355). A ditch's *direction* relates to the contour of the land, which it must follow closely but with just

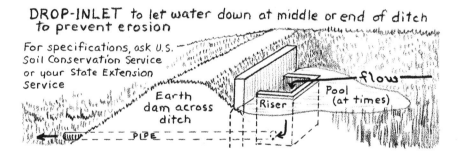

DROP-INLET to let water down at middle or end of ditch to prevent erosion

For specifications, ask U.S. Soil Conservation Service or your State Extension Service

Earth dam across ditch

Riser

Pool (at times)

flow

PIPE

enough gradient to give a slow flow. Too steep a pitch will erode the ditch and too slight a grade will sediment it. Avoid sharp angles, which alter rate of flow and cause erosion or clogging. Layout must also terminate the ditch appropriately, preferably in a low, well vegetated spot. A poorly protected slope may quickly erode from the outpourings of a new ditch. The ditch may end in a water body, though a substantial flow from a ditch may disrupt stream energetics (p. 211) or cause a delta of sediment. A ditch may terminate in a previous larger ditch, gutter, or storm sewer. If it must empty beyond your

DROP SPILLWAY across a ditch or small gully
to prevent erosion

First study the
stream gradient
downstream,
then watch for any
erosion or sedimentation

wing

Apron

Apron can be
concrete or stone
riprap, to absorb
the water's energy

property, get written permission for it to flow there (a *flowage right*).
If the ditch cannot empty into something at the same grade, make
an outfall (p. 355).

Width and *steepness* of banks depend on the volume of water to
be carried and the kind of soil. A flat or U-shaped bottom is less
apt to erode or clog than a V-shaped one. Banks should usually not
be steeper than a 1:3 slope, one vertical foot for each three feet horizontally. In heavy clayey or peaty soils a steeper bank may be feasible; while across cultivated fields, haylands, or pastures a much
broader and shallower ditch, a *grassed waterway*, permits farming
operations to cross it rather than having to go around. Avoid deep,
narrow, weed-hidden ditches in which unwary walkers may break an
ankle.

Spoil dug from a ditch can often be used constructively for some
nearby project, such as a low ridge to give shelter from wind or
noise (p. 278) or a slight knoll for relaxing or observation. Sometimes it can form a spoilbank paralleling the ditch and far enough
from it so it will not wash back in (p. 184). Or the spoil can be scattered so as to have minimal effects in any one place.

MATERIAL EXCAVATED from DITCHES

Single spoilbank

Double spoilbank

Broadcast spoil

Spoilmound

stabilized
with grasses, forbs, and shrubs
as a picnic & observation site

Gutters. A ditch lined with impervious material is called a gutter. It may be paved with cobblestones, concrete, asphalt, or plastic. Its hardness prevents erosion in the steeper places and decreases the growth of weeds. However, expense is initially greater than for an unlined ditch, and it tends to look more artificial.

Drainpipes. Where a drainage system must be buried to keep it out of sight or permit surface activities such as farming or playing ball, it is necessary to use pipes. Traditional drainage pipe, called agricultural tile, is of baked clay. Composition pipe is commonly used today, its lighter weight making it easier to handle. Short lengths, usually four inches in diameter, are laid in a carefully dug ditch which is level-bottomed, floored if possible with gravel, and pitched downhill just enough to carry off water, for instance at a drop of between six inches and a foot per hundred feet of length. In extensive drainage, the four-inch collector *laterals* lead into larger *mains*. With clay tile, sections of pipe are lined up accurately but left about one-quarter or one-half inch apart to allow water to enter. The top half of this circular crack is then covered with a piece of tar paper or the like to prevent overlying soil from falling in. The pipe is then "blinded," that is covered with a layer of gravel to help water percolate into the drain but keep clogging soil out. The gravel is then covered with soil even with the surrounding surface or a little higher at first, to allow for settling, so that it will finally be even with the surface.

Drainpipe outfalls must be made carefully to prevent erosion. As described above for ditches, the pipe should discharge into dense vegetation in a nearly level area if possible. Sometimes artificial devices may be needed, such as a deposit of rough stones or rubble too

SOME DRAIN OUTLETS into a water body
to prevent erosion

Gently graded | Spilling onto riprap | Paved chute | Angled pipe | Propped Outlet

Usually best | Usually worst

coarse to be displaced by the outflowing current, to absorb erosive energy. Smooth stones or paving of concrete or asphalt can spread the water to diminish possible cutting into the soil. Where the pipe must end atop a bank, a paved or wooden chute enables the water to run down the bank without eroding it, but what happens at the foot of the chute must be of concern because the water can exert considerable power at that point. A well-constructed flat apron of hard material, and possibly a series of *baffles* to use up the water's energy, will diminish scouring of the valley by the outflow. A *propped outlet* is sometimes used but is seldom a thing of beauty. It consists of a pipe, held up by posts or a wall, which projects well beyond the bank so that the plunge pool the water will excavate beneath its end will not cut back into the bank. Avoid such an out-fall if possible.

MAKING SOILS MOISTER

The usual reason for adding water to soil is to help plants grow. Sprinkling water to imitate rain is *aerial irrigation*, and flowing water over and/or through the soil is *soil irrigation*. Agricultural watering of crops is a fascinatingly complicated business beyond the scope of this book; but for help in establishing vegetative cover on bare soil or keeping green plants around your home, see page 373. Be careful not to apply so much water that it breaks down the crumb structure of the soil, leaches out minerals contributing fertility, causes erosion, or fills the pores continuously, thus waterlogging the soil and excluding air needed by most roots for healthy growth.

Maintaining moisture in the soil may be more important and more efficient than adding it. Mulching (p. 340) helps keep water from being lost into the air. Shading with vegetation also conserves soil moisture, as does blocking off dry air with windbreaks (p. 276).

USING SOIL TO GROW PLANTS

This most important aspect of soil is dealt with in *Maintaining Vegetative Cover* (p. 339) and in Chapter 14, *Vegetation Management*. Understanding the particular soils of your area and how best to use them for growing plants is a challenge to which you should give continuing attention. See reference 67 and consult some of the many excellent books on gardening and farming when you become involved in agriculture or horticulture.

While many modern techniques of growing plants may seem remote from the way vegetation grows in more natural areas, anybody who grows even one plant in a bottle with nutrient solutions, artificial light, and ventilation still is having to work with nature and must supply the support and fertility which is the natural contribution of soil. (44, 289)

So-called *organic gardening* and *organic farming* devote particular attention to developing and maintaining soils as they occur naturally. In these soils vegetation and animals have contributed, over a period of time, considerable organic matter from their decaying bodies and wastes. Thus high fertility and good crumb structure can often be achieved by intensive soil management with minimal, if any, resort to concentrated fertilizers and pesticides. More people should become much more knowledgeable of nature's ways, more willing to give closer personal attention to growing things, and less willing to consume wholesale crops from soils managed on a vast scale by machines. Our soils would then be used more wisely.

USING SOILS FOR GRADING

We move soils around to alter the topography, excavating here and piling there for many purposes, for instance to dig a pond, build a trail or road, make a foundation for a building, control erosion or sedimentation, or create pleasing contours to the land.

Saving topsoil.   Because topsoil is complex and precious, slow to form and easy to destroy, we must never waste it. When establishing new grades, that is changing the contours of the land, pile the topsoil carefully to one side. Then level or pile the exposed subsoil as you desire. Finally, replace the topsoil evenly over any exposed subsoil, so that it can with its fertility and structure promote the best possible cover of plants. Animals too will thrive where fertile topsoil is conserved. Six inches is a good depth of topsoil for establishing a lawn, but in many cases you may wish to plant a few plants in holes with deep topsoil while skimping on the general covering of the subsoil. Sometimes there may fortunately be more topsoil than is needed at a graded site, so some can be moved for improving plant growth elsewhere.

Compacting soil.   Preventing excessive soil compaction is important wherever plants are to be grown after grading. Heavy machinery can do long-lasting damage by breaking down crumb structure of soil and thereby decreasing insoak and increasing runoff, which may cause accelerated erosion and sedimentation. Also, compacted soil makes a poor seedbed, too dense to catch seeds and permit the growth of the delicate roots of seedlings. Restrict machines so that they do not cause undue compaction.

Sometimes, however, maximum compaction may be desirable, as when building the core of an earthen dam, which should be as impervious as possible to infiltrating water, or when building a roadbed or trail tread, which should have minimum subsequent settling. In these cases heavy tamping is desirable (p. 30).

Preventing erosion and sedimentation.   All too often contractors fail to prevent washing of freshly exposed soil. Good soil is frequently carried away; streams are clogged with sediment; and fertile soils downstream are covered with sterile sand and gravel. It is not enough to replace topsoil and seed it when construction is over.

CONSIDER DOWNHILL EFFECTS of roofs, paving, and other non-absorptive areas.

Little insoak and much runoff can cause   bad erosion and sedimentation.

Steps should be planned and taken to keep soil in place during grading, even though that may be difficult and expensive. One technique is to work on the lower part of an area first so that the watershed is protected as long as possible on the upper part. Another method is to make temporary sedimentation ponds on the site to catch any runoff and make it drop its load of soil as close as possible to its source *(517)*. Of course it also makes sense to operate as much as possible along the contours rather than up and down hill, so that the downhill sides of ruts make little dams restraining the downward flow of surface water. Because wind as well as water can cause erosion and sedimentation, it may be wise to erect drift fencing across the wind (p. 277). Sometimes it is effective to seed bare soil even before operations are finished. The U.S. Forest Service recommends sowing seeds on logging roads when they are first built rather than after the logs have been hauled out. While some seedlings of the protective cover crop are, of course, destroyed by the tractors and logs, enough survive to help hold the soil.

USING SOILS FOR BUILDING

Many soils make good building materials. For gravels, see page 37; for sands, page 41; and for clays page 46. Some loams can be used in *rammed earth* construction, an arduous form of building, inexpensive except for time and labor. For ridges of soil as sound barriers and wind deflectors, see page 278.

Mounds of earth can be heaped up to relieve the monotony of flat land, to provide observation hills, and to give children a place to slide. We need to take a much more creative approach to grading

The dense fibrous roots of plains grasses made it possible for pioneers to cut turf in blocks for building sod houses to give protection from the extreme heat and cold of the midcontinental climate. Ash Hollow, Nebraska.

in developing home sites, school grounds, parks, and industrial parks.

USING SOILS FOR WASTE DISPOSAL AND RECYCLING

The more crowded the world becomes, the greater the problems of waste disposal. Formerly body and kitchen wastes could be absorbed by the local soil and broken down by natural processes. But today we congregate in enormous cities and have a culture devoted to making things, many of which we soon find we do not want or discover we must throw away because they have worn out much faster than did the few prized belongings of our ancestors. We regularly and thoughtlessly insult our environment with our discards. The middens of so-called primitive people were one thing. The tremendous piles of glass bottles, metal cans and foil, and plastics are something else!

Composting.   The countryman worthy of the name separates glass and metal from food wastes and biodegradable papers and composts the latter, mixing them with soil to inoculate them with soil organisms which will break them down and create a fertile soil for farmlands and gardens. To hold in the soil and moisture, the compost pile should have walls made from poles, old boards, building blocks, or stones. It should be built up a layer at a time: wastes, soil, wastes, soil, etc. In dry climates the center should be kept slightly lower than the sides to help retain the moisture needed by the decay-causing organisms. Lime can be added to control the acidity and to provide calcium for fertility. From time to time the pile should be mixed with a shovel or spade. A second pile is started

COMPOST PILES produce improved soil

Add poles, blocks, or boards as pile grows

Poles in center keep soil aerated (hole-in-doughnut principle of cooking)

Keep top of soil level to promote insoak of water

Stir mixture occasionally

Build up piles with alternating layers of loam and organic matter, such as garbage and weeds.

while the first is maturing its organically rich soil. The time needed for breakdown of the wastes will vary with several factors including the heat and moisture available and the careful turning to help create crumb-structured soil. *(444)*

Disposal of glass, metal, and durable plastics. These resistant materials are best returned to "civilization" for reprocessing. If that is impossible, they can with much labor be buried deeply in the mothering soil where nature will eventually recycle them; for some materials that may take a few thousand years. Whenever possible, reuse these things rather than jettison them; you can thus reduce demand for production, keep dumps from filling in our remaining lowlands, and prevent incinerators from polluting the air.

Sewage. Wastes from toilets, sinks, and washtubs not connected to municipal sewers can be piped (usually via four-inch "soil pipe") to a primitive cesspool or its more modern version, the septic tank. In it, microorganisms break down organic matter, hopefully as fast as it is contributed. The resulting liquid is led away through an overflow pipe to an underground *drainage field*, a system of perforated or segmented pipes which distribute the effluent so that (again hopefully) it seeps away through the soil. It is most important that the soil of the drainage field be porous, therefore of coarse-textured sandy or gravelly soil. It is important that the drainage field be so located that it cannot contaminate a water supply for drinking or other domestic use. State and local health codes should be consulted.

In less affluent cultures, human excrement is termed *night soil* and is an important source of fertility which is systematically returned to the soil. In this country, experiments are promising some improved methods of recycling human wastes safely and efficiently so that man operates within nature's systems rather than pouring his concentrated wastes as environmental insults into streams. These new methods should be followed closely and applied as soon as possible.

Many a new house these days is built and equipped with a sewage system in a site where the soils cannot handle the effluent, either because of high water table or because they are fine-textured soils and do not allow the effluent to percolate away. Often the builder has moved away before the purchaser discovers his waste disposal problem, made all too evident when the clogged soil causes unhealthy backup in toilets and sinks. A little more soil-consciousness and conscience on the part of developers would help.

Washing machines are best led to a septic tank or cesspool separate from the ones to which toilets and sinks run. The washing machine detergents may not be conducive to the bacterial action required to break down toilet and kitchen wastes. While your best friend may sometimes seem to be your plumber, more fundamental is your relationship with the soil technician who can help you plan efficient waste disposal by helping you learn about your local soils.

CONCLUSION

Soils are much more than ground-up rock which makes plants grow. In fact, soils are the mix of which mortal men are made and to which they return, as has been long known but recently unheeded by too many. City people today often think of country people as dirty, because they grub in the soil and spread manure. On the other hand, country people, living closer to unaltered nature, think of city people as dirty, because of polluted air and accumulating trash where people are too remote from the soil to let it handle their wastes for them. Soil can be dirt when mishandled. But in its nobler moments, when it is not subjected to accelerated man-induced erosion and sedimentation and contamination by paving and human wastes, soil can be a beautiful and productive foundation not only for man's existence but also for his loftiest aspirations. . . If you are lucky enough to have access to a little soil, see what you can do with it. It may surprise you if you really care for it.

(See also *49, 197, 226, 290, 328, 493, 531, 532, 539, 542, 544, 548.*)

14 *Vegetation Management*

Environmental Roles of Plants
The Kinds of Plants
What Plants do
  Plants begin
  Plants grow
  Plants get around
  Plants reproduce
Plants at Your Site
Transplanting
  The site from which a plant is moved
  The site to which a plant is taken
  The new environment
  Digging the hole for a tree or shrub
  Bottoming a hole
  Seasons for digging
  Time of day and type of weather for digging
  Plastic spray to reduce water loss
  Width of digging
  Depth of digging
  Root pruning
  Bare-root method
  Heeling-in
  Ball and burlap method
  Placing transplant in new hole
  Frozen ball method
  Filling the hole
  Watering a transplant
  Mulching a transplant

363

Removal by digging and pulling on the tree
Removal by pulling
Removal by drilling
Removal by burning
Removal by digging and burning
Removal by dynamiting
Removing stones
Removing herbs
Removing litter

Handling Cut Brush
Uses of brush
Stacking brush
Location of piles
Sledge piece and piling
Size of piles
Separating species
Burning cut brush
Site for burning cut brush
Weather for burning cut brush
Kindling
Feeding
Emergency tools
Extinguishing fires

Peeling Logs
Season
Tools

Prescribed Burning
Disadvantages
Advantages
To remove flammable hazards
To control pests
To prune and weed blueberries
To promote pines
To improve grazing
To create or maintain certain wildlife habitats
To maintain low vegetation
To preserve certain biotic communities for
education and research
Methods of prescribed burning

Harvesting
    Considering demand
    Getting marketing information
    Sustained yield
    Multiple uses
    Public relations
Training Plants
    Stimulating growth
    Stunting growth
    Pruning and shearing
        Pruning a large branch from a tree
        Tree climbing for pruning
        Pruning a shrub
        Shearing shrubs and trees
        Seasons for pruning and shearing
    Bending woody plants
    Grafting
Fertilizing
Watering
Protecting Plants

When you want to work with nature, you take a close look at an environment and are alarmed by its dynamic complexity. Humbled and uncertain, you are tempted to sit back and do nothing. Where can you start to exert a positive influence? The best answer is, usually, "Work with the plants first." They are more tangible than air, softer than rock, more stable than water, and more dependable than wildlife. Although there are many exceptions, the rule is to start with the vegetation of an area. Manage that and you influence the whole environment.

ENVIRONMENTAL ROLES OF PLANTS

Wherever land has enough moisture, plants colonize the rocks and soils, breaking down the hard stone of the earth and creating that softer blanket, much more hospitable to animals, which we call soil. Plants live in the waters of the earth too, as multitudinous microscopic forms and as visible scums, reeds, and seaweeds. In water as on land, plants make animal life possible. Taking elemental matter like carbon, hydrogen, oxygen, and minerals, they synthesize organic materials which animals use as food and protection. They liberate oxygen from its natural compounds, thus enabling animals to breathe. And they hitch and unhitch (recycle) many other materials in nature's storehouse. To do this work, all but certain microrganisms catch solar energy by photosynthesis. When animals eat plants, some of this energy becomes theirs—and ours.

In their processes of living, plants develop and stabilize soil. They exert a major control of the water cycle by influencing condensation, evaporation, insoak, and runoff, as well as transpiring vast amounts of water into the atmosphere. They slow down wind currents and water and curtail erosive waves. They capture or exclude solar radiation at and near the ground. In these and many other ways, plants modify the physical environments that determine the lives of all plants and animals, including us. *(304, 450)*

In talking practically about the roles of plants, we must not restrict ourselves to coldly calculated matter-and-energy relationships. The whole story of the downy cattail seeds used by hummingbirds to line their nests cannot be told by saying that they give good insulation in relation to weight. There must be what we can call a *cuddle factor*, some parameter which involves the joy of being cradled in anything so soft, of being snug, of being at home in the felted mini-fibers. Extending this concept, we are reminded that plants make our whole planet a *home*, a place where millions of years of evolution have evolved our senses along with our organic environment so that we delight in the greenness of leaves, the bright colors and fragrances of flowers, and the sound of wind in the branches. As we work with nature, we can reflect that "ecology" comes from the Greek *Oikos*, home, and that plants provide not only roof and walls but also carpet and curtains and, on the wooden table, a vase of flowers beside the loaf of bread.

THE KINDS OF PLANTS

The more you know about the plants you are dealing with, the more ably you can work with them. Up to a point you do not need to know a plant's name or even what family or other larger group it belongs in. But when you want to ask about it or look up information about it or tell somebody about it, then it is most helpful if you can call it by a name used by others. When you are in earnest about managing vegetation so as to improve an environment, you will take seriously the matter of nomenclature (naming) and taxonomy (grouping) of its organisms *(67)*.

Recognizing groups according to *life form* helps. The simplest classification of land plants divides them into *trees, shrubs, vines,* and *herbs.* Herbs and some vines lack woody tissues, and include vegetables, flowerbed flowers, wildflowers, grasses, reeds, ferns, mosses, and other relatively soft plants. Shrubs, also called bushes, are woody and have two or more stems coming from the ground or close to it. Trees, also woody, usually have but one such stem,

LIFE FORMS of WOODY PLANTS (woody vines omitted)

TREES				SHRUBS		
Evergreen		Deciduous		Evergreen		Deciduous
Narrow-leaved	Broad-leaved	Narrow-leaved	Broad-leaved	Narrow-leaved	Broad-leaved	Broad-leaved
Spruce & Pine	Live Oak	Larch	Sugar Maple	Juniper	Mt.laurel Kalmia	Forsythia

which becomes taller than those of a shrub. More complicated classifications of life form recognize such groups as *rosette plants*, whose radiating leaves hug the ground, and *geophytes* (earth plants), which survive unfavorable seasons by dying aboveground but persisting as a bulb or tuber protected within the soil. Noting how the form of a plant enables it to live in an environment helps when trying to make it grow happily or when trying to cope with its apparently excessive growth.

Recognizing evolutionarily related groups is also a help in practicing ecology. Many texts and manuals of identification are available. Look also for manuals which describe the flora of your region. Ask local biology teachers, librarians, and nature center or museum personnel. In addition to published floras (accounts of plants of a region), look for books devoted to special groups such as trees or grasses, which may include written descriptions, illustrations, and keys (devices to speed identification). Do not expect any one book to have all your answers. One which does well, though, is Palmer's *Field Book of Natural History (405)*; see also *3, 134, 141, 188, 191, 192, 216, 234, 288, 412, 415, 452, 476,* and *506.*

WHAT PLANTS DO

A living plant is busy. It does not just sit rooted to the spot waiting for somebody to classify it. Watch things happen to a plant from season to season, from day to day, and sometimes from hour to hour. What time do your evening-primroses open their flowers on August 1, at your latitude, at the end of a sunny day?

Plants begin. Some plants grow out of a *spore;* some sprout from

LIFE FORMS of NON-WOODY PLANTS (=HERBS)

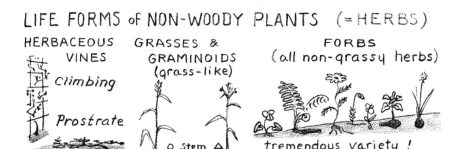

HERBACEOUS VINES — Climbing, Prostrate

GRASSES & GRAMINOIDS (grass-like) — o Stem Δ

FORBS (all non-grassy herbs) — tremendous variety !

a much more complicated device, usually sexually produced, called a *seed*, borne in a cone or fruit; and some start from a non-sexual piece of a parent, by what is known as *vegetative reproduction*. With the help of books and knowledgeable people, plus your own eyes, get curious about how the plants in your area begin.

Plants grow. Roots get longer; shoots, that is, the aboveground parts, get longer too. Roots may get a little thicker; shoots may grow much thicker. Such growth is the result of cell division in special tissues called *meristems*. These occur at the tips of roots and shoots of the seed plants, which are the most conspicuous land plants. Nipping the bud from a tree or shrub removes this terminal meristem and can markedly change the growth of the plant (p. 439). This can also influence the growth of many herbs, for instance the windowsill geranium *(Pelargonium)*, which slows its upward stretching and begins to bush out sideways when we thus *pinch back* (disbud) its growing tips. Such growth effects are determined to a large extent by *growth hormones* produced at tips of shoots. These normally inhibit the growth of buds and side branches farther down the stem. When the tip containing these hormones is pruned off, the parts nearer the roots are freed from this hormonal restraint and may well begin to grow much faster. While natural growth is far more complicated than this brief paragraph suggests, even this little knowledge can help you encourage plants to grow more according to your wishes as you prune, shear, and graft them, working with their natural growing processes. A rich literature of plant physiology includes excellent books written for amateurs, especially gardeners. A notable one is Kenfield's *The Wild Gardener in the Wild Landscape (293)*, a book relating plant growth substances to the esthetics of wildland management.

Plants get around.   Most land plants are more or less rooted to one spot through most of their lives. This makes people underestimate their mobility, which is often great in their spore or seed stage. Also, the minute male plants called pollen grains float vast distances on wind and water or hitchhike on insects and birds to foreign destinations. Consider any tract of land where you wish to work with nature. Every plant there somehow arrived there, did it not? In some environments, notably those in early stages of vegetational development, which are sunny and windy, plants come and go much more dramatically than in later, more stable stages. In managing plants, give thought to how they arrive and become established. Note also those which come to live in the new environment but fail—unless perhaps you give them help.

Plants reproduce.   For each species, ability to reproduce is a criterion of success. An individual plant may live a long time and grow to great stature. It may be a venerable old beech or pine, a dominant factor in its patch of woods. But if young beeches or pines do not grow to take its place, its species will eventually be eliminated from the scene and other species will take over. A beech, however, will probably produce female flowers and male flowers which will fertilize them. The sexual fusion will produce beech seeds in heavy nuts which, on maturity, drop to the forest floor; there some of them will grow happily in the shade of the parent tree and eventually replace it. In contrast, the pine will also produce female and male parts, creating seeds which are light weight and winged. Instead of dropping to the forest floor, where they are physiologically incapable of growing in the shaded environment, they fly away to become established in some sunny field, wood margin, or roadside verge.

Beech nut, from burr, is HEAVY

Young beeches in shade under parent

Pine seed, from cone, has wing, is light

Young pines start growing not in shade but sunshine.

These examples indicate that different reproductive methods help determine what grows where. Texts on plant ecology have much to say about such matters. Most of them are technically written and require study of the terms used to describe the complex but fascinating reproductive processes. The beginner may wish to start with books on plant propagation written for gardeners and then expand his understanding by watching closely the flowering and fruiting of the plants in the area to be managed *(5)*. The sexual reproduction of the so-called lower plants is equally challenging to study. And often the non-sexual (vegetative) reproduction of plants may be very significant, as with some weeds which proliferate even as you chop them up. Try *Botany for Gardeners (440)*, perhaps followed by *Plant Propagation (242)*.

PLANTS AT YOUR SITE

The following sections cannot tell you how to handle the plants in the areas where you work. Each environment has its own problems and possibilities. Be assured, though, that in all but the bleakest barelands the plants will be a significant part of the scene, deserving your close attention.

Vegetation management involves three basic techniques: (1) *removing or killing* plants; (2) *modifying* plants where they grow, as by pruning; and (3) *planting* them. Planting is one of the most important ways to work with nature, promoting the kinds of vegetation which you feel desirable to improve your corner of the world. You have a delightfully wide choice, in most climates, of what landscape architects call *plant materials*, that is the kinds of plants available to do a job; for instance, among others, Lombardy poplars or Norway spruces for a windbreak (p. 279). You also have to decide on the method of planting, for instance transplanting rooted stock or scattering seeds. Your successes will compensate for some inevitable failures and you will become more and more intrigued by the varieties of plants and the ways that you can help them. *(566)*

TRANSPLANTING

Because plants sprout, grow, travel, and reproduce, there are often more plants in one place than we want or need. The surplus can sometimes be used elsewhere. Before moving any plant, however, we must ask ourselves a basic question in conservation, "Is what we want really best for the environment and for other people, present and future?" We must be concerned about both the site from which the plant comes and the place to which it is moved.

The site from which a plant is moved.   Will removal of a plant impoverish an area or improve it? If you dig a little tree or other plant from woods, field, or flowerbed, take one which the land use of that particular area can spare. If the area is certain to be bulldozed, flooded, or in some other way catastrophically changed, you can (with the owner's permission of course) feel free to take all the plants for which you can find new homes. But many sites must continue much as they were before you took away a plant; in such cases, try to cause minimal ecological disturbance. Remove a plant which will leave remaining ones well spaced. Take pains to do as little damage as possible to roots and shoots of surrounding plants. Leave the soil smoothed so that people and animals will not stumble into a hole. Do not leave bare soil susceptible to erosion; mulch it (p. 340).

The site to which a plant is taken.   Consider the possible ecological effects of introducing a plant to an environment. Will the transplant be rejected by the new site, perhaps because of too much or not enough shade, unsuitable moisture in the air or soil, or inappropriate soil chemicals such as those which cause too high or too low acidity? Will the transplant be too successful for its new associates and crowd them out? Will the newcomer introduce a new disease or harmful insect? In this connection, consider federal and state laws governing transport of rooted growing plants across regional and state borders, and abide by them faithfully. We cannot afford more disasters such as the introduction of the Dutch Elm Disease and the American Chestnut Blight. Consult your local U.S. Department of Agriculture or other responsible governmental agency.

The new environment.   Always plant a plant where it can grow happily. An old saying goes, "You can put a 50-cent plant in a ten-dollar hole, but never put a ten-dollar plant in a 50-cent hole." A poor environment can ruin an otherwise good investment, so it pays to be concerned about the new environment. The amount of sun and rain and growing space is of course vital, but here emphasis is on the importance of the soil.

Because it is difficult to modify the soil of an environment to accommodate a plant brought to it, we usually study the environment where we wish to put a plant and then seek species which will enjoy it as it is, in other words ones growing in a similar environment. If our soil is strongly acidic, we look for *acidophiles* (acid-loving plants) such as blueberries and other members of the heath family, rather than *calciphiles* (calcium-loving plants). Occasionally we do make a special effort to remake an environment to which we move a plant. For instance in a region of granites, which disintegrate and form acidic soils, we may bring in a few limestone rocks to make a rockery for calciphilic ferns to round out a collection of living ferns.

Digging the hole for a tree or shrub.   Usually a round hole is best. A trench is good for setting in a row of closely spaced plants, as for a hedge. The hole should be wider and deeper than the root mass of the plant to be set in it, to give space for fresh soil for new roots to penetrate. Slant the sides of the hole a little toward the center, to avoid overhanging sides which might permit air pockets drying out the roots.

If you dig the hole in a lawn or other groundcover which should be protected from dirt, spread out an old cloth, burlap bag, canvas, or plastic sheet on which to pile excavated soil. If atop the hole site there is good turf which can be used elsewhere to patch a lawn or lay

KEEPING LAWN CLEAN
WHILE DIGGING

Turfs
Roots on roots
Grass on grass
Subsoil
Topsoil
Tarpaulin

across an eroding bank, dig it out in rectangular pieces with a spade (straight-bladed shovel). Make sure the cuts are vertical and uniform so that the pieces will fit tightly against each other when set tile-wise in their new site, to keep their roots from being exposed to the air and drying out. If there is inferior turf, pile it beside the hole with the topsoil.

As you dig, pile the subsoil separately from the topsoil. To save energy, make your piles close to the hole but not so close that the soil tumbles back into the hole as it is widened. When digging on a slope in a dry climate or a sloping dry site in a wet climate, pile the topsoil on the uphill side of the hole and the subsoil on the down-hill side. This procedure increases soil moisture; the topsoil is shoveled back into the bottom and lower sides of the hole to encourage new roots to grow downward, whereas the subsoil is used in the top of the hole and around the downhill side of the top to form a crescentic rim for a little dam to catch water running down the slope, thus promoting insoak for the roots.

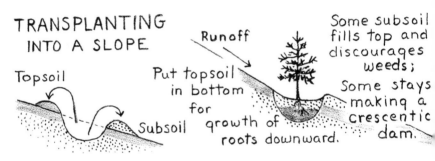

If you are bringing in a transplant with a large ball of earth on its roots (p. 382), you will have some subsoil left over after planting. To save shoveling this soil twice, as you dig load some subsoil directly into whatever you will use to remove it, for instance cart, wheelbarrow, basket, or tarpaulin. If the hole is not to be filled immediately, make sure that nobody will fall into it. Crisscross your tools or conspicuous sticks or logs over it, or set brush upright in it as a warning. If people or vehicles may come by after dark, set out a light.

Bottoming a hole.   The texture of soil under a transplanted tree or shrub is very important (p. 335). If it is coarse-textured (gravelly or sandy), water will drain away rapidly from the roots whenever the water table is low in critical droughty periods. Also, such light-textured soils are often quite infertile. On the other hand, a very fine-textured soil (of silt or clay) may hold enough water to keep a soil waterlogged, excluding air needed for root growth and more than offsetting the high fertility expected of heavy-textured soils. So dig a hole deeper than the transplant's roots; then you can put the best possible soil in the bottom of the hole to underlie the roots, to make a "ten-dollar hole."

If the soil is coarse-textured, you may wish to bring in some loam (p. 335), perhaps from the site where you get your plant or elsewhere. It will provide nutritious "fines" (fine particles) whose minute capillary spaces retain water in time of drought. If loam is unavailable but you can get silt or clay, mix that with the soil at hand to make loam. In very coarse soils, a sheet of plastic at the bottom of the hole can make a "perched water table" to hold moisture for your plant; make sure it is laid in saucer-shaped fashion. If the soil is fine-textured, you may want to get some sandy soil to mix with it, thus making a coarser-textured soil with better drainage and aeration.

Whatever the texture of the soil, its *structure* (p. 336) will almost always be improved by adding organic matter. Take whatever plant material may be around the site, such as dead leaves, weeds, and turf not needed elsewhere, and put it in the bottom of the hole, chopping it up and mixing it with some of the topsoil which you piled beside the hole. You can also bury old papers found lying around too many sites; these also will increase the water-holding capacity of a coarse soil and aeration of a fine soil. If compost is available, use that (p. 360). Animal manure, not too fresh, well mixed with mineral soil, will improve both structure and fertility of bottoming soil.

Place enough of your "ten-dollar soil" in the bottom to support your plant at the right height when it is set into the hole and gently snuggled into the loose soil. Gauge the correct height by estimating or measuring the distance from the base of the roots to the root-shoot juncture, also called the *root crown*, at the top of the roots. Usually there is a slight swelling at this point, at the level of the surface of the soil where the plant was growing. Many plants die if soil is piled against the stem above or below this juncture. In most sites the root crown should be a little lower than an imaginary line straight across the top of the hole, with the surface of the soil sloped down saucer-wise from the rim to the root crown. This depression helps collect moisture and holds leaves or other mulch to protect the soil around the transplant. In wet sites, however, a plant may benefit from having its root crown at the top of a slight mound like an inverted saucer. In very wet sites like low swamps or peaty mountain moors as in Scotland and Wales, trees may be planted in the tops of ridges formed when plowing drainage ditches. Each site must be considered individually when deciding the style of planting.

Seasons for digging.   When digging, you will almost always damage some roots which the plant was using to drink in water and nutrient chemicals. Try to transplant when the plant is drinking least and transpiring least moisture out to the atmosphere through stems and leaves (especially leaves, with their broad surfaces and myriad of microscopic holes). A dormant season is best. Many plants go dormant in cold winter months when the temperature drops into the thirties and below. Some plants in hot deserts are dormant in the hottest months, losing their leaves in summer and thus conserving water. Deciduous plants, those which lose all their leaves at the beginning of the unfavorable season, go almost completely dormant, but evergreen trees and shrubs retain some of their leaves all the time and transpire some moisture from their foliage into the atmosphere at all seasons.

Deciduous plants, therefore, can be dug best after their leaves have fallen and before the buds open up to form new leaves, but not when the soil is frozen hard. In other words, dig deciduous plants in late fall or early spring in cool climates, or farther south, at any time during the fall, winter, or spring. With special care (p. 384), deciduous plants can be moved in summer.

Evergreen plants, both the needle-leaved cone-bearing trees and shrubs and the broad-leaved evergreens such as rhododendron and mountainlaurel kalmia, can be moved at any time of year when the ground is not frozen but must be handled with much more care to avoid damage to the water-supplying roots (p. 384).

Time of day and type of weather for digging.   Because evaporation is usually greatest in the middle of the day, transplant during the higher humidity of early morning or evening, or on rainy or cloudy days. If possible avoid dry days and windy days when the air keeps tugging at water molecules in the leaves, pulling them out into the atmosphere. To keep from wilting, the plant calls for more water from the roots; but if the roots are being transplanted they may not be able to balance the water loss from the shoots. Remember that water absorption is made possible by microscopically small root-hair cells with very thin and delicate cell walls. The plant does not drink through the coarse brown roots visible to the unaided eye. As you dig, keep in mind the finest visible roots with their invisible root-hairs. Give them the best possible chance.

Plastic spray to reduce water loss. One of the commercially available plastic transplanting sprays can greatly help reduce transpiration and still permit exchange of oxygen and carbon dioxide between the plant and the air. It should be used *before* transplanting, prior to possible wilting.

Width of digging. Ideally we should dig all of a plant's roots. For a small plant that may be practical, and often we should choose a small plant rather than a larger one so that we can move a greater percentage of roots. Sometimes, however, we need a larger plant, for example to give a quicker landscape effect, to control erosion sooner, or to supply more food and cover for wildlife. How much of the root mass should you take to give the plant enough water-absorbing root surface to become well established? As a rule, dig straight down under the drip line (real or imagined) at the tips of the branches; within that circumference you will get enough roots. For a symmetrical plant this line will be circular, but if branches extend farther on one side, perhaps because of a sunny opening there or better soil in that direction, the pattern of digging will be more

TRANSPLANTING: ROOT MASS & HOLE

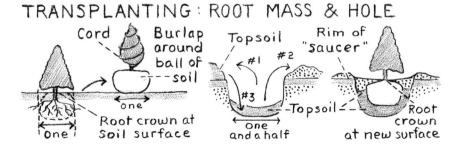

Cord Burlap around ball of soil

Root crown at Soil surface

one

Topsoil Rim of "saucer"

#1 #2

#3

-Topsoil-

one and a half

Root crown at new surface

irregular. Note that many roots do extend beyond the tips of the branches, but usually enough will be included if you follow the above rule. The wider the circle the more work will be needed, not just according to area but by the cubic mass, because depth is also a factor.

Depth of digging.   Roots of many plants are restricted to the more fertile topsoil enriched by organic material, so relatively shallow digging may yield enough of the finer absorbing roots along with the coarser transporting and supporting ones. However, some plants send one or more major roots almost directly downward, so-called tap roots. Oaks, pitch pines, and many other plants of dry sites are apt thus to tap a low water table. In semi-arid and arid regions, many shrubs send roots deep into the soil; these are called "well plants," or *phreatophytes*, and drink copiously from lower levels. Some of these plants are very difficult to transplant once they are established; it is best to move them in their seedling stages before they have grown deep roots. Do not expect them to grow well close together; plants of dry areas need to be widely spaced and may even kill each other chemically if crowded.

When digging, do not let your shovel angle in shallowly under the plant; keep the sides of the root mass as vertical as possible, to insure getting as many roots as you can handle. Do not dig blindly; feel and look as you progress, exploring for the natural patterns of the root system. Be curious and learn as you experiment. With all but the smallest plants, it is best to remove a "doughnut" of soil by making a circular trench around the root mass, to facilitate digging and minimize damage to roots. Also this reveals neighboring plant roots which should be cut off with hand clippers or loppers to free the transplant with minimum disruption. Any damaged major roots of the transplant should also be cut off clean to promote healing. Splintered or abraded roots are a liability to the plant.

Root pruning.   Wide-straggling root systems are more difficult to transplant than compact ones. To encourage a small mass of active roots, nursery-grown trees and shrubs are often root-pruned. A sharp spade or special plow cuts the tips off the longer roots and thereby stimulates them to sprout more thickly near the center of the root system. The same technique is useful when plants are to be dug from woods or fields, where roots often wander under the land-scape and tangle with those of other plants. A year before a desired plant is to be moved, dig a trench around it to cut off the longer roots and to cut away competing roots of neighbors. Then imme-diately refill the trench with the soil, or if it is of poor quality replace it with good loam. New, actively absorbing root tips will grow out into the trench. The next year, after a growing season, the plant is dug up with this compact mass of vigorous roots. Forgetful people do well to mark the tree and next year's calendar to make sure that they remember to harvest the tree of their labors.

Bareroot method. Deciduous plants which have lost all their leaves at the beginning of the dormant season can be transplanted without taking soil along on their roots, which are therefore bare. Many root-hairs are damaged, but this does little harm because the shoots are not actively transpiring moisture and new root-hairs will form at the beginning of the next growing season. To lift the trans-plant, loosen the soil carefully around the roots, starting at the tips; pry the plant up gently and let any soil fall off which comes off easily. Be careful to keep the roots out of the sun and dry air, especially avoiding dry wind. Times of high humidity give best survival. If the transplant is not to be set in the new hole at once, set it in a bucket of water or wrap it in wet newspaper, burlap, or other cloth. It helps to enclose wet wood shaving, old leaves, peat moss, or other damp materials to maintain high humidity while the plant is being moved or stored. (Nurserymen may store bare-rooted plants all winter, from late fall digging to early spring planting, by maintaining them in storage sheds at high humidity and around 36 degrees Farenheit.) Plant bare-rooted material as soon as you can, though, after digging.

The bare root method is also used for evergreen stock when it is very young, for instance seedlings up to three or four years old of pines and spruces for reforestation. These may be shipped from nurseries in lots of 100 to 500 in a bundle wrapped in peat moss or shavings. They should be planted in humid weather in early spring, after the soil has warmed a little but is still wet. While planting, carry them with their roots in a bucket of water, wet peat moss, or shav-ings.

Heeling-in. This is a method of temporarily storing bare-rooted plants if they are obtained before the local season is advanced enough for planting or when time or labor is unavailable until later. Dig a trench as deep as the transplants' root systems. Make it vertical on one side and about 45° slope on the other, with all the excavated soil forming a ridge above the vertical side. Lay the plants close together on the sloping side with the root-shoot juncture at the surface of the soil. Replace the soil over the roots and stamp it down firmly to eliminate air pockets. Your heel gives especially good pressure, hence, presumably, the term "heeling-in." Water thoroughly and keep the soil moist until planting. Plants can be kept happy in such a trench for two or more weeks or until their buds begin to open; but do not leave them in the temporary trench longer than necessary.

Ball and burlap method. This method, indicated often as B&B in nursery catalogs, is used for evergreen trees and shrubs other than seedlings and for deciduous plants when they are in leaf, and also for all trees with trunks over five or six inches in diameter, whether or not they are dormant. For these plants, it is important not to disrupt

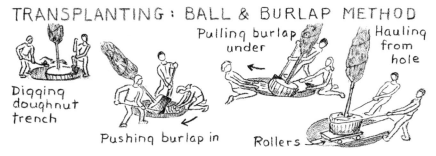

TRANSPLANTING : BALL & BURLAP METHOD

Pulling burlap under

Hauling from hole

Digging doughnut trench

Pushing burlap in

Rollers

the drinking roots any more than necessary because of the volume of water being transpired by the shoots. Therefore a ball of the soil in which the plant has been growing is carefully held around the roots with burlap sacking or some such material. This ball of soil is heavy, so do not try to move large plants by this method unless you have a lot of help. A ball about two feet in diameter may weigh over a hundred pounds, and it is an awkward shape to handle.

The technique for getting the burlap under the root mass is similar to that used by a nurse changing the sheets under a sick patient. Tip the dug-around ball to one side and push the cloth, pleated, as far as you can underneath. Then tip the plant back onto the cloth and pull out its pleats toward the tipped-up side. Sometimes a still uncut downward-growing root will prevent the pulling out of the cloth and will need to be clipped. Disrupt the soil around the roots as little as possible. If the soil is moist, it will adhere to the roots better than when dry and therefore forms a better ball; so watering beforehand helps in a dry spell. It is easier to maintain a coherent ball in a fine-textured soil than in a coarse one of sand or gravel.

Tie the diagonally opposite corners of the cloth tightly across the top of the ball, or use a wrapping of strong twine to hold the cloth against the soil, or overlap the corners of the burlap tightly and skewer them with 6d (six-penny) box nails. (Box nails are thinner than common nails and therefore penetrate between the fibers more readily; common nails are less convenient.) The burlap must be tight to hold the soil against the roots, maintaining contact between the delicate root-hairs and the soil particles.

Lifting the plant with its heavy ball can be a problem. Always lift from under the ball; never hoist by grabbing the stem of the plant, even though it looks like a handy handle, because that tends to loosen the roots from the soil, which, because of its weight, tries to stay behind. An inclined plane can help in sliding a plant up out of the hole where it is balled. For a heavy plant, a small platform under the ball can be rolled up the plank on sections of pipe, broomstick, or other rollers. If you have three helpers, slide a second burlap or tarp under the wrapped ball and have one person lift each corner, so that each lifts only a quarter of the weight. Do not attempt to move too big a ball; the most desirable plant is not worth an injured back. Use brains and leg muscles, not back muscles. And after digging, be sure to fill in the hole from which the plant was dug, to prevent accidents.

Placing transplant in new hole. After bottoming the new hole, lower the plant into it. If the plant is not symmetrical, orient it so that it looks its best from the side whence it will be seen most. Or if one side has skimpier growth, place that side toward the sun or other favored direction so that it will grow out. If the roots are bare, snuggle them into the loose bottom soil. Then add more good loam (topsoil or better soil brought in) between and around the roots, poking it in gently with a stick where your fingers cannot reach. Fingers work best for small plants. If the roots are ball-and-burlaped, unwrap the burlap carefully and remove it if you can do so without unduly disrupting the ball of soil; otherwise lay back the flaps and cut them off close under the ball. Some people leave the burlap spread out to the side of the hole and buried, to contribute organic matter, but some burlaps contain chemicals which slow the growth of roots. Check to make sure your plant stands vertical, or is set at a desired angle; push extra loam under a low side to lift it and hold it in the best position.

Frozen ball method.   For an especially valuable tree or large shrub, the frozen ball method permits transplanting with minimum dislocation of roots and their root hairs. Ask a nurseryman about it.

Filling the hole.   After positioning the transplant, continue adding the best possible loam around the sides of the roots. As you do so, keep compacting the added soil to make sure there are no air pockets which will dry out the roots. A short, stout stick makes a good tamper; so do your feet if you can jump up and down hard straddling the plant without stepping on it. Some people use copious water to wash the soil in around the roots, but this often leaves a soupy soil of poor structure. If you do pour in water as you add soil, don't try tramping—it will be too muddy. Fill the hole with soil, except for a saucer-shaped depression slanting in from the rim of the hole to the stem or stems at the center. Be sure that soil is not piled against the stems higher than it originally was where the plant formerly grew. If planting on a slope, mound the subsoil to make a little crescentic dam on the downhill side to retain surface water and help it soak in. Tamp the dam and, if necessary, sod it or mulch it to keep it from washing away. If water is available, water the transplant thoroughly by filling the saucer, repeatedly if necessary to provide a thorough soaking. Watch for any air tunnels which may develop and fill them in.

Watering a transplant.   Repeated waterings may help spring plantings and summer plantings. Don't keep a plant soaked; its roots need some aeration. Early autumn plantings also benefit from watering in dry spells, because this helps establish young roots before winter; but late autumn waterings may induce new growth which will be too delicate to survive the winter and will prevent the plant from going dormant as early as it should. If the following spring is dry, water the autumn-planted stock then.

Mulching a transplant.   Protecting the soil with a mulch can benefit a transplant greatly (p. 340), preventing weed competition, holding in soil moisture, and, in some climates, avoiding the cracking of soil caused by alternate freezing and thawing or wetting and drying.

Pruning a transplant.   The greatest peril to most transplants is loss of water from the shoots when it cannot be replaced adequately by damaged roots. Pruning immediately after transplanting reduces the area aboveground from which water loss can occur, keeping the shoots in better balance with the reduced amount of roots. Just how much to cut off is anybody's guess, but it is best to err on the side of too-heavy pruning. A considerable amount can be cut off the ends of major branches, and many small twigs can be removed (p. 439). If you think you have done considerable damage to roots, be sure to prune the top back heavily to reduce the transpiring area. With specially shaped broad-leaved evergreens, like hollies, which would be spoiled by heavy pruning, up to three-quarters of the leaves can be cut off one at a time (cut, not picked). A plant sprayed with plastic before transplanting (p. 379) will not need nearly so much pruning as an unsprayed one.

Supporting a newly planted tree.   Wind tends to shake newly planted trees and thus prevent their rootlets and root hairs from becoming established. To steady a tree, run two or three guy wires out to stakes set firmly in the ground where people will not trip over them. Each wire is looped around a fork at appropriate height, giving about a 45-degree angle. The wire is run through a short length of old hose or bicycle tire or other soft tubing placed around the tree to prevent chafing and undue pressure on the bark. Each guy must be tightened by twisting the doubled wire with a wooden toggle (stick) until it is taut. After two growing seasons the wires and stakes should be removed.

Continuing care.   After all this work you should either hate your transplant or love it. If you love it, watch it, enjoy it, and give it help

A newly planted green ash, with wrapping, stake, and a mulch of clinkers, at a rest stop on the interstate highway west of Lincoln, Nebraska.

from time to time, watering it in a dry spell, pruning it to keep it strong and handsome, controlling undue numbers of insects or fungi, and showing it to those who may care for it after you yourself have left the landscape of which it is an important part still.

SEEDING (SOWING)

The sowing of seeds enabled early man to take the step from hunter-gatherer to farmer and live a more settled life. Today's agriculture, from the subsistence farming of one family to the vast agribusiness of national and international corporations, depends mostly upon reproducing plants by seeds.

Each viable seed contains an embryonic plant which will start to grow if, after a suitable dormant period, it is provided with an appropriate amount of moisture and warmth. Seeds as sources of new vegetative cover for bare ground bring protection, productivity, and beauty to an environment, a function this book can only touch upon. For information on the selection of appropriate seeds and their special environmental requirements, you must turn to more specialized books devoted to farming and gardening (233).

Seeding compared to transplanting. The small size of seeds and their dormancy makes it possible to store them and disperse them in large numbers, whereas larger, rooted plants, in most cases, require space—and time-consuming individual handling. If you have a small area of, say, only tens of square feet or square meters which needs rapid covering with vegetation, transplanting may be the best method, especially if sods can be cut and laid down systematically or if irregular clumps of small native vegetation close at hand can be readily moved onto the site. Otherwise, seeding at an appropriate season will normally be best, establishing many small plants as soon as growing conditions permit.

Seasons for seeding. When seeds sprout (germinate), the resulting young seedlings are delicate; so mortality can be high if environmental conditions are poor. The tender roots need warm, moist soil with good tilth (p. 336). The shoots need light and air with enough moisture to keep the thin leaves from shriveling before they can develop their protective waxy coating. Each climatic region has its own best seasons for planting seeds, especially climates with alternating wet-dry seasons or warm-cold seasons. For instance, after New England's hard winter the month of May shows the new greens of natural vegetation coming to life; and man's agriculture follows suit. Farmers used to sow their seeds when the white oak leaves were the size of a squirrel's paw. Planting later in the summer would often require protection from hotter, drier weather. Today we may provide irrigation unless thundershowers or rainy spells bring favorable conditions. Sometimes a mulch can protect seedlings planted in dry summer weather. Early autumn with its more temperate circumstances may again provide suitable planting weather in climates where young plants can survive the winter.

Find out from farmers, gardeners, or agricultural extension workers about the best time to plant in your locality. Published maps of hardiness zones are helpful, as are maps showing frost-free seasons and patterns of expected rainfall. Note also the local importance of soil types. Light-textured (sandy) soils (p. 335) dry out and warm up earlier in spring then heavy-textured soils. Also the aspect of a slope (direction in which it faces) makes a difference. Land sloping southward in the northern hemisphere is better for early planting than land facing northward. The cooler slopes are better for later planting. When land management requires removing vegetation and baring soil which will need reseeding, plan the operation so that it will be completed at a season suitable for seeding.

Sources of seeds. Plants already growing successfully in your neighborhood are adapted to the local climate. Their seeds can sometimes be harvested at no cost. Dry fruits, such as the grains of grasses, the pods of legumes, and the capsules of evening-primrose, can be collected into a paper sack of unglazed paper which will let moisture escape. Seeds of fleshy fruits must be spread out to dry before storing so that they will not become moldy. In cold climates most seeds require a period of cold weather, to which they have become evolutionarily accustomed for their survival, before they will germinate. So seeds collected in early autumn may need to be hung up in an unheated shed or put in a cold but non-freezing portion of a refrigerator for a few weeks. Protect them from rodents.

Commercially available seeds can be bought at farmers' supply companies, garden shops, hardware stores, and other such outlets. If in doubt as to where it is best to buy, consult the Yellow Pages and also your agricultural extension agent. Make sure that seeds are fresh enough to assure that a high percentage will germinate. Packages often give the date of production and per cent germination expected. If you have held over a large quantity of seeds from an earlier year, try germinating ten or twenty in a paper towel or absorbent cloth kept moist but not inundated, to see whether a high enough percentage will sprout to warrant the effort of planting them.

Treating seeds before planting.   Some seeds need to be soaked or *scarified* (scratched) to help moisture penetrate the seed coat to activate the enzymes which start the embryo growing. Some seeds even need treatment with acid. Consult books or knowledgeable people.

Chemical deterrents are often used by commercial seedsmen because fungi, insects, and rodents frequently attack stored seeds. Some, including for instance mercury compounds, are very poisonous. Do not let anybody eat seeds sold to be planted! Keep them out of reach.

Preparation of the seedbed.   Try for a balance between disruption of the soil and freeing of the expected seedlings from competition with neighboring plants. Consider on the one hand the welfare of the soil, especially if on a bank or larger slope susceptible to erosion by water or in a windswept site, and on the other hand the needs of the seedlings. Some loosening of heavy-textured soil will almost always be necessary, for burying the seeds and allowing the new roots to push down. A light-textured soil, however, may need only minimal cultivating. Aborigines have done fine farming with only a digging stick, growing enough food to support their sparse population. For most of us, multiple-gang steel plows are used to produce the inexpensive food making possible our dense urban life; but a bigger price may have to be paid later wherever long-term effects on the soil have been inadequately studied or studiously neglected by self-centered agribusiness.

Liming soil before planting can improve the structure of some soils and raise their pH if it is too acidic for the kinds of seeds to be planted. Chemical testing of dry samples of your soil, using commercially available soil test kits, helps indicate acidity and elements for plant growth in which the soil may be deficient. Organically composed soil may give you and your plants the greatest satisfaction, but you may wish to experiment also with commercially available mineral fertilizers. Be wary, however, of over-application, forced productivity, and subtle long-term effects on the soil and soil runoff. What seems good for your seedlings may not be best for the total environment in the long run.

Sowing.   Seeds may be *broadcast* by hand in the age-old manner. A little practice gives the knack of scattering seeds fairly evenly. Mechanical spreaders made for lawn seed are useful on even terrain when one doesn't want to bother with the pleasure of sifting seeds through the fingers of an outward-swinging hand. Too thick a seeding creates competition between seedlings. Too sparse a scattering leaves too much bare ground and deprives seedlings of mutual aid in colonizing their environment. In your sowing, may you have good luck at first; then may the skill of experience take over.

Seeds may be *drilled* into the ground, that is dropped into little parallel trenches. On level ground the drills may be straight but on slopes they should curve carefully along the contour. The distance between drills depends upon the spatial needs of the mature plants, and sometimes upon the dimensions of the machines used to plant, cultivate, or harvest. You can twiddle seeds between thumb and finger, a pinch at a time, into the drills, trying to achieve a spacing which will give the seedlings enough room yet provide mutual protection. Thinning later can sometimes compensate for early crowding. Farm machines drill seeds faster for large areas. The depth of the trench is determined by the size of the seed; a general rule is to plant seeds at a depth about three times their longest diameter. The finest seeds may be broadcast on the surface and merely pressed into the ground. Drills need to be back-filled, by shuffling feet or by hoe or machine, with tamping light enough to stabilize the soil without compacting it so much that air and water are kept out.

If you are a bit of a mystic, plant with a prayer. There is always something in nature to mystify you if you stop and ponder.

METHODS OF PLANT PROPAGATION

Cuttings to supply new plants.   Some plants can be multiplied by cutting off pieces and urging them to grow roots. The resulting plants will be genetically the same as the parent plant, whereas seeds have who-knows-what genetic contributions from the sexual fusion of the germ cells of their parents. Usually it is a piece of stem which is severed, or sometimes a fragment of root.

Hardwood cuttings—These are made from healthy twigs of dormant trees and shrubs. Select twigs growing in full sun that are rich in stored food, not fast-growing suckers of weak branches in the middle of a plant. Cut a piece of last year's growth four to twelve inches long and including at least two nodes. The basal cut should be just below a node and the upper cut one half to one inch above a

HARDWOOD
CUTTINGS
in autumn
of deciduous
trees and shrubs

4 to 12 inches
of previous
year's growth

Include at least 2 nodes

— — Node

Tie in bundles for
cold storage over winter

node. Cut, pack, and tie the twigs all oriented one way in little bundles. Store them until spring in a cool, moist place in polyethylene film, sand, sawdust, or peat moss. If a cool, non-freezing shed or cellar is not available, you can bury the bundles in the ground at a depth which will prevent their freezing or sprouting. In early spring, plant the twigs in sharp sand such as builders use (not sea sand with its excessive salts). A light powdering of the bottom of each twig with a commercial plant growth substance such as Rootone or Hormodin will promote root formation. Plant into small pots, flats, paper cups, or other containers with drainage holes in the bottom. Keep the sand constantly moist in a place with warm, humid atmosphere. When roots have formed, the new plants can be lined out, that is, transplanted in a row in a nursery bed where they can be cared for two or three years until they are large enough to be transplanted to a desired site.

Semi-hardwood cuttings—These are taken from broad-leaved evergreens such as mountainlaurel kalmia which never go completely dormant. Pieces are cut in summer after new growth has slowed down. A twig from three to six inches long is cut on a cool early morning or cloudy day. Lower leaves are removed, and so are parts of the upper leaves, to reduce the area from which water will be lost. After treating the base with plant growth powder as with hardwood cuttings, the twig is planted in sand and kept warm and humid until rooted.

SEMI-HARDWOOD
    CUTTINGS
in summer of
broadleaved evergreens.

3 to 6 inches long,
after new growth
has begun to
harden.

Cut below
a node

Some of larger
upper leaves cut
in half

Lower
leaves removed

Cuttings can help you start a small conservation nursery to supply desirable plants for various situations. Because plant propagation includes tricks for different kinds of plants in various climates and soils, you will profit from gathering more information than the brief amount here. Get advice from a professional nurseryman, gardener, botany teacher, or well-informed garden club member. Consult books and government pamphlets on plant propagation to stimulate and supplement your own experimentation.

Layering plants to multiply them. Some plants have stems which sprout roots as they run along on the ground or bend over and touch the ground. This is called *layering*. After roots are well formed, the stem can be cut and the newly rooted portion transplanted to a desired site. Layering can be induced in shrubs with supple stems and even in some trees while they are young. Bend a lithe, vigorous stem gently to the ground, bury it slightly, and pin it down with one hooked stake or two crossed stakes, or weight it with a stone. Make sure the tip of the stem then bends upward and is held that way, stimulating growth. After a growing season with adequate moisture, roots should have formed at the point of contact with the ground. Then cut the original stem and transplant the shoot, or enjoy it where it is near its parent.

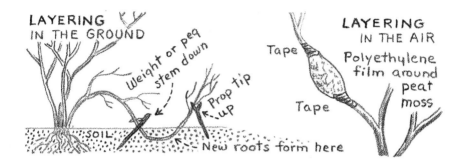

Air layering is more difficult. Instead of bending a twig to the ground, fool it into thinking that it is in the ground. Select a vigorous twig. Six to twelve inches back from the tip, in last year's growth, cut an inch-wide ring of bark and remove it. Wrap a handful of sphagnum moss around the wound and the bark for two or three inches above and below it. Wet the moss thoroughly and wrap it with a ten-inch square of *polyethylene film*, which permits exchange of atmospheric gases but reduces water loss. Other plastic films may not work, so do not trust breadwrappers. Secure the moss and plastic film by tightly wrapping both ends with a waterproof adhesive tape. Start the wrap on the bark and finish on the plastic film. Spring or early summer is best for air layering. Three or four months, with moisture maintained in the moss, may be needed for good root formation. Then the stem can be severed and the rooted tip planted. Use maximum care because even a well-rooted "layer" has a difficult time adjusting to its new environment.

Trench layering and *mound layering*, along with other methods, are described in books on plant propagation *(242)*.

Grafting and budding. Sometimes an already rooted plant in the right place does not have just the characteristics which you want for it, but these are possessed by one of its close relatives. You can try taking a piece of the latter and growing it on the former. The rooted plant is called the *stock* and the added piece the *scion*. For instance a scion of a sweet-fruited cherry can be grafted onto a stock of bitter-fruited wild cherry such as may be found growing along a fence row. Note that both plants are in the genus cherry. Only very seldom will plants of different genera be compatible enough for grafting. Often it is best to use varieties within the same species. *Grafting* is best done at the beginning of the growing season. There are many tricks to this ancient horticultural art, for instance special modes of cutting to insure a really strong union. Many plants valuable to conservation, especially fruit trees, are multiplied by grafting *(209)*.

Budding is a special form of grafting whereby a single bud from a desired plant is used as the scion. It is carefully removed together with an elliptical bit of bark, using a sharp knife, slipped into a usually T-shaped slit in the bark of the stock, then waxed and taped.

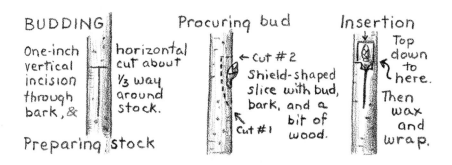

BUDDING

One-inch vertical incision through bark, &

Preparing stock

horizontal cut about ⅓ way around stock.

Procuring bud

←Cut #2

Shield-shaped slice with bud, bark, and a bit of wood.

Cut #1

Insertion

Top down to here.

Then wax and wrap.

Division and separation. Plants for conservation can often be obtained by *division* of a large plant already at hand. Many shrubs can be cut down through the root crown into two or more sections, each with stems and roots. If given appropriate growing conditions, each of these can form a new shrub. Similarly, many non-woody perennials can be divided by cutting apart their roots or underground stems, as one propagates potatoes by cutting apart the "eyes" (buds) of the tubers. Irises and daylilies, for instance, often make desirable groundcovers which prevent erosion and contribute beautiful blooms. Clumps of so-called *bunchgrasses* or portions of the more regular *turf grasses* can be cut apart, spread out over bare ground, and planted as *plugs* to speed revegetation. Many other mat-like plants can be similarly propagated.

Separation is similar to division except that the plants to which it is applied have a natural tendency to form separable pieces. Lilies, daffodils, and crocuses, for example, form new bulbs beside the old ones, which are readily separated without cutting. Consult gardening books for details on planting methods; or when dealing with native plants use your eyes to note how they are growing and use your common sense to try to relocate them happily where you want them.

Other methods of propagating desired plants. The plant kingdom is full of surprises. Its diversity challenges anyone who wishes to work creatively with nature. So you want more water lilies? Then you had better study water lilies. You have a cave and want to grow mushrooms? Better study mushrooms. There is a voluminous literature on plant propagation waiting for you, and the plants themselves are waiting to teach you as you watch them grow and reproduce. There is much still to be learned and written. Perhaps you can be the first to discover how to grow a lichen garden on a city wall. Most if not all lichens seem to be killed by city smog. Perhaps by browsing through a city cemetery you can find an old gravestone with a resistant variety of lichen, maybe in the moist niche provided by the chiseled inscription. Maybe you can propagate that lichen to bring more plant life to our dingy cities. While learning the old ways, keep looking for new ones. *(566)*

WEEDING

A weed has often been defined as a plant in the wrong place. When you call a plant a weed, you have made a value judgement. You have decided that the plant is bad for that particular site. A dandelion flower may be objectionable in the front lawn but delightful in someone's hair, delicious in dandelion wine, and dazzlingly beautiful in company with a hundred others in a moist meadow. There can be no simple rules for judging weeds. We must consider each case. Removing weeds can increase an Iowa corn crop sixfold, but at another time the same field lying fallow may be protected from erosion by weeds.

The commonest concept of weeds is that they are plants giving *competition* to more desirable plants such as crops or ornamental plantings. They compete for space, sun, soil moisture, and mineral nutrients. Also weeds may harbor insect pests and diseases which may then move over onto our crop plants, backyard vegetables, flowers, and other desirables. Weeds sometimes offend us even when causing no real harm, just because they remind us of their alleged sins at other times. That "ugly" ragweed may be truly beautiful, but we do not see it that way because of our allergies in preceding Augusts when it was liberating pollen.

Today with chemical planticides, flame-throwers, and multigang cultivators pulled by huge tractors, we can almost keep ahead of weeds. In one sense agribusinesses are winning the battle and providing bountiful crops. The war with weeds, however, will be won only when much more scientific knowledge and greater humility bring more subtle balance between the few plants which we know we want and raise largely in vast monocultures and the many plants which we do not yet adequately appreciate. Who knows what miracle drugs may lie waiting to be discovered in weeds which we now consider irritating and which we try so hard to erase? *(124, 415)*

Weeding by cultivating. In garden beds, plowed fields, and some orchards, weeds can be kept down by more or less frequent stirring of the soil to uproot them and let them shrivel. This *cultivating* should be done early and often, while weeds are young and their roots still shallow. Hoeing or machine cultivating is best done in the afternoon of a hot day to give maximum exposure of the weeds' roots to killing sun and air. Repeating cultivation five to ten days later, when another batch of weed seeds may have germinated, will continue the battle. Most weeds of exposed soil are annuals, that is, going from seed to seed in one growing season. They often produce prodigious quantities of seeds; for instance, up to 50,000 in one average plant of purslane. Because of minute differences in physiology and variability in soil conditions, all the seeds do not germinate at the same time. Evolution of weeds has not put all their eggs in one basket. So repeated cultivation is necessary, at least until crop plants get a good head start. Even thereafter it is best to keep cultivating to prevent weeds from sending down deep roots and forming the flowers which produce more thousands of seeds. Cultivate shallowly and carefully to avoid damage to crop roots. After harvest, repeated cultivation, deep at first and then progressively shallow, can prepare a good seedbed for a winter cover crop, summer fallow, or the next regular crop, according to the climatic region and season. Along with all these efforts to hold back the propagation of weeds, be sure to plant crop seeds which are as weed-seed-free as possible.

Weeding by hand-pulling. Small quantities of weeds in small areas can be tackled by hand, especially when the soil is moist and loose. If removing a weed's roots disturbs those of a desired plant, tamp the soil back around it and perhaps water it to help it reestablish intimate contact with the soil particles. A narrow trowel or large knife can help eradicate weeds with deep central *tap roots*, and can help loosen soil under shallow-rooted weeds to make them yield more readily. A pronged hand-cultivator can be used to scratch out tiny weed seedlings. Weeds can be dried in the sun and then thrown in the compost pile, assuming that the pile is well handled (p. 360) and not just a weed garden. A little weeding each day is better for both gardener and garden than a valiant effort more rarely.

Weeding by mowing or grazing. Cutting the tops off herbaceous weeds, by either blades or teeth, can keep many of them from flowering and setting seeds. Frequency of cutting is important. Be careful not to cut too low in an effort to thwart the rosette and sideways-spreading weeds which grow close to the soil. Cutting too close may let the sun kill shallow-rooted plants which will die and leave bare soil as an invitation to more weeds. Too much mowing or grazing can cause accelerated erosion, as well as favoring specialized weeds.

Weeding individual woody plants by cutting them down.   A tree in the wrong place in a forest can be a weed as surely as can a plantain in a lawn. Weedy trees also spring up in hedges, shrubberies, and other places where they must be removed one at a time and with minimum disturbance to surrounding plants. When possible, try to spot such intruding trees in their youngest stages, when they can be pulled up by hand. Later they can be cut with lopping shears prior to their reaching a diameter of one and a half to two inches, depending on the style of loppers available. When a weed tree is a little too large to cut with loppers at its base, it can often be cut shoulder-high. Protect your face from its branches, however, as it falls. Then cut the trunk at the base with a bow saw, pruning saw, or carpenter's cross-cut saw. For trees larger than three to four inches in diameter at the ground, see *Felling Trees* (p. 411).

When cutting out weedy trees and shrubs, differentiate between *sprouters* and *non-sprouters* (p. 419). The latter die when their shoots are cut off and thereafter they give no more trouble—unless new seedlings start. Sprouters, however, often send out new shoots, either the same season or the following one. Usually each stem cut will stimulate sprouting of two to several new stems; these must be either cut off, tolerated, or enjoyed.

Sprouting, sometimes a miserable nuisance, often has benefits, as when a plant undesirable as a tree can by repeated cuttings be turned into a desirable shrub. For instance some oaks and maples, among many other kinds, when repeatedly cut make beautiful bushes, especially in autumn when their brilliant foliage makes bright patches close to the ground. Sprouts of many woody plants make good cover and browse for several forms of wildlife, including rabbits and deer. Numerous shoots close to the ground tend to catch leaves in windy places and hold them as a soil-protecting mulch. And sprouts can be harvested for toasting forks and craft uses of many kinds.

When persistent sprouters must be eliminated, you can try being a persistent cutter, removing stems as fast as they appear so that they do not grow leaves to make food for the roots. Theoretically at least this starves the roots so that the plant dies. That may be a long time, though. Digging up the root crown (top of the roots where they join the stem) may help, but it is often a lot of work, and some species send up sprouts optimistically from remaining segments of roots. A blow torch or flame-thrower can be an effective weed killer in sites where it can be used without hazard of starting wildfire. Chemical planticides, very carefully used, are often the best agents for killing sprouters (p. 400).

Weeding by girdling.   Sometimes a live tree is undesirable but if it were dead it would not be objectionable, or might even be desirable. For instance, a living tree in a closed woodland (p. 149) competes increasingly with its neighbors for light and space as it grows larger. A dead tree, on the other hand, contributes more and more to its neighbors as it gets smaller and gives its minerals and organic matter back to the soil. Mistakenly, most people try to improve a woods by removing dead trees; they would usually be helping the woodland community far more if they killed live ones! Of course some keen observation and good thinking must be used to determine which trees should be killed and which should be left to prosper freed from the competition of the weedy ones killed. Girdling is an excellent technique for killing trees to be left standing.

Before girdling, decide on the purposes of the woods (see Chapter 5, *Treelands*). Then take note of the tree species and individual trees which will help most in achieving these purposes. Fell or girdle those trees which give greatest competition to the desired trees. *Fell* them if you can use them for fuel, lumber, crafts, or other purposes. But *girdle* trees not worth the trouble of felling. Leave them to die standing. Woodpeckers and a host of other animals, fungi, and other lowly plants will soon be making use of the dead trees for homes and food. Also, a dead tree can be very beautiful (if necessary, meditate on the high cost of driftwood in a city gift shop).

To girdle a tree, cut through the outer and inner bark to expose the wood in a ring an inch or more wide all around the trunk, at ground level or any more convenient height. Cutting and removing the inner bark prevents food made by the leaves from flowing down to feed the roots, which are thereby starved. A vigorously growing tree may heal and bridge over a too-narrow band, requiring recutting. An axe is the most frequently used tool, but any sharp instrument which is handy may do the job if only a few trees are to be girdled.

Weeding with chemical planticides. As every chemist knows, molecules are mighty. Plant growth depends upon just the right chemical happenings in roots, stems, and leaves. If we contribute foreign chemicals to a plant, they may disrupt its normal functions. Some stimulate growth, some inhibit it. Too much of either stimulation or inhibition can kill a plant. Killing a plant with chemicals is almost always very easy—very.

Chemical *planticides* are also called *phytocides*, plant killers. The term *herbicides* is less desirable, being often loosely used for chemicals which kill not only herbs but also woody plants. Some, like ammonium sulfamate, creosote, calcium chloride, and sodium chloride, have been used for decades, as have very toxic compounds such as those of arsenic and mercury. Since World War II, a great variety of new planticides, mostly complex organic compounds, have been and are being developed. They are a major factor in the high productivity of croplands in technologically advanced countries. They make weeding amazingly easy, compared to the back-breaking hoeing which men and women have had to do for thousands of years.

Unfortunately planticides have often been used wholesale by unthinking, careless, or ignorant people without due regard for their subtle ecological effects, some of which can be disastrous to vast ecosystems. Like a surgeon's scalpels, planticides do have their place in environmental operations. When used with thought and skill, they can eliminate a plant in the wrong place. But if you want to use chemicals, do so with care. Know what you are doing. Take only calculated risks. Meticulous following of manufacturers' instructions may not be enough, because some chemicals have been inadequately tested for their ecological effects. Always consider your applications experimental. Use only small amounts until you can assess what happens in your situation. Watch the effects. Do not become so preoccupied with watching a weed die that you are oblivious to any effects on surrounding plants—and they include the unseen micro-

The willows and other shrubs along the creek in the valley have been killed with a planticidal spray. Gained: a little more grass for cattle. Lost: a little more habitat for wildlife. Dubois, Wyoming.

flora of the soil. Also consider effects on animals, including insects and worms. Think too about whether you are diminishing ecological diversity in your area and thus promoting major ecological changes instead of the smaller oscillations which tend to keep an environment in a more steady and hence more easily managed state.

As a rule, if you must use a planticide, select one which is as specific as possible for the kind of weed you wish to eliminate. Avoid broad-spectrum planticides, those that kill many kinds of plants; they have the most unpredictable effects on vegetation. So far as possible, apply the planticide only to the kind of plant to be killed; do not broadcast the chemical. Instead of killing dandelions by spreading weedkiller all over the lawn, use an ecologically safer wand-injector. That is often more tedious; but we are learning that what is immediately easiest in environmental management is not always healthiest in the long run. The long run, perhaps for our children or their children, may be very tiring indeed, if we contribute to irreversible pollution or other ecological adversities.

With large plants like trees and shrubs, apply chemical to no more of the plant than necessary. Use a basal spray or paint the chemical on the base of the stems rather than drenching the foliage. Remember that the vehicle in which the poison is carried, for instance fuel oil, may have its own toxic effects in addition to those of the phytocide.

Use planticides at the seasons when the plants to be killed are most susceptible to them. That way you can use less chemical. For instance, phenoxy planticides such as 2, 4-D; 2, 4, 5-T; MCPA; Silvex; 2, 4-DB and many other phytocides are most effective when plants are growing rapidly—when buds are bursting from woody stems or seedlings are emerging from seeds of herbs.

Use all precautions for handling poisons, such as (but not limited to) the following. Store poisons only in tight, clearly labeled containers kept out of reach of children or ignorant people. Use poisons only in suitable equipment in good condition for efficient application. Wash yourself and your clothes after involvement with poisons, and be careful of what becomes of the wash water. Know first aid antidotes for the chemicals you are using, and know how to contact your nearest emergency poison center.

Risks must always be weighed against potential values. Dangers cannot always be avoided. Planticides can be a great boon to the human race if we can learn to use them wisely and curb those who indulge in them for short-term gains inimicable to society. Selective weeding of crops is of obvious benefit if we do not overdo it. Careful selective spraying of Poisonivy, Poisonoak, and other plants irritating to the point of danger also makes sense. There is logic too in treating cut stumps along trails and vistas or other places where their sprouting would require endless maintenance. It is sensible also to mix an appropriate planticide in mineral jelly (such as vaseline) and apply it to a poisonous stem growing up in a hedge rather than to disrupt the hedge by digging up the poisonous roots. But just as we think of a weed as a plant in the wrong place, so must we realize the dangers of a chemical in the wrong place.

CULLING

Culling removes less desirable plants which would be detrimental to remaining ones, or which occupy space that would be better held by new plants. It achieves some of the same results as thinning (p. 405) but focuses on conspicuously inferior plants to be removed with less consideration for the vigor, form, and spacing of crop plants to be left. It can be thought of as weeding, except that weeding means elimination of plants not of the crop species, while culling removes crop species. *(329)*

In farming and horticulture culling is familiar; inferior plants, flowers, or fruits are removed to favor the remaining ones. In forestry also, the value of culling has long been recognized, but too often this theoretically sound practice has not seemed economically justified. Today, as our inherited forest resources dwindle and we begin to feel more responsible for developing future forests which will pay their own way with sustained yield, we must give far more attention to intensive forestry practices such as culling. Also, although the market for household firewood from forest culls has diminished, there is an increasing use of charcoal and firewood for recreational fires and a tremendous increase in the number of people who might enjoy or otherwise profit from outdoor work such as culling (see also *Harvesting*, p. 435).

The principle of culling can be applied to many intensively managed plantlands, not just fields, gardens, and forests. While the following comments focus on treelands, thought should also be given to the possibilities of culling bushes in shrublands, and to opportunities in relatively natural herblands also.

Culling leaners. A leaner is a tree which is not upright. It is as unpopular among sawtimber as a thoughtlessly leaning person in a crowded elevator. It is sure to rub somebody the wrong way. It bruises the bark of other trees and makes them liable to infections and takes up space which several other trees could use effectively. The sooner leaners are removed, the less damage they cause to trees around them, and the less felling hazard to young trees beneath

Sprouts from
cut Ash

Cut conifers
very seldom
sprout

Wolf
tree

Leaner

Girdled Tree
dies standing

(plants which foresters call "advance reproduction"). In felling leaners, let them fall along the direction of lean; to do otherwise you have to overcome their tremendous mechanical advantage. Ropes, block and tackle, and power sources such as tractors can influence direction of fall to some extent (see *Felling*, p. 411), but to work easily with nature, fell in the direction of lean. When felling, remember that a leaner will tend to break its hinge (p. 415) much sooner than an upright tree; so be extra careful, watching for premature splitting and back-kick of the bole. Make the notch deeper than for an upright tree and be very cautious with the third cut.

Note in defense of leaners: If other values than straight lumber are to be considered, remember that leaners are highways for squirrels and other wildlife, and that there is beauty in diversity of slanting lines as well as in the uniformity of upright trunks.

Culling wolf trees. A wolf tree is a wide-spreading tree which is a predator on the rest of the forest. Its sprawling branches, indicating growth in the open, make a wide crown (top) which utilizes the sunlight of a space large enough for several narrow-crowned trees (indicating growth amid other trees), and the light energy goes into making wood in crooked limbs rather than in straight trunks which are more readily harvestable. If sizable shade-tolerant trees have already grown up beneath, damage to them can be minimized by pruning the large branches of the wolf tree and lowering them on ropes before felling the trunk.

Note in defense of wolf trees: Wide-spreading trees are often hollow and therefore good as den trees for many forms of wildlife which depend on them. Also, in some sites their beauty is worth more than the dollar value of whatever lumber trees they may be hindering.

The space under a spreading wolf tree may be ideal for a gathering place for a class or picnic. Don't remove *all* wolf trees from a woodlot. Leave those which are best for the above purposes.

Culling diseased trees. Fungal diseases take a heavy toll of standing wood. Much of the damage seems inevitable because of the expense of giving individual care to forest trees (as one does to shade trees along the street or in the front yard). Because fungal spores capable of infecting trees are almost everywhere, efforts are best directed at maintaining vigorous trees which are well spaced so that they do not wound each other. However, when fungal fruiting bodies emerging from bark indicate heart rot or other disease, the sooner the tree is culled the more wood it will yield; and in isolated woodlots, as in the midwestern United States, removal of such trees may decrease the incidence of the disease. *(66)*

In some cases efforts are made to restrict the spread of an introduced or otherwise new disease which seems to lack adequate natural control. Woodland managers should support government foresters and others trying to check the spread of such diseases as Dutch Elm Disease. Cull trees when they first show symptoms. The culled trees must be disposed of so as to avoid spreading the disease; for example, infected elm wood must be burned to prevent its harboring the bark beetles which act as vectors (carriers) transferring the fungus to healthy elms.

THINNING

When there is overcrowding, it is often beneficial to remove some plants. Nature often stocks stands of plants heavily, with the result that only the fittest survive, and the fittest often show many scars of the battle. Man, by trying to figure out an ideal quantity of plants, say carrots or pines, for a given area, and by early elimination of the excess plants, can work with nature to develop plants which, freed from the tensions of the battle for survival, are of more uniformly high quality in certain respects. The following paragraphs refer primarily to forest management, but the principles of plant growth and plant removal can be extended, with some adaptation, to other environments.

Need for thinning. When the branches of two plants come in physical contact, they are apt to compete for light and to suffer mechanical injury from rubbing, with resulting wounds being liable to infection. Also, crowding may affect the shape of a plant of esthetic importance, as in foundation plantings where too many small woody plants were originally set out. In recreational woodlands, thinning can remove trunks which are in the way of active play or pleasant vistas, even though crowded crowns may not be a concern. Experience and deep thought are often needed when trying to decide how much to thin. It is easier with a row of radishes than with alders in a shrubswamp. If you do not have the experience yet, start acquiring it, and don't be so serious that you spoil all the fun of experimenting.

Results of thinning. Removing a plant closely adjacent to another tends to make the remaining plant spread sideways. Branches grow longer and thicker, producing more leaves, which make more food for the plant. However, with plenty of room to the side, the plant does less stretching upward, so the trunks of thinned trees and stems of other plants tend to be shorter and stockier. This reaction to environment is similar to that of the open-grown pasture oak, which is short, stocky, and widespread compared to its forest-grown brother which is tall, straight, and short-limbed. These growth responses should be considered when thinning, so that spreading is not excessive.

Thinning young softwood plantations. "Softwood" is the foresters' term for the needle-leaved cone-bearing trees, even though some of them have fairly hard wood. Many plantations of pine, spruce, larch and occasionally other softwoods are planted with close spacing, such as six feet between trees. While at first seedlings or cuttings so spread look far apart, five to fifteen years of growth (depending upon soil fertility, availability of water, and other growing conditions) will bring their branches into contact. Ideally every alternate tree should then be removed, but modifications are in order where a tree thus designated for removal is superior to an adjacent tree to be left, or where a volunteer (self-planted) tree, perhaps a hardwood, seems more worthy than an adjacent planted softwood. Healthy, well-shaped trees with room to grow are usually more to be desired than geometric precision in their arrangement. Also, diversity of species like that created by a few volunteer hardwoods improves the conditions for wildlife and reduces the threat of rapid spreading of disease in a pure stand (a stand of only one species). Where supervision of thinning operations is difficult, instructions may be given to remove every third or fourth row regardless of the quality of the trees removed.

Whenever possible, a harvest from thinnings should pay for the labor involved, through production of Christmas trees, holiday greens, posts, pulp, fuel, or material for specialty products such as barrel staves. Sometimes helping the woods may be pay enough.

Thinning older softwood plantations. Trees between fifteen and thirty years old may be profitably thinned again, so that a six-feet by six-feet planting thinned to twelve feet by twelve feet may become spaced twenty-four feet by twenty-four feet. This repeated thinning will give the crowns room to spread, thereby increasing their food-making ability and promoting better health and increase of wood production. Larger trees are harder than small ones to remove from among their neighbors because of increasing problems of lodgement and damage to the remaining trees. There is a tendency today in the United States not to thin older plantations to develop optimum sawtimber, but rather to harvest plantations younger and use them for pulp, boxwood, or the like. Where esthetic considerations are primary, there is real joy in extending thinning into the later stages of the life of a plantation, as in recreational areas where the advance reproduction of shade-tolerant plants on the forest floor is also being managed to give the shady openness of a cathedral. European foresters excel in the management of old forest.

Thinning natural treelands. Natural woods usually have a greater variety of species than plantations and may be uneven-aged instead of having trees all of one age (although young woods started after logging, fire, or abandonment of open land may be of one age-class). Natural woods are complicated. If you must thin, be subtle about it; consider many of the environmental factors involved, and thin bit by bit, with much thought, to enable you to develop a good feel for what you are doing. Of course some natural woods should remain untouched.

Selecting crop trees to be left. Start by considering the dominant trees, those whose crowns, composed of well-foliaged branches, are the largest and the highest in the canopy. In a pure stand of pines, which are typically even-aged, no trees may stand out as particularly dominant, but some may be healthier or of better form than others. Next, consider the age of these trees in relation to harvest. They may be saplings only an inch in diameter or great forest trees two or more feet DBH (Diameter Breast High), or any size in between. If they are ready for harvest, and you think the woods can spare them, don't thin them, fell them (see *Felling Trees*, p. 411). If they are not ready for harvest, see if the canopy still has openings which give their crowns a little room to expand sideways without touching neighbors; they should have a little space but not enough to let them grow wide-spreading. If the canopy is closed (with no room for crowns to spread), it should be opened by judicious removal of certain of the trees extending up into the canopy. Decisions on trees to be removed are based primarily on which trees should stay. The trees of greatest vigor, straightest form, and most suitable spacing should usually be left.

Vigor is indicated by (1) a densely leafy crown (indicated in dormant deciduous trees by many twigs with buds), (2) healthy-looking bark devoid of scars or fungal outgrowths, (3) current-year twigs well elongated beyond budscale-scars of the previous winter, and (4) wide growth rings of wood of recent year, as revealed by a forester's borer or increment hammer. Straight form of the trunk should be judged from two views at right angles to each other. Spacing depends upon the size of the trees. The following rules may help.

D plus rule: One spacing rule to use as a general guide is the D plus rule of thumb. D is the average diameter breast high in inches of potential trees to be left. The plus factor is a number between 2 and 6, to be added to the DBH. Two seems best for slow-growing trees, such as spruces in the north, while 6 may work well for fast growing pines in the south. The diameter in inches plus the factor gives a number which is the recommended spacing in feet between trunks; so two slow-growing spruces of 5 and 7 inches DBH should be 5 + 7 + 2 = 14 feet apart (roughly!). The formula should be used experimentally in any region to find out what plus factor works best locally for various species at various ages.

D times rule: The DBH is multiplied by a factor determined experimentally, and does not usually vary so much with trees of different diameter classes. A factor sometimes recommended in the South is 1.75. The multiplication gives the appropriate space in feet.

H divided rule: The height divided by a factor from 4 to 7 gives a recommended spacing in feet. The lower factor is used for shade-intolerant trees. This rule is easier to apply to conifer plantations than to natural hardwoods, whose heights may be harder to determine.

You should not get so busy calculating with diameters that you fail to consult the canopies to study their need for space! Also, nature may not have happened to plant a vigorous or straight tree at the desired spacing, so compromises are often necessary.

The vigorous, straight, well-spaced dominant trees to be left for later harvest are sometimes called the *crop trees.* (Note, though, that other trees cut from between or beneath them may also constitute a crop.) They are sometimes called the *final crop trees,* a useful term in a plantation where they are the last of the planting to be cut, but not in sustained-yield operations where younger trees keep coming to form subsequent crops. Crop-trees-to-be-left-for-later-harvest is probably the most accurately descriptive term, although admittedly cumbersome.

Selecting trees to be removed. Any trees in the canopy which are not crop-trees-to-be-left can be removed in the thinning process, but if removing all of these makes too-wide holes in the canopy (ones that would not close in, say, five to ten years), only some of the trees should be removed at one thinning. Otherwise the crop-trees-to-be-left would become overly widespreading. Culls (p. 403) should be removed first. In felling, special care should be taken not to damage the crop-trees-to-be-left by felling trees into them, breaking their bark with careless attachment of chains or other tackle, or hitting them with machinery (see *Felling,* p. 412).

When the first thinning is in young woods, a subsequent thinning or thinnings should be made when crowns again come in contact.

Thinning from beneath. Some trees fall behind in growth, their tops just reaching into the bottom of the canopy. These suppressed trees are skinnier than the dominant ones, although they may be of the same age (as revealed by counting seasonal rings). Removing them, while not necessarily beneficial to the crop-trees-to-be-left, utilizes them before they are lost to decay and gets them out of the way for the felling of the dominant trees and for the growth of younger trees. Their removal is called "thinning from beneath." It is important not to confuse such suppressed trees of declining growth with shade-tolerant trees just pushing up through the canopy, whose best years are ahead of them.

Thinning by girdling or planticiding. Normally thinning is by felling, which yields harvestable products such as posts, poles, or firewood. Where the expected yield is less than the investment of labor for felling, the trees may be left standing but eliminated from competition through killing by girdling or planticiding (pp. 399, 400).

Thinning very young growth. Because competition starts early, attention may well be given to selecting crop-trees-to-be-left when they are only saplings (or in a nursery, seedlings). Young people especially, at home, school, or camp, can have the fun and beneficial experience of selecting and helping potentially valuable plants in youthful stages. They may not be able to handle a power chain saw; but a five-year-old can thin seedlings with hand clippers, a nine-year-old can use loppers to thin older saplings, and a twelve-year-old with a pruning saw or a small bow saw can make a vast improvement in a pole-sized stand. Let them help, and be themselves helped to appreciate our natural resources. Ideally, a young person should grow up with his or her own woodlot.

RELEASING

Some promising trees and shrubs are imprisoned by neighbors which overshade them. *Releasing* gives desirable plants a new lease on life by removing taller ones which are suppressing them. The ones removed to let light in on those being released should be used in any way possible, as saw timber, pulp, or firewood, for example. In cases where they may not be worth the cost of removal, they can be killed by girdling or planticiding and left standing, their dead and leafless branches admitting enough light for the plants released. These dead trees are not useless; they will be utilized by many kinds of wildlife for homes and food as they decay, (p. 463). Shade-intolerant plants are more obviously benefited than shade-tolerant ones. Blueberries, for instance, may start fruiting again if they have not been suppressed too long before being released.

FELLING TREES

Should you?   Many treelands suffer from the inability or unwillingness of people to cut down trees. While of course some woods are best left natural, others can be vastly improved by careful culling, thinning, or harvesting, or by cutting out trees to shape the woods — sculpture which involves working with a living medium. There are thus two arts involved in felling: deciding what to carve out of the woods and skillful use of tools to accomplish a tree's removal. In these arts, one needs all the science he can get.

When you are sure that a tree needs to be felled, to improve the environment, supply needed materials, or give fun and exercise, decide whether you yourself can safely fell it or whether an expert is needed. Don't forget that the sharp tools required and the tremendous weight of trees can be very dangerous, creating hazards which only an expert can foresee — and even he will sometimes be in for uncomfortable surprises. Practice first on small trees away from buildings, wires, cars, etc. Don't chop alone. Wear a safety hat (hard hat). Keep your tools in good repair. Don't chop when tired or in failing light.

Seasons for felling.   Felling deciduous trees when they are leafless makes the removed branches ("brush" or "slash") easier to handle because they are lighter and not so unsightly and flammable when dried. Cooler weather is more comfortable for chopping and sawing. Farmers and gardeners usually do their felling in the non-growing season because they are not so busy with cultivated crops. However, if logs or poles are to be de-barked to increase their durability, trees should be felled in late spring or early summer when the bark peels ("slips") most readily.

Direction of fall.   Carefully check all the following factors for safety and efficiency: (1) where the falling tree will cause the least damage; (2) where the fallen tree can be most conveniently trimmed

FACTORS INFLUENCING DIRECTION OF FALL →

Lean   Crown   Wind   Interior   Feller's
        lopsided   rot   notch

(good footing, minimum of small trees and bushes); (3) rough ground which might damage the trunk; and (4) direction in which wood and slash are to be moved, to shorten haul.

After deciding where *you* want the tree to fall, consider where *nature* wants it to fall. Does the tree lean some other way so that it will be too difficult to throw in the desired direction? Even a slight lean of a tree too large to push can cause great difficulty and danger. Does the tree have a lopsided crown, with most of the branches creating one-sided weight which will influence the fall? Is there wind which would affect the direction of fall? Is there heart rot at the height of the proposed cut, perhaps off center? If there is any question of the tree misbehaving, leave it for an expert or take good precautions using the following.

Rope.—Fasten a strong rope to the tree, as high up the trunk as possible. Run it in the desired direction of fall well beyond the expected distance it will fall, and pull on it or have a helper pull on it when the tree is cut to the hinge (see below). More (and safer) tension on the rope results from running it through a pulley and tugging from the opposite direction (non-fall side) well beyond the zone of possible fall or butt jump. Or after tying the rope to the base of a tree beyond the line of fall, fasten another rope to the first rope's middle and pull it sideways from a safe distance. The more the first rope is bent, the less mechanical advantage and control of direction, so it helps to have another person keep snugging up on the far end of the first rope if the tree is hard to pull over.

Push-pole.—Use a straight pole with a strong fork which can be placed at least at a 45-degree angle as high on the tree as possible. Push against the base of a strong, live branch to exert leverage at exactly the right moment to induce and guide the fall. A push-pole

STARTING THE FALL

Forked Push-pole   Rope   Sledge & Wedge

cannot be used safely on larger trees. Professionals sometimes use a metal-tipped "pike pole" to stab into the tree for pushing.

Sledge and wedge. — Use sledgehammers and wedges on large trees, driving them in behind the saw to keep the kerf (crack) from binding; or, drive them in after removing the saw when the cut has reached the hinge. Three wedges are often needed, two being needed to effect removal of the third in case it needs to be relocated. With power saws, use only soft-metal wedges or homemade hardwood wedges, in case they touch the blade. Never drive wedges with an axe if you value the axe; always use a sledge or heavy block of wood. If the saw has been withdrawn, always set it at a safe distance before driving wedges. Avoid using wedges on trees with dangerous dead limbs or top which hammering might dislodge so they fall on you.

Preparing the space. Clear out of the way any unwanted smaller trees and brush. Trimming lower branches from the tree to be felled will minimize the damage to desirable trees to be saved. Around buildings or wires, it is wise to cut off upper branches or the whole top, and lower them by ropes before felling the trunk. In a close stand of young straight trees like pines or spruces there may be no room for the crown to fall. If such a tree is light enough to be lifted at the base after severance, the direction of fall is best determined as opposite to where the butt can most easily be dragged. The crown thus ends up near the stump, having fallen straight down through the opening created by cutting the tree.

Axe or saw? A saw is almost always the more efficient tool; it wastes less time and wood than an axe; it leaves a flatter stump than most axemen can make; it is safer. However, if it is dull, incorrectly sharpened, or poorly set, one might as well use one's own teeth! An axe is better for cutting saplings, at least when a slanting or V-shaped stump is not objectionable. Never allow sharp stumps in areas for active recreation. An axe is more fun for most people, each stroke being a test of skill. It is, however, much more dangerous than a handsaw.

Power saw or handsaw?   A power saw in the hands of a skilled operator accomplishes wonders. It is very dangerous, however. (Power saws, of all kinds, account for more accidents than any other tool.) Never use a power saw until you have a great deal of practice with handsaws. Using hand tools makes you more sensitive to the natural problems involved in any job; in sawing, for instance, it gives you a chance to feel the binding of the blade which forewarns of the tree's falling and gives you more time to consider what is happening and what to do about it.

Handsaws.   Bow saws with tubular frames (modern versions of the old wood-framed bucksaw) are usually best for amateur felling and cutting up. They cannot cut through such large trees as can a two-man crosscut saw, but they are safer and easier to handle. A coarse-toothed straight pruning saw (push type) or even a coarse-toothed carpenter's crosscut saw can be used where only one or two small trees are involved.

Height of cut.   Stumps should be cut low to provide minimum waste of wood and more pleasing aspect, except: (1) where people might trip over a low stump; (2) when a stump is to be pulled out and more height gives a better place for attaching the chain for exerting leverage against the roots; (3) when the stump is to be used as a base for a birdbath, feeding tray, planter, or stool; and (4) when the stump serves as a buffer to restrain cars, as a fence post, or as a base for attaching a flagpole. On a tree with flaring bole (base of trunk), the bulging portions can be cut off prior to felling, to permit a low cut and yield a maximum length of straight-sided log.

Undercutting (notching).   (Not necessary for small trees when a companion with push-pole or rope is available.) *The first cut should be:* (1) at the height of the stump to be left; (2) horizontal; (3) at right angles to the desired direction of fall; (4) on the fall side of the tree; and (5) straight, not cutting back farther on either side than in the middle. This cut is much easier to make with a saw than with an axe. It should extend about a third of the way through the tree, or deeper if the tree is leaning in the direction of fall (to minimize premature splitting when making the final cut).

The second cut is also on the fall side, above the first, slanting down to meet it in a straight line at its inner edge. It takes skill to start the second saw cut so that it will end up exactly at the inner edge of the first cut. The intervening chunk is knocked out on completion of the second cut. With small trees, this can be chipped away with an axe about as easily as it can be sawn.

Felling. The third is the last cut but should *not* cut the tree down. It starts on the non-fall side 1 to 3 inches higher than the first cut. It should usually be horizontal and like the first cut should be at right angles to the desired direction of fall, hence parallel to the first cut. Do *not* extend this cut to reach the first cut. A uniformly thick piece of vertical wood should remain between the two cuts as a *hinge*, to control the direction of fall and to minimize the chances of the butt jumping off the stump.

FELLING

#2   #1
FOR SAPLINGS:
2-CUT METHOD

#3   #2
      #1
      Remove
      notch
LARGER TREES
3-CUT METHOD

Always leave a hinge
to prevent butt-jump

Hinge

This hinge is tremendously important; your life may depend on it. The big question always is, how thick should it be? Since every tree is different, there can be no stock answer. Careful experience is the best teacher. Stop cutting before the hinge is too thin! Do not *cut* the tree down! Cut it so far that it can be pushed down by a push-pole or wedges, or pulled down by a rope considerably longer than the tree is tall. If the hinge is too thick, this may be difficult or impossible. It is always disconcerting to remove the saw, drive in the wedges, and then have the tree refuse to fall. (Where the radius of the tree is considerably more than the length of the wedges, the wedges can follow the saw, which then need not be removed.) If the hinge is too thin, the tree may fall prematurely with jumping butt, flying splinters, and crashing branches. This is extra hazardous if you have misjudged the direction of expected fall. Remember that a tree with decayed center may provide only a minimum hinge at the outside and therefore fall before you expect it to. Don't take chances! Better to have too thick a hinge, which can be tested and then made thinner, than too thin a hinge, permitting premature falling.

To be prepared for all eventualities, be sensitive to any pinching or opening of the third cut which may indicate sway of the tree. It helps to have somebody else watching the crown to note any suspicious motion and to signal it immediately. If you are using a power saw, the signal must be visual, because of the noise. Always have your feet balanced under you so that you can jump and run. Know in advance where you can run without tripping; if working in pairs, each of you should know where the other person expects to run so that you don't collide. Abandon your tool in an emergency. But make every effort to avoid emergencies. If you must run, do it with care, not panic. Make sure that others are at a safe distance, remembering that the danger zone is not just under the falling trunk but also extends beyond the spread of the branches, which may even fell other trees like cards in a card house. Play it safe or leave felling to experts.

Cutting up.   Normally all limbs are removed from a felled tree by *limbing* or *lopping*. Start at the butt end by the stump and trim toward the crown; an axe is the preferred tool unless the limbs are large enough to make a saw more practical. Occasionally the smaller power saws are used for heavy limbing when one can work from the ground. Climbing fallen trees with a power saw is excessively dangerous. Never chop off limbs on the same side of the trunk that your legs are on. Remove the branches on the top and far side, then go to the other side and cut off the remaining ones, or roll the log over, or both. This may seem a long way to do it, but it is shorter than a trip to the hospital. Always chop toward the top of the tree. With large trees, a skilled axeman can work standing on the trunk, but this is extra hazardous.

Good footwork is essential for all axing; plant your feet carefully and never swing until you are well balanced. Don't walk blithely along the trunk whacking at branches. When limbing, keep slashed branches thrust aside in an organized fashion. Don't work close to anybody else. After a large limb has been cut off, a companion may drag it by its tip to a safe distance to trim it.

Be fussy about lopping smooth with the trunk. Sharp stubs are dangerous when logs or firewood are being handled, and they prevent close stacking in the woodshed. Keep different kinds and sizes of wood sorted and stacked carefully to expedite future handling and to conserve wood.

A good way to limb a tree with a team of inexperienced young people is to start them at the periphery of the crown in pairs, one using loppers to cut off branches four to six feet long, the other stacking the branches neatly (see *Handling Cut Brush*, p. 426). Then let them rest and watch a demonstration of how to chop and saw the larger branches. They can then take turns "bucking" into sections the main limbs and trunk with saws, or possibly they can be taught chopping, *one at a time.*

When cutting up a felled tree, consider carefully how the wood can best be used. It is wasteful to burn it just to get rid of it.

Saw logs—If logs are suitable for lumber, make advance arrangements with a sawyer, with the aid of a government or private forester; then cut the logs to give maximum length and minimum curve, working around poor spots.

Logs not for lumber—Straight logs eight to twelve inches in diameter are useful as risers in trails. Cut them long enough to extend well beyond the tread of the trail. Remove bark to minimize rotting and treat with preservative. When the log is large enough, the top may be hewn flat with axe or adz to make a safer step. Logs twelve inches or more in diameter make good seats for wayside benches and council rings. For the latter, diagonal cuts alternating with straight cuts give seats which can be put together slightly angled to face center, with square ends on aisles. Remove bark and treat log with preservative for durability. Don't sit on pitchy species until they have dried adequately, sometimes a year or more. Logs twelve inches and up can be used for bump-logs and posts in parking areas. Short sections of stout logs can be used for chopping blocks, individual benches, and tables; for supports for birdbaths, feeders, and planters; and for steps in trails.

Poles—Straight saplings or tops of larger trees may be used for fence rails, woven fences, and hedges; poles for flags, birdboxes, or tents; rustic furniture; clothes driers; spars for boats; or corduroy road in wet places. Cut them for maximum length. In recreation areas, short lengths of green wood are useful for camp crafts; cut some so that they have a fork at the end for campfire cranes, rope beds, rustic tables, and the like.

Posts—Straight pieces six to eight feet long and four to twelve inches in diameter at the base should be considered for posts, especially if they are of one of the species most durable in contact with the soil (arborvitae, baldcypress, eastern redcedar, black locust, Osage-orange, catalpa, and white oak). Many other species make good posts if treated with wood preservative. For electric fences, thinner posts (down to two-inch diameter) may suffice. In cutting posts, remember that about two and a half feet is usually set in the ground; allow accordingly. Because slanting tops shed water better than flat, alternating diagonal cuts and right-angle cuts along a long trunk will give several posts which do not need shaping later. All wood to be in contact with soil should have the bark removed to retard rotting as soon as possible after felling. Bark peels (slips) much more readily when tree growth is most active in spring and early summer; so plan most harvesting of posts for these seasons.

Cordwood—Short lengths of wood for pulp (four feet) and firewood (four feet, a meter, two feet, eighteen inches, or other) should be neatly stacked with an even, vertical face, preferably across two poles to keep the bottom sticks off the ground with its rot-promoting moisture. A *cord* is the most commonly used unit of measurement in America. A *standard cord* is a pile 4' × 4' × 8', neatly stacked to give minimum air space and maximum wood. Crooked pieces make more air spaces and lower the value of the cord. A *face cord* has firewood which is shorter than 4 feet but is stacked 4 feet high and 8 feet long as in a standard cord. A *long cord* has sticks longer than four feet.

Faggots—Pieces under two-inch diameter can be stacked in cords with larger sticks; they make the pile more solid. Often, however, they will be in shorter lengths or crooked so that it is better to handle them separately. When piled neatly, they provide a fine supply of faggots for campfires. Those up to at least an inch and a half can be cut with compound-leverage loppers; cut the larger ones a bit on the diagonal, when green. Or cut them with an axe across a stump or a chopping block made of a thick section of trunk. Many people think it is a waste of time to utilize these smaller pieces, and possibly it is where wood is inexpensive and labor is not. But remember that time spent harvesting small sticks reduces time spent handling brush, and results in a neat job. Besides, in small doses such work is good medicine with a sweet taste, more satisfying than an exercising machine.

Brush—Twigs small enough to produce leaves are termed *brush* (sometimes called *slash*, but this may include the coarser branches). Brush is often a problem because it looks bad, gets in the way of operations, or is a fire hazard. However, it also has many uses which should be considered before it is disposed of wastefully (see p. 426).

Stumps—If the stump is removed (p. 424), it can be used for a stump fence; for a chopping block, the spreading root bases giving steadiness; or for fuel. When cutting up a stump, use an *old axe*, because stones sometimes become buried in the wood as the upper roots grow around them. If the stump is to remain, consider whether it will sprout. Many hardwoods will sprout, notably maple, chestnut, elm, ash, oak, basswood, catalpa, and black locust. To deter sprouting, spray with one of the modern planticides such as 2, 4-D or 2, 4, 5-T or a mixture thereof, commercially available under various proprietary names (p. 400). Sprouts are desirable in certain cases: they create cover close to the ground and browse for wildlife, form a wind barrier at the edge of a woods, supply toasting sticks ("supper suckers") near an outdoor fireplace (when cut on a sustained-yield basis), keep people or stock off an eroding area, and add beauty. In Europe, managing sprouts is called *coppicing*. A coppice of sprouting stumps provides thin stems for laying hedges and a supply of kindling which does not have to be split. Sometimes sprouts carefully thinned will grow into commercially valuable shoots useful for specialty products such as tool handles, for poles, fuel, and wood for chemicals; and occasionally, preferably with pruning, they can grow into harvestable sawtimber.

Certain species are worth special consideration. Pitch pine, unlike most softwoods, will sometimes sprout when young if cut in the spring and will create a beautiful groundcover which stays low and evergreen for many years to protect sandy soils. Other evergreens, though they do not sprout, can be kept alive if there are several live branches close to the ground which can be left undamaged while the trunk is cut off just above them. Young open-grown white pine, for instance, bushes out beautifully when so cut. With care, a succession of little Christmas trees can thus be produced by one stump.

Roots—While felling a tree does not normally dig up the roots, they may be available where stumps are removed. Normally they are useless things to practical humans, but don't overlook an opportunity to enjoy sassafras tea or other root concoctions of a frontier sort *(192, 213)*. Some roots are useful for primitive cordage or dyes. Stumps with roots make excellent stump fences. Small stumps carefully dug and set in the sun to bleach make "driftwood" ornaments beautiful in themselves or attractive for planters or lamp bases.

Bark—Bark is a by-product of peeling logs, posts, or poles; finding a use for it is challenging. Indians and pioneers made rope from braiding inner bark of hemlock, aspen, basswood, elm, and other species. Barks of certain oaks and hemlock have been commercially important for producing tannin. Sheets of bark were used to cover pole frames for certain types of Indian shelters. Slippery elm bark has been used for medicine. Paper birch helped shape the history of North America by contributing the bark canoes of the explorers and early traders. Today, shredded bark of cedar, pine, and redwood is used for fancy mulching of paths in woods and gardens. In European forests, bark is sometimes carefully stacked to use as fuel. When trees are felled near playgrounds, camps, or schools, bark can be used by the children to learn nature crafts. Otherwise it can be left broadcast (spread out) or laid across trails as mulch, or can be stacked out of the way to rot or be burned if unsightly or a fire hazard.

Wood chips and sawdust—These by-products are often left at the site of cutting as a meagre return to the producing soil. They are valuable mulch for gardens (p. 340) and playgrounds in heavily used recreational areas. Both are used in animal husbandry for bedding. Minor uses of sawdust include lightening plaster of Paris in models, absorbing spilled liquids, insulating ice at camps, stuffing in taxidermy, and packing breakables for shipment. Remember that dry chips and sawdust can create a severe fire hazard.

Wood-using industries utilize chips and sawdust for fuel, with special burners to contribute a forced draft, and for various chemical and mechanical treatments to create synthetic products. Write for information to Forest Products Laboratory, U.S. Forest Service, Madison, Wisconsin, or to American Forest Products Industries *(71, 170, 406)*.

CLEARING LAND

Clearing land means removing something to increase the value of the land or to improve neighboring land by providing an open space or view. Boulders, flood-deposited gravel, or perhaps cultural debris such as ramshackle buildings or old beer bottles may need to be removed. But usually our first thought, rightly or wrongly, is removal of trees and shrubs. As with all conservation practices, we should first inventory the existing resources and *then* develop plans for improved use, trying to use to advantage as many as possible of the existing resources. Make sure you know the value of whatever you plan to remove! All too often woods are completely cleared to make a parking lot (p. 24) or a house site when a little careful planning could have saved at least a few trees for shade, beauty, and wildlife. Sometimes a few big old trees are saved without any middle-aged or young trees to replace them later—regrettable negligence.

Marking area to be cleared. Tie strips of white or brightly colored cloth or plastic to trees or bushes at margins of areas to be left, or set conspicuous stakes. Then walk these bounds with the person in charge of clearing. Make sure it is understood that bonfires must not be close to these margins and that machinery is not to be driven or parked beyond these limits unless by special arrangement.

Protecting trees to be spared. Where isolated trees are to be saved and surrounding trees removed, avoid sun-scald of trunks. Leave as many live branches as possible to shade remaining trees. For thin-barked trees, wrap the lower trunk with asphaltum-impregnated paper to shade it until the tree has time to adapt to its modified environment. Avoid unnecessary compaction by machinery of soil under trees to be saved. Branches located so as to be susceptible to breakage by tall machines such as cement-mixers should be pruned beforehand (p. 439). Erect temporary protective fences to safeguard trees and other valuable resources if there is to be construction or grading by machinery.

Before removing trees. If possible, plan to use the wood from trees or find a market for it, asking help from a government or private forester in writing the contract and supervising the cutting (if it is done by the buyer or a third party). Also consider transplanting valuable shrubs or herbs ("wildflowers," ferns, etc.) which might be used around your house or at a local school or park. Sometimes a school class can make an educationally valuable project of transplanting them.

Removing trees. See *Felling Trees*, p. 411.

Removing brush. "Brush" is a term often used to signify unwanted shrubs and/or small trees or sprouts. It may occur as native shrubland, as brush which has invaded a field or right-of-way, as understory in treelands, or as planted shrubbery.

Cutting brush—Cutting seldom kills brush, for many species sprout rapidly and thickly. So while in a sense cutting brush will remove it, the removal is usually only temporary, often a waste of time unless one wants it thicker (as indeed one may in a hedge), or unless one wants the cut brush.

Loppers are best for selective cutting of brush in recreational areas or clear-cutting relatively small areas. One good lopperman can keep ahead of at least one stacker. Good lopping leaves low, flat stumps. Where leaving sharp stumps is no hazard, various styles of "brush-hooks" or "bill hooks" may be used by skilled adults, but they are too dangerous for children. Hatchets and axes are inefficient, hazardous, and easily knicked; they should not be used for brush. For extensive clearing, portable gasoline-powered rotary blades do a fast and clean job; they can be either swung at the end of a shoulder-hung pole or pushed on wheels. Ordinarily mowing machines can cut light brush. Brush growth is sometimes set back several years by chopping and uprooting with an Athens disk pulled by a 35 hp crawler-tractor. In the southwestern United States, monstrous tractor-drawn weighted drums with sharp blades triturate unwanted brush in large-scale operations of so-called range reclamation.

Burning brush as it stands—Burning standing brush effectively controls a few species such as juniper in a pasture, but it often stimulates sprouting or growth of other species which may be undesirable. Wild blackberries, for instance, thrive on burned-over ground (see *Prescribed Burning*, p. 431); and they may or may not be desired.

Uprooting brush—Pulling up by the roots gives more complete eradication, although root fragments may sprout unless the ground is cultivated afterward. Hand-pulling of lightly rooted plants may be arduous, but it works well for small areas, such as trails, where cut stumps would create hazards. Use work gloves and pull by straightening your legs while keeping your back upright. With a horse or tractor, chains and brush-pulling hooks can be used effectively on heavier brush. For combination root-cutting and pulling use a grub hoe, or a mattock for heavier-rooted plants. For extensive areas, a bulldozer with blade or brushrake does an unexcelled job. Although these machines cannot be expected to be selective, a skilled operator can work around patches of brush to be left and can even do considerable transplanting of shrubs and small trees by underdigging them and sliding them with soil still around their roots, especially if the soil is clayey and moist. Tag in advance specimens to be saved or moved; then be on hand to give directions (you will have to use prearranged sign language once the bulldozer's motor starts). Realizing how much a bulldozer costs an hour, you may hesitate to slow down operations by giving directions; but an hour so spent may give one's planting plan a fifteen-year head start. (If you have no plans, send the bulldozer home; you are not ready for clearing!)

Poisoning brush—Hormonal planticides such as 2, 4-D and/or 2, 4, 5-T give most effective killing, including root-killing, but they do not remove the brush. Dead brush, however, may not present a problem, because it gradually disintegrates. For complete and permanent clearing, it may be destroyed by controlled burning as it stands, when dry, by uprooting when dead, or by cutting while still alive (p. 422).

Browsing brush—Intensive browsing by fenced or tethered goats does a good job of brush removal; over-extended, it can cause soil erosion.

Removing stumps.   For uses, see *Stumps* (p. 419). Stumps can be a headache. If not too inimicable to the planned land use, leave them

Carefully shaped and finished oak planking adds years of use to the stump of a felled tree. Colonial Williamsburg, Virginia.

and enjoy them, admiring the beautiful fungi and insects which will eventually remove them for you, helpfully creating humus in the slow but sure process. Often a stump makes a fine bench or planter for several years.

Removal by digging—This is as challenging as it is difficult. Dig away enough soil to give access to the roots, using a sharp, round-pointed shovel. In stony ground a pickaxe may be necessary, or even a crowbar. Where soil is compacted or with many small roots, use a mattock with obtusely sharp blades to loosen soil. As roots are exposed, cut with loppers those under about an inch and a half diameter. Use an old axe or mattock for the larger roots, keeping it sharpened somewhat obtusely, sharpening edges of stone-caused nicks rather than trying to grind away nicks altogether. Power digging by excavating with a bulldozer is quick but may tear up a sizable area. Undercutting with a special shearing blade designed for heavy equipment is one of the newer techniques and disturbs less soil.

Removal by digging and pulling on the tree—A prying action, using the trunk as a lever, helps uncover or break roots. Therefore, small trees whose stumps are to be removed are often best felled by digging them up before severing the trunk from the stump, unconventional as this may seem. Use a rope, preferably with block and tackle, attached as high on the tree as possible. After one or more roots are cut on the non-fall side, pulling on the tree may pry out the rest as it falls. Make sure that the rope is long enough to keep the operator out of danger from the falling tree or other trees which it may knock down or break. A truck or tractor may be used for the pulling. Professional arborists use a winch with an A-shaped support on the rear of a heavy truck.

Removal by pulling—Small stumps can sometimes be pulled by hand after some roots have been cut, or with the help of a mechanical stump-puller. Various contrivances involving levers, block and tackle, or hand winch can be used. It helps to leave stumps about four or more feet tall and fasten the pulling chain near the top, for leverage.

Removal by drilling—Some professional arborists and park departments have power drills designed for diminishing stumps. These cannot be expected to remove large horizontal roots. Any wood drill used carefully and often enough can hasten the demise of a stump; any cavities which hold moisture hasten rot.

Removal by burning—An old trick is to drill inch-wide holes in the fresh stump and fill them with saltpeter. A year later, brush is stacked over the stump and burned. For best results, a stump furnace is made from two open-ended drums on top of each other, placed on the stump with a blower at the base to create a forced draft. Burning is often undesirable in recreational areas because residual carbon may soil clothing.

Removal by digging and burning—Dig a slanting ditch to and away from the stump in line with the prevailing wind, low enough to go under the center of the stump (if no taproot) or under major side roots, and kindle a fire. In porous soil, guard against fire spreading along roots and starting a ground fire. (See *Burning cut brush*, p. 427).

Removal by dynamiting—Dynamiting should be done only by

trained and licensed persons. Powder is less used since powerful tractors and bulldozers have been developed. It is oftenest employed in sites difficult for these machines to reach.

Removing stones.   See *Moving Rocks*, p. 325.

Removing herbs.   Herbs are non-woody plants such as grasses, wildflowers, and ferns. If no large woody plants are present, the herbs may be plowed under to create bare ground, burned (p. 431), or poisoned (p. 400). Such complete removal of vegetative cover may create serious problems of soil stabilization so that hard-topping and drains or special soil conservation practices may be necessary. Wherever possible, keep herbaceous cover.

Removing litter.   Unfortunately this is a most commonplace and necessary form of clearing. (p. 318)

HANDLING CUT BRUSH

Brush accumulates from felling, clearing, and pruning operations, often posing problems of fire hazard or disorderliness. While burning is sometimes the best procedure, one should first consider various possible uses.

Uses of brush.   These include the following: brush fences and hedges; horse jumps; brush dams; mulching for erosion control; wildlife shelters; screens for observation hides; kindling for campfires; chips, made by chipping machines for mulch or stock bedding; supports for peas and other vines; protection of seeded lawns; and crafts.

Stacking brush.   Except when immediately to be broadcast (spread out) for mulching (p. 340) or fed to a chipping machine (see *Wood Chips*, p. 420), brush should be neatly stacked to facilitate handling and reduce fire hazard and disorder.

Location of piles—Small piles of no more than armful size should be made while you cut, within a couple of steps of the cutting. They should be far enough away from the trunk of a felled tree not to be underfoot when you are bucking it into sections. Keep the piles distinct from one another so that they do not intertangle when one is picked up. When clearing a road from which brush will be trucked out, stack brush at right angles to the road along its edge to facilitate

HANDLING CUT BRUSH

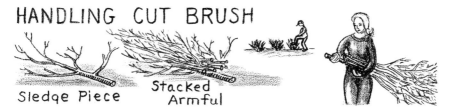

Sledge Piece   Stacked Armful

passage and loading, but keep brush back from any ditch. For subsequent piling for burning, see *Burning brush* (p. 427).

Sledge piece and piling—The bottom branch of the pile, called the *sledge piece*, forms a base on which the pile is dragged or carried. It should be carefully chosen to be flat and as wide as the finished pile. Point it with the butt in the direction the pile will be moved, or if along a road or trail at right angles thereto, with the butts toward it. Succeeding pieces are flicked down on the sledge bough with butts pointing the same way but back six inches so that the sledge butt protrudes as a visible handle. Keep the pile compact, stepping on it if necessary.

Size of piles—The length of the pieces will depend somewhat upon the type of material and upon whether faggots are being cut off. Sometimes it pays to make an extra cut in the branches to shorten the pile for easier handling, especially when children are to move it. Keep piles small enough to put one arm around near the butt end while the other hand grasps the butt of the sledge piece.

Separating species—Where thorny or poisonous species are involved, stack them separately. Plants with markedly different growth form are also best piled separately; uniform piles are easier to handle. And having them sorted may be useful when certain kinds are to be used for special purposes, for instance evergreen boughs for mulching under broad-leaved evergreen shrubs and hardwood branches for supporting garden peas.

Burning cut brush. When brush creates too big a hazard left broadcast, neatly piled, or chipped, and when it cannot be disposed of more usefully, it should be carefully burned. Be sure to obtain a permit from the authorized persons in your locality whenever local ordinances so require. Ask your local fire department and air pollution control officers, if any. Common sense requires that the fire be kept under control at all times and be completely out before it is left.

Site for burning cut brush — Select a spot with minimum flammable material, preferably bare mineral soil. In a garden, untraveled dirt road, or beach, first dig a shallow hole the size of the fire so that (unused) ashes may be buried. It helps to have a road, bare garden, body of water, or rock outcrop on the downwind side. Where there is no bare spot, carefully burn one out for a distance considerably greater than the size of the fire. Keep fire well away from trees, overhead as well as alongside, especially under evergreens or deciduous trees in leaf. The steady draft of warm air rises and dries out the leaves and twigs; this killing action may not show up for days or even weeks. Many people ruin their prized ornamental plants by burning too close to them.

When the site of the fire has been prepared, place the brush in distinct armful-sized piles in concentric semi-circles on what you expect will be the upwind side during burning weather, at a safe distance beyond the reach of sparks should the wind veer. DON'T make one big pile in the center of the area, where the fire will be built; this space should be left open until kindling (see below).

Small quantities of brush in suburbs are best burned in incinerators, where these are allowed, after being reduced to small pieces with loppers. Cover the incinerator or stay by it until the brush is burned. If laws prevent incineration, bundle the brush for removal with trash, facing the branches to both right and left.

Weather for burning cut brush — Snow on the ground is ideal (unless you have left the brush broadcast instead of piling it). Fire hazard is greater when weather is warmer, windier, and drier. Fires often get out of control on the first warm days of spring when people are burning with the same precautions they used safely on preceding cooler days. Early morning and evening are usually safer than midday. Don't try to burn during dry spells, even though rain seems imminent. Really wet days are best; the added safety is worth the extra work of kindling. A fire well started can withstand light rain. If weather becomes hazardous, put the fire out at once.

Kindling — Finely divided material with plenty of *small* air spaces makes good kindling. Fine, dry sticks criss-crossed, close together but leaving air spaces, or arranged tepee fashion are laid on tinder of crumpled newspaper, dry grass, dry leaves, or the like, in the center of the fire site. In wet weather give temporary protection from rain with a sheet of cardboard or bark. Kerosene poured over this kindling *before ignition* insures starting. NEVER USE GASOLINE! Its highly volatile fumes, invisibly surrounding the pourer, may ignite or flash back to the container and explode it. For burning large quantities of brush in wet weather, an old tire shoe soaked with kerosene maintains a hot fire (but gives off volumes of black smoke). DON'T kindle a large brush pile by stuffing newspaper under one side and lighting it. One has almost no control over such a fire and cannot gauge how long it will take to burn out. Most fires left burning when people had to leave were started in piles that were too large and therefore did not burn up completely while supervision was available.

Feeding—Add brush to the kindling when it is hot enough not to be extinguished by the added cooler wood. Don't smother the fire by putting on too much at a time. Maintain plenty of spaces for air. When the fire is hot enough, throw on one armful-size pile at a time, lining it up with the preceding sticks on the fire; this alignment makes it easier to keep the diameter of the fire small and to extinguish it. Do not wear floppy clothing in which the brush may catch as it is thrown on the fire. Wrist watches are apt to get caught and should be stowed in a buttoned pocket or left home. Neat stacking pays off during the feeding. Often one person can keep two or more fires burning if there is a safe site and the brush has been well piled. Keep the fire(s) small.

Emergency tools—Unless wildfire danger is nonexistent, as with snow cover, have fire-fighting tools on hand and know how to use them.

Extinguishing fires—The safest way to extinguish a bonfire or campfire is to burn up completely all the combustible material and then to cool down the ashes and adjacent soil. Make sure that there is no chance of heat from the ashes kindling surrounding vegetation (roots as well as shoots), or dried leaves which might blow across the fire site. This is one reason for keeping fires small at all times—so that you can gauge how much can be burned completely before you have to leave. Stop feeding the fire early enough to allow all the brush to be consumed. DON'T count on a pail of water to finish off a bonfire. The hot ashes or a couple of charred logs may easily evaporate the water, being only temporarily cooled thereby, and then heat up again to their kindling point.

As the fire burns down, use a long green forked stick to push unburned butts and tips to the hot center. When even these have burned to coals, you should stay until they have been further burned to ashes by occasionally being stirred to admit air to all pieces. Wood ashes, rich in potash, make valuable fertilizer for lawns and leafy cultivated crops. The ashes should be used before being rained on, because the potassium leaches out fast.

Another method, quicker but less complete, is to rake the embers back and forth, keeping them well within the burned site, to expose them to cooling air so that they are extinguished without being entirely ashed. Use a green stick with one or two feet of a branch base left at the tip; or an iron garden rake kept cool, by dippings in a water bucket, so it will not lose the temper of its metal in the heat. If copious water is available, deluge the coals. If there has not been enough time to burn all heavier wood, roll each piece over so that all sides and cavities are soaked. Leave pieces separate from each other so that they cannot share heat and rekindle.

When you have only a limited water supply, *sprinkle* the coals or ashes to cool them completely while stirring them to expose all hot embers. Wet down vegetation around the edge of the burned spot. When you can hold your hand on the fire site, all over and down inside, the fire is *out*.

Don't be deluded into thinking that a buried fire, with cool earth on top, is out. This ostrich-head-in-sand concept can start ground fires. To be sure, moist earth can have a cooling-and-smothering effect that helps extinguish fires, but it can also insulate a fire from cooling air and keep it smouldering for days; it may pop up later as a monster.

The above lengthy procedures seem shorter when mixed with toasted marshmallows, baked apples, and singing. Festivities or not, somebody must stay until the fire is *out*.

PEELING LOGS

Removing bark from logs makes them more durable, especially where they will be in contact with soil, because bark holds moisture which benefits the fungi and other organisms which cause rot. Make wood last as long as possible after sacrificing a tree and investing the labor of harvesting it. Treating with preservatives after peeling is also recommended for posts, trail risers, and any other wood which will be in contact with soil. Although the wood of certain species such as catalpa, chestnut, redcedar, and black locust is very durable, even these will serve longer if peeled and treated with chemicals.

Season. In late spring and early summer when growth is active, the cambium (the microscopically thin cylinder of tissue between wood and bark) is full of sap and therefore breaks easily; thus the bark "slips" easily. This is the season for "sap peeling." An axe cut or slash across the top of the fallen log enables one to start sideways peeling down around the trunk.

Tools. The tool used for sap peeling is usually a homemade *spud*, with which the bark is pried off, although a small job can be done with an axe or hatchet. If sheets of bark are to be saved, circular cuts around the trunk should be made before spudding. In seasons when the bark does not slip, tight bark is removed with a carpenter's *drawshave*, or better, a *timbershave*, which is heavier, curved, and with handles at a better angle. Since pulling these tools upwards facilitates peeling, lift one end of a long trunk onto another log; then straddle the one to be peeled. Bolts (four-foot lengths for pulp) are peeled on a shaving horse which has one pair of legs shorter.

Uses of peeled bark. See *Bark*, p. 420.

PRESCRIBED BURNING

Controlled burning of primarily uncut vegetation to improve ecological conditions for certain purposes is sometimes recommended. Control of the fire is, of course, imperative to avoid wildfire which would create adverse ecological conditions. Although this technique has been used for centuries, there is still much experimentation and evaluation to be done; it is never a technique to use without careful thought and planning.

Disadvantages. Prescribed burning may turn into wildfire if a human error is made—and such errors are made. Most people are blissfully unaware of how complicated burning conditions can be. Fire may not have the expected effect on vegetation, because of unnoticed ecological factors. Fire destroys organic matter in the soil unless careful attention is given to season, weather, condition of vegetation, amount of combustible material, rate of burning, and intensity of heat resulting from these and other factors. Destruction of organic matter in soil and of vegetation on it leave the soil exposed to erosion by wind and water, ruining the area as a watershed. Minerals released by burning may give a quick, temporary greening to vegetation but be quickly used up and/or leached away. In burning to control pests, helpful forms of wildlife (many of which might be feeding on the pests) are killed along with the pests.

Advantages.   Fire often quickly and inexpensively removes vegetation which might be prohibitively expensive to cope with otherwise. Since it has a selective action on vegetation, some species being benefited by fire, resistant to fire, or eliminated by it, fire can be used to control or develop certain types of vegetation for various purposes. Fire releases to the top layers of soil minerals which plants have derived from lower layers, making them quickly available for use by shallow-rooted species. Fire kills all but the more mobile forms of wildlife, including some insect pests.

Note: the following are only generalized prescriptions for burning. In each specific instance, local conditions must be taken into consideration and careful plans must be made with professional help from local foresters, wildlife managers, or others who have studied the effects of fire locally.

To remove flammable fire hazards—A backfire is a type of prescribed burning used *after* a wildfire has started. The same principle of removing combustible material by burning is often applied *before* a wildfire starts. Fuelbreaks, zones along roads where cigarettes might be tossed by passers or parkers, and grassy fields around buildings are the areas most often burned for this purpose. In these cases the loss of organic matter is considered less significant than the fire protection acquired. Had settlers in the chaparral of California years ago realized that wildfire was a natural component of that vegetation, they would have used controlled burning to prevent the abnormal accumulation of combustible plant material which now presents a tremendous hazard to communities in that dry climate. The situation is such that it is now too dangerous to burn in most places.

To control pests—Sometimes when insect pests build up excessive populations in weedy field borders, farmers resort to controlled burning. Some weeds are also controlled by burning.

To prune and weed blueberries—Dry hay or brush is spread over lowbush blueberries on developed blueberry lands in early spring while the ground is still wet. Ignited, the spread fuel burns just the tips of the shrubs. It destroys many weeds and animal pests as well, and releases minerals to the surface of the soil.

To promote pines—Careful burning reduces hardwood competition, prepares seedbeds, and controls some diseases among southern pines, especially in the longleaf and slash forest types. In the northeastern United States, only pitch pine can withstand burning. In the Great Lakes states, fire is sometimes used to manage jack pine.

To improve grazing—Certain woodland herbs in southern pinelands are maintained by burning and have their palatability and nutritive value increased thereby. What is good for woodland grazing, however, may well detract from the wood yield of the treeland in the long run. As with all environmental management, one must make choices (p. 144).

To create or maintain certain wildlife habitats—Burning arrests natural plant succession and tends to maintain cover closer to the ground, to favor certain food plants of some species such as deer, and to increase edge between habitats under some conditions. In the upper midwestern United States, for instance, burning is sometimes prescribed to maintain sedge meadows valuable to game birds, and in Scotland patches of heather, about an acre at a time, are burned to favor grouse (p. 457).

To maintain low vegetation—Where vistas, broad views, or other open spaces are desired, burning may be prescribed to eliminate or stunt taller vegetation while maintaining low-growing plants for watershed protection, wildlife cover, or beauty. Grass around estates, summer cottages, or other places where the land is not grazed or cut is sometimes managed by burning when there is ample moisture in the ground. Burning is particularly helpful where fire-dependent kinds of grass such as the prairie bluestems are desired; some of these beautiful grassland types should be utilized more than they are in landscaping, by means of prescribed burning.

To preserve certain biotic communities for education and research—Some ecological types of vegetation and their characteristic animal life will be lost if man continues to extend his culture and to eliminate wildfire as a natural agent. For instance, the fire-dependent pitch pine-scrub oak forests of New England, scraggly but ecologically fascinating, are being markedly reduced locally; they should be encouraged here and there on sandy soils by burning.

Methods of prescribed burning. Map the area to be burned and study thoroughly its topography, type of soil, and vegetation. Make a study of the local weather conditions. Know what special plants and wildlife will be sacrificed and try to minimize their loss by transplanting or providing another habitat. Consider the long-term as well as the short-term effects on the soil and on the plants thought to be fire-resistant.

Work out plans with the help of experienced people such as foresters, fire wardens, and fire chiefs.

Determine the best season (usually late winter or early spring in most climates) and the type of weather needed to render flammable the material to be burned while leaving soil moist enough to save its organic matter. Plan the time of day for maximum allowable humidity and minimum wind (usually early morning or evening). Figure what parts of the vegetation will burn most hotly. Know the wind direction and plan to burn upwind from the downwind side, and plan what you will do if the wind should change direction unexpectedly. Don't ever try to burn alone; arrange to have help on hand or near. Gather appropriate tools in good working condition and see that your helpers know how to use them efficiently. Apprize your helpers of the plans.

Clear a fuelbreak or fire line of all combustible material completely around the area to be burned. Make it wide wherever combustible material bounds the area. In an extensive area, make interior fuelbreaks; then just portions can be burned, should fire danger be increased by rising temperature or wind, and the rate and extent of firing can at all times be kept under control.

Kindle a small length along the fuelbreak or fire line on the downwind side of the area and let it burn slowly upwind with smoke and sparks therefore blowing back across the fire line and across the burned area. When a wide burned area has developed, some people kindle a fire on the upwind side, the first kindled fire acting as a backfire stopping the second. While this speeds the burning, it may trap many forms of wildlife which would escape a single fire. Nevertheless, if there is a change of wind, a second fire should be started to backfire the first if there is any question about controlling it. *Never* set fire to more than can be readily extinguished should the wind rise.

Be sure to control the rate of burning. Speed it by spreading the fire sideways with a torch of dried grass or branch, or with a manufactured flame-thrower. Slow the burning by extinguishing the ends of the fire edge or by backfiring. Do not leave the fire unsupervised; patrol it until it is dead.

HARVESTING

Harvesting is gathering plants or parts of plants for specific uses such as construction materials, foods, or crafts. Innumerable plant products are harvested in innumerable ways, which this book cannot enumerate. Among the many publications available, these are noteworthy: *71, 134, 170, 213,* and *406.* A statement of certain conservation principles, however, is in order.

Considering demand. Try to harvest natural resources when there is genuine need of them. This minimizes waste and brings highest prices and greatest appreciation. If there is no current need, leave the resource unharvested if it will either improve or maintain itself in good condition. If the unharvested resource would deteriorate or hinder development of a more valuable resource, harvest it and try to store it with maximum protection until there is need. Remember the old slogan for vegetable gardeners, "Eat what you can; can what you can't." If possible, try to develop demand through honest advertising, education, or invention of new uses. These concepts apply not only to material resources like trees being cleared from an industrial or home site but also to such intangibles as beauty of a proposed parksite. For even beauty can be stored to some extent, by an artist with camera, brush, or pen, when otherwise it might be totally lost. We must create more demand for beauty derived from naturous areas, and sometimes even attempt to put a dollar value on it to convince the mercenary-minded of its value.

Getting marketing information. Consult governmental agencies such as county agents, state departments of natural resources or conservation, federal agencies such as the U.S. Soil Conservation Service and Production and Marketing Administration, and departments such as agricultural economics at your state university. Also consult industries; these often have buyers in the field and written material describing their needs and prices. If possible, and it usually is, get prices from more than one source. Study specifications carefully so that the resource is harvested according to them. Otherwise there may be considerable waste.

Sustained yield. Except where one type of resource is being harvested completely to make room for another, as in lumbering an area to be flooded, harvest in a manner which leaves the area permanently productive. In forestry, leave seed trees and a good seedbed, or replant, just as in wildlife management we should leave breeding stock. In a recreation area, see that those recreating (which includes harvesting beauty) leave the area productive of beauty. If possible, increase the perennial yield; at least don't let it dwindle.

Multiple uses. Often an area can yield two or more harvests, for example a shrubland providing blueberries, wildlife, and water from the protected soils of its watershed. Harvesting of each resource should be carried on so as not to damage other resources, and if possible so as to benefit them.

Public relations. Let the consumer in on what it takes to produce our natural resources. Include conservation literature with the product. For instance if you sell Christmas trees or greens, give out a simple leaflet describing the species and the importance of protecting them from fire and vandalism. Make the public your partner and the partner of nature.

TRAINING PLANTS

Satisfaction comes from working with an individual plant, helping it grow happily yet partly to our personal specifications. We must know something of the genetic characteristics which determine its

This cherry tree is espaliered (trained flat) against the brick wall to conserve garden space. The warmth of the brick ripens the backs of the fruits. When the cherries begin to ripen, the net is lowered to protect them from birds.

potential, for we cannot train an apple tree to produce oranges. We need information on its growth processes so that we can more or less control them. We should have some imagination to help us plan for the plant's future in ways that can contribute to our own future or that of others. Continuing close observation is needed, and some dedicated work at crucial seasons.

Caring for individual plants is called *horticulture*; it is a felicitous mix of art and science—and for some of us religion too because we feel ethically responsible for another living thing sharing our environment. Of course training a plant is not quite the same as training a dog, but there are some similar pleasures, plus some additional benefits in shaping the environment. A plant cannot wag its tail when it is happy, but it will show other signs to those who watch it, for instance producing flowers and fruits, healthy green leaves, and perhaps deep shade in the heat of the day for its roots and for our lawn chair or rustic bench.

Training plants mostly involves influencing their stature. We manipulate their growth direction and rate, size, and shape; and we sometimes stimulate or suppress their reproductive processes, notably flowering and fruiting. The following discussion centers on perennial woody plants (trees and shrubs) as they relate to somewhat natural environments. For training house and garden plants, you can find much more detailed descriptions in the many excellent gardening books at your library or bookstore *(35)*.

Stimulating growth.   To make a plant grow faster, try to figure out what environmental factor is holding it back, for instance inadequate sunlight, too little water, insufficient minerals in the soil, too much grazing or trampling, or too much highway salt. Then try appropriate treatment, such as cutting away taller plants to permit more light. When the limiting factor is taken care of, there may be another factor which becomes limiting, and maybe you can correct that for even greater growth. When the environment is as perfect as you can make it, the plant may be able to grow up to the limits of its genetic possibilities.

The above paragraph may seem useless, because it tells you nothing specific about any particular plant whose growth you may wish to stimulate. But the concept of limiting factors is tremendously important; and the challenge of thinking about the environment from your plant's point of view should many times help you solve your problems by experimentation. Often your own powers of observation closely applied can tell you more than a trip to the university. At other times you will of course benefit from identifying the kind of plant with which you are working and then reading what others have already discovered about its needs. If that fails, ask for help from a well-informed person at a university or nature center.

Non-environmental methods of stimulating plant growth can also be effective, especially pruning and fertilizing, discussed below. Also, applications of plant growth substances, very similar to naturally occurring hormones, may be administered directly to a plant to increase or stunt growth.

Stunting growth.   Using the environmental concepts above, experiment. If your lawn grows too fast so that you have to mow it too often, hold back on the water or fertilizer or both—and treat your neighborhood to a little less mower noise. If a branch of your flowering plum tree is growing too fast across the middle of your picture window, bend it downward with a weight or with a spiral wrapping of stiff wire. Growth of most branches is suppressed by bending the tip down—and stimulated by bending the tip up. Pruning roots with a sharp spade or shovel can hold back the growth of a tree or shrub, decreasing the vigor of the shoots; but because root pruning can have a delayed stimulating effect, it will usually need repeating after another growing season has produced new roots.

Dwarfing plants has been a major art in the Orient for centuries. In Japan it is called *bon-sai*. Today growing miniature trees and shrubs is becoming more popular in Europe and the United States. As we become more crowded in the Occident and more prone to find our joys locally rather than dash around so much, we shall do well to give more attention to the techniques of adapting plants to small spaces.

Pruning and shearing. Cutting off parts of a plant often has remarkable results in addition to reducing its size and trimming its shape. Terminal buds of most trees and shrubs produce hormones which tend to inhibit the growth of other buds farther back along the stem, thus insuring that the tips of branches grow faster than the side shoots. Therefore removing a terminal bud (disbudding), or a considerable portion of the end of a branch with its terminal bud, usually has the effect of releasing from this inhibition one or more of the remaining lateral buds; at the next growing season they may grow much more actively. Even this one bit of knowledge can help you control the size and shape of many plants.

When pruning twigs, cut with sharp knife or clippers just beyond a bud which you want to become the new *leader* of the branch. If the buds are alternately arranged, you can influence the direction of

CONTROLLING PLANT GROWTH by DISBUDDING

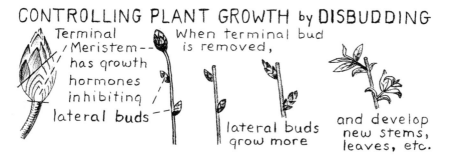

Terminal / Meristem-- has growth hormones inhibiting / lateral buds

When terminal bud is removed,

lateral buds grow more

and develop new stems, leaves, etc.

the new growth by cutting back to a bud pointing the desired way. Do not cut very close to the bud, because that may cause it to dry out and wither before scar tissue forms. However, do not leave much of a stub, because healing sap is not drawn much past the bud; a long unhealed projection beyond it invites fungus spores and harmful insects. For example, on a pencil-thick twig, do not leave more than an eighth of an inch projecting, with the basal end of the slanting cut nearly opposite the bud. *(262, 495)*

Pruning a large branch from a tree — Cut an unwanted branch back to a trunk or major branch to be left. If the branch is small enough to be supported with one hand while the other saws it, cut very close to its base so there will be no projecting stub. If the cut is close enough, the resulting scar is almost always more elliptical than round, because of the buttressing shape of the branch base. Be sure to hold up the branch as the cut is being completed, so that its weight does not cause it to split back into the trunk, causing a wound difficult for the tree to heal quickly.

For a branch too heavy to be supported with one hand, use three cuts. Cut #1 is upward from the lower side of the branch a foot or two out from the trunk. Cease cutting before the down-bending of the partially severed branch pinches the saw blade. Then start Cut #2 downward from the top of the branch a couple of inches outward from the first cut. This cut descends until it is near the level of the first cut; then the branch will suddenly split back to it. At the instant of severing, the branch still lacks any momentum and can usually be thrust quickly in whatever downward direction seems desirable, for instance away from you — or from your ladder, if you are on one. If the branch is really heavy and/or springy, watch out that it does not bounce up from the ground and strike you or your ladder. Cut #3 is finally made close to the trunk to remove the stub, which you can hold with one hand to keep it from tearing back into the tree. As stated above, the scar should usually be elliptical rather than round.

If a branch is very heavy or if for other reasons it might cause damage in falling, it should be tied at its estimated balancing point with a rope passed up over a higher crotch which can serve as a pulley for lowering it slowly and carefully.

Each year it must take some real gymnastics to pollard this sycamore (trim it back to the knobby bud clusters). Colonial Williamsburg, Virginia.

Professional arborists usually paint large scars on valuable trees, using commercial tree surgeon's paint. This keeps the wood from cracking and excludes fungus spores and harmful insects. Because most if not all paints tend to slow healing, do not apply paint quite to the edge of the wound where the delicate cambial tissue should soon produce protective scar tissue. Ideally, paint should be re-applied as it wears off in successive years until the scar is healed. Practically, this is seldom done. Sometimes it appears that the painting is done more to please the customer than to please the plant. When cutting large branches along trails or during other extensive woods operations where scar-painting is totally impractical, the unsightly newness of wounds can be readily camouflaged by rubbing a little fine soil over the fresh surface.

Tree climbing for pruning—To get the maximum fun from tree climbing, study the dangers and develop the skills to cope with them just as you might with rock climbing or skin-diving. Learn how to distribute your weight on two or more branches, staying close to the trunk unless you are roped to a strong crotch above. In rope climbing, which is great sport, learn the appropriate knots and practice their use close to the ground until you have skill and confidence. Learn to carry your sharp tools hung sheathed at your belt. Watch out for electric wires. Know always what kind of tree you are climbing, avoiding brittle species such as poplars and aspens. When there is wind, saw upwind from your cut so that sawdust does not get in your eyes. When using a ladder, tie the top to the tree and make sure the base is firm and not too close or too far out. Do not be lazy and overreach when you should move the ladder to a safer position. Watch out lest a falling branch knock the ladder from under you. And do not sit on the branch you are cutting! Indeed, to have the fun and avoid the dangers, keep all your wits about you.

Pruning a shrub—To reduce the size of a shrub and at the same time stimulate dense new growth, use *selective destemming*. Cut a few of the oldest stems at or near their bases. These are probably the tallest as well as the thickest stems, so removing them shortens the shrub. This pruning stimulates growth of new basal shoots. Repetition every few years maintains low, dense growth good for wildlife cover, soil protection, windbreaks, visual screens, and certain types of landscape design like the bottom frame of a vista. Sometimes a shrub benefits by having a few branches cut here and there at different heights or having its top and/or sides sheared (see below), but usually selective destemming at the base is preferable.

Shearing shrubs and trees—Shearing is a special kind of pruning which cuts the tips off many branches simultaneously without focusing on any one branch at a time. Long-bladed shears are used and the resulting surfaces of the plants are relatively smooth. The style will determine whether these are flat planes or curves or mixtures thereof. The results seldom look natural, but shearing is often desirable around buildings, parking lots, and other geometrically laid out areas because it helps blend artificial and natural components of the environments. Because shearing promotes dense growth of many kinds of plants, it is useful in creating and maintaining hedges, screen plantings, windbreaks, and wildlife cover.

Hedges should be sheared narrower at the top than at the base, to provide adequate light for healthy growth of the lower branches, which keep the hedge dense to the very bottom.

Some plants are much more *shear-tolerant* than others and respond happily to trimming by development of numerous buds on older twigs and sometimes even on thick branches. Yew, juniper, and arborvitae are examples of narrow-leaved evergreens which respond well to shearing. Boxwood is a broad-leaved evergreen justly celebrated for its fine texture, excellent for shearing into simple or fancy shapes, and so favored that people get used to—and even enjoy—its odor reminiscent of cat urine. Privet and barberry are common deciduous shrub genera which include species excellent for shearing.

Some native shrubs can be somewhat sheared right in their natural habitat to improve their usefulness and beauty. (See *Dune Shrubland*, p. 101). Many of the heath family, for example blueberries, huckleberries, and billberries, can be subtly sheared along trails and at picnic sites in ways which add to the landscape design and accessibility.

Topiary is a horticultural term for fancy shearing of shrubs and trees. It goes in and out of style in landscape design, partly because of cultural factors such as the presence of a landed gentry with money to hire gardeners or such as the suburban cottage style of land use where people with leisure can do their own thing.

Seasons for pruning and shearing—An old gardener's saying is, "Prune when the knife is sharp." Doing a good job is more important than choosing the best season. Where there is a dormant season, for instance winter in upper latitudes, pruning of deciduous plants is best done near its end, for soon healing growth will begin to protect the cut surfaces. However, some plants such as maples, dogwoods, and grapes lose sap ("bleed") markedly in spring so are best pruned in fall or winter. Summer pruning of deciduous plants can create a problem because the cut green leaves dry out. The resulting *slash* (cut branches) may be both unsightly and highly combustible, creating a fire hazard. Disposal is especially difficult where fire laws and air pollution standards prevent burning. Chipping with a machine is often the best procedure, but a machine may be hard to find or expensive to obtain (p. 420). Dormant-season pruning of deciduous plants avoids these problems to some extent. Conifers can be pruned at any season, their pitchy sap soon coating the cuts. Their needles on the slash are a fire hazard, whether cut in winter or summer, and should be handled to minimize that danger.

Ornamental flowering plants should be cut at seasons permitting maximum bloom. There are two groups. The first produces flowers

Topiary (fancy trimming) at "Wakes," home of Gilbert White, famous eighteenth-century author of *Natural History of Selbourne*. Selbourne, Hampshire, England.

on the new growth each spring; these should be pruned during the dormant season, to stimulate a lot of new shoots. The second group produces flowers on the twigs made the preceding growing season or seasons; prune these soon after flowering, to encourage many shoots which will bloom the following year. To find out which plants are in which group, watch to see what parts of the twigs produce the flowers. Usually bark color will enable you to distinguish current-year growth from preceding-year growth. For horticultural plants, much information is available from appropriate books and gardeners and nurserymen.

Bending woody plants. Horticulture has a goodly share of old sayings, another of which is Alexander Pope's "Just as the twig is bent, the tree's inclined." Some trees and shrubs, willow for instance, are supple. Twigs of some species can even be tied in loose knots. Older stems as well as younger ones can sometimes be bent slowly and carefully, as in the Japanese art of bon-sai (p. 439), or for some practical purpose, such as fencing made from interwoven stems or a tree platform made from interlocking limbs. Be careful not to bend stems so sharply that they split or break; a little practice with unwanted stems helps give the feel of the material and its limits.

To hold a branch in a desired position until the plant can maintain it that way, a wire or rope may go from it to another part of the plant, to a stake or stone, or to a hanging weight. The wire or rope should not make a constriction all around any living branch, for this might cut off the downward flow of food, made by the leaves, through the inner bark. Either wrap stiff wire around and along the branch in a long spiral, or fasten wire or rope to a screw-eye or to an eye-bolt passed through a hole drilled in the branch. (The bolt should fit tightly, precluding entrance of fungus spores or chafing.) If wire or cord must go around a branch, run it through a protecting length of old hose or bicycle tire where it passes over the branch and change its position slightly from time to time to distribute the wear.

Grafting. Bringing into intimate contact two branches which will grow together is called grafting. Natural grafts sometimes occur when branches rub together or roots cross each other. Artificial grafting can be used to *inarch* one branch to support another on the same plant. Grafting can also take a piece *(scion)* from one plant and attach it to a *stock* of another plant of the same kind or a very closely related kind.

In grafting, the growing tissue (cambium) just under the bark of the scion must be exposed by whittling and then be firmly placed precisely against similarly exposed cambium of the stock. This must be done when the tissues are actively growing, as in spring. The junction of scion and stock must be protected with a layer of grafting wax (usually mostly beeswax) and then securely wrapped with a flexible, durable tape to maintain their position until they have grown firmly together. Books on plant propagation and tree care should be consulted for the many fascinating techniques of grafting, procedures which can add much fun to creative vegetation management. How about grafting rungs on a living ladder to give access to a tree platform? *(209)*

FERTILIZING

Plants depend on nutrient minerals in the soil. Each mineral makes special contributions to healthy plant growth, for instance cell wall formation or synthesis of chlorophyll. In native vegetation, only those species survive which find adequate amounts of the particular minerals they require. Therefore if we are working with only native plants in their usual habitat, we can assume that they will grow well without any supplementary fertilizing. However, if we wish to encourage certain plants more than others, for example native flowering shrubs along a trail, particularly desirable wildlife cover plants, or shrubbery to serve as a buffer between a road and a natural area, then we may wish to experiment with applications of fertilizer. It may help to make chemical tests of the soil and look up the known preferences of the species involved, but the requirements of many native plants are known only in general terms. Small experiments are best; treat the soil around a few plants and leave some similar ones untreated for comparison, making records of the date, amount, and method of application to help evaluate results.

There are two more or less distinct major categories of fertilizers: organic and inorganic. Commercially available inorganic fertilizers are mostly relatively simple chemically, designed primarily to supply nitrogen (N), phosphorus (P), and potassium (K), which are listed in that order on the package as a per cent; for instance 5-10-5 is a fertilizer with half as much nitrogen and potassium as phosphorus. The balance of the hundred parts is inert material to aid in spreading. Such fertilizers have made possible great harvests in modern agriculture. However, thoughtless or careless application of inorganic fertilizers can sometimes have detrimental long-term effects, for instance influencing soil fauna and soil flora which have subtle but substantial effects on the continuing productivity of the soil. By comparison, organic fertilizers, such as animal manures and plant residues, are chemically much more complicated, their diversity helping preserve nature's balances. In excess organic fertilizers too can be harmful, but their usually slower release of minerals and their positive contribution to soil structure make them preferable in most situations where short-term economics are not seen as controlling.

Spring and early summer are usually best for applying fertilizers, at least in climates with cold winters. Fertilizing too late in the summer may stimulate new growth which will winterkill, because the tender shoots do not have time to harden before cold weather.

Trees are usually fertilized by making crowbar or auger holes in a circle under the tips of the branches, about where most of the actively absorbing rootlets are guessed to be. Fertilizer is poured into these holes, which are then capped with soil up to the level of the surrounding earth. Shrubs can be similarly treated, or fertilizer can be scratched into the soil around their bases. Newer methods of spraying the foliage are worth watching, including experiments with broadcasting of sewage effluent on woodlands, which have significant abilities in recycling wastes. Because people in our urbanizing culture have insisted on concentrating themselves and their wastes, there must be compensating efforts to redistribute nutrient materials and toxic substances back on the land rather than concentrating them all in our overworked bodies of water.

Fertilizing herbaceous areas is best done by following the advice of local agriculturalists. Fertilizers can be especially helpful when we want to reestablish vegetation as rapidly as possible on exposed soil where building developments, highways, or trails have removed the vegetative cover. When lime is used to condition soil before planting, it should be applied well before fertilizing, for lime not only acts as a fertilizer (by contributing calcium and sometimes magnesium) but has other chemical effects which may counteract NPK fertilizers.

In special cases, pelletized seeds are used to help insure quick revegetation, as after forest fires on steep land subject to erosion. The seeds are encased with fertilizer and other chemicals to prevent their destruction by rodents and fungi. Sometimes seeding is done with a slurry, that is, a liquid suspension of seeds and fertilizers together which can be sprayed on exposed road cuts and similar barelands. Information about such special techniques can be obtained from state universities and government extensionists. *(126)*

WATERING

Water is a life-giving environmental factor for plants, just as for us. Plants in their normal environment usually get along well without our watering them—or else die because they·are poorly adapted individuals. Nature permits only the fit to live. We may, however, be so interested in some individual plant or plants that, during an abnormal drought, we do not want to go along with nature and let these plants perish; so we water them. For instance we may have been studying crevice plants struggling for years in a boulder or bedrock crack. In a bad drought these might be the first plants to succumb, just as a lawn that is smooth but with unevenly graded subsoil will burn out first in those spots where the topsoil is thinnest, over the humps in the subsoil. A little water carefully applied to the crack plants may mean survival.

Non-native plants or native plants moved from their natural environs are much more apt to need supplementary water in dry spells. Particularly watch recently transplanted specimens for the first signs of wilting or offcoloring of leaves. If a plant has been moved from a moister to a drier site, it may be wise to start watering it even before any signs of droopiness or dehydration of leaves. A plant worth the trouble of moving should be worth the bother of maintaining.

When watering, be sure that the water sinks in deep enough to reach to the young root tips whose root-hair cells do the drinking. Clay soils baked by the sun may need to be loosened to promote insoak and mulched to prevent rebaking. Water should not only reach the rootlets but should sink below them to encourage their growing tips to extend downward. If the soil is moist only around and above them, they tend to grow upward and there become more susceptible to drying out. To ascertain the probable depth of insoak of a given amount of water, water the same kind of soil away from the plant and do some investigative digging.

Irrigation of gardens and crops is beyond the scope of this book. It is an exciting form of environmental management, making possible plant life where it would not normally grow or not grow well. Irrigation involves such fascinating factors as the living plants themselves; the climate and its expected and unexpected weather; the soil—not just the mineral particles but also the air spaces between them, the soil solution, and the soil microorganisms; the engineering of flowing or spraying the water on the land and removing any excess; and the economics of water procurement and application. You may wish to look up information on irrigation and try it on a small scale as an experiment in working with nature. You may bring to bloom what otherwise would be a dry and sterile corner of the earth—or you may end up with nothing but dead plants and mudpies, at least at first: Water can make all the difference. (p. 294)

PROTECTING PLANTS

Plants contribute much to our environment. They protect soil, regulate the water cycle, balance our oxygen and carbon dioxide, modify winds, recycle minerals, make homes for wildlife, supply us with food, drugs, fuel, and raw materials for industry, and beautify our surroundings. Some portion of people's lives should be dedicated to caring for plants or to helping others care for them.

There are no easy rules for protecting plants, because different kinds in different situations have different problems. There is no one enemy. Even fire while killing some plants favors others. What we must do is observe plants and note their difficulties, lending a sensitive hand whenever we can.

For example, perhaps we can build a little but sturdy fence around a small tree which is not yet appreciated by children as they run in and out of school. Maybe we can place a bumper log at the edge of a parking lot to keep people from backing into the lilac hedge. Sometimes foundation plantings need a little slatted shelter to protect them from snow sliding off the roof. Perhaps a newly planted tree can use a mulch of stones to reflect the bright sun away from the soil over its struggling roots.

Plants are like other aspects of nature: if we watch and wonder, we can work along with them to help supply their needs. That is a large part of what vegetation management is all about.

(See also *32, 44, 54, 142, 189, 202, 323, 371, 460, 498.*)

Old age brings special kinds of beauty. A very ancient mulberry attracts youngsters and still has young buds of its own each year. Dying is a relative matter, so don't give up on a plant too soon. Colonial Williamsburg, Virginia.

15   Wildlife Management

We know today that there is a limit to the number of animal passengers the planet earth can carry, human and non-human together. We are all animals, with the same basic needs of food, water, protective cover, and space. As people preempt more and more of the world's natural resources, most forms of wildlife have less and less. While some of our best scientists and philosophers are beginning to deal with the whole-world life-support problem of sharing resources, most of us should be tackling it on a small scale, puzzling about the animal-carrying capacity of some little piece of the planet, such as our own yard, the schoolgrounds, or even the cemetery— which in some ways can be the most lively place in town because it still has some green plants and wildlife. The facts we learn on such lands and the understanding we develop in ourselves and others may well contribute to appreciating and solving the whole-world problem. *(196, 319, 575)*

KINDS OF ANIMALS

From a hundred or so chemical elements organic evolution has created an astounding variety of animals. Zoologists have spent uncounted hours studying them and still there are untold kinds not yet named and classified. For managing wildlife at a site, we can begin with simple classifications such as those in basic biology and zoology texts, and then progress to the excellent texts on wildlife management. These are worth study if you are interested in how we humans evolved, how we live and reproduce, and how we share the world with other forms of life. *(127, 150)*

While zoologists have been concerned with taxonomy (arranging animals in evolutionarily related groups), other people have developed classifications based on how wildlife appear to them in daily life: *predators* feed on other animals *(prey); parasites* live in or on

453

A swale of sedges and meadowsweet spiraea in a roadside ditch makes excellent cover for a rail. Deer Isle, Maine.

other animals; *grazers* feed on grasses and *browsers* eat buds, bark, and tender twigs of woody plants; and *game*, which is hunted, includes such groups as *upland game, waterfowl, shorebirds, shell-fish, finfish,* and *fur-bearers.* Sometimes people oversimplify, trying to classify wildlife as "good" or "bad," using terms such as *beneficial wildlife* and *vermin.* A raccoon may be vermin to the farmer whose corn he steals, a fur-bearer to the boy trapping and selling pelts to put himself through college, and a good subject for pictures to the wildlife photographer. *(206)*

We do not all see the world and its wildlife from the same view-point; that is often the major problem in wildlife management. Texts on ecology and wildlife reveal much about how animals do and do not seem to fit in with man's ideas of what the world should be like. As you give increasing attention to wildlife around you, see which classifications work best for you but keep an open mind, ready to consider another's views. The squirrel which "steals" your "bird-seed" does not think of it as birdseed; and another person may find the squirrel more interesting and desirable than the titmice at your feeder. *(292)*

NUMBERS OF ANIMALS

The quantity of animals always relates to an area. Seventeen house sparrows in my yard; twenty woodchucks on Brown's hundred-acre farm; fifty-six whooping cranes left on earth. So one of the most important procedures in wildlife management is censusing populations to find out how many individuals are present in a particular place at a certain time, whether the concern is ducks in a marsh or mosquito larvae in a discarded rain-filled can. Numbers help reveal the *carrying capacity* of land, and of water too. When an area has more animals than it can sustain, it becomes overworn, or the animals become ill, or the population moves out to other areas, or all these phenomena occur, often with much attendant sorrow. At other times an area may be understocked with wildlife of appropriate kinds, perhaps even without enough individuals to find each other and mate and perpetuate the species. *(252, 582)*

The wildlife manager is therefore always having to consider the number of animals as they affect their own health and the condition of their habitat. But he is also alert to the viewpoints of other concerned people. He must reconcile the way of thinking of a school biology class making a rabbit shelter in a corner of the schoolgrounds with the feelings of a suburban gardener next door trying to grow lettuce and carrots. In such a situation, what is the optimum number of rabbits? Similarly, what is the right amount of wild deer and domestic cattle on a ranch, when the state owns and manages the deer herd with hunters' taxes and the farmer owns the cattle and manages them with whatever money he can get from their sale? What is an appropriate number of pigeons for people to feed in a city park,

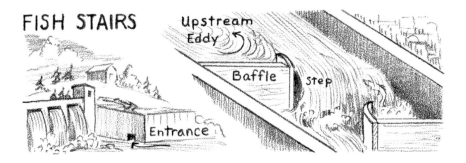

FISH STAIRS   Upstream Eddy   Baffle   Step   Entrance

where urbanites have so little other contact with nature but taxpayers have to pay to have pigeon droppings cleaned off the library steps? Sometimes the appropriate carrying capacity of the land is less a matter of what the natural resources can withstand than what men can agree upon, though the latter must always be within the limits of the former.

LIFE HISTORIES OF ANIMALS

Each kind of animal has special ways of being born, staying alive, and reproducing its kind. To trace the story of an animal's life is to discover a multitude of relationships with its environment, such as its initial nursery, its feeding grounds, its mating territory, and the habitat where it raises its young. At the same time we learn about its physiology, what it can eat, how old it must be to mate, how many young it can produce at a time, how many years it can be productive, and what age it can expect to reach. The *reproductive capacity* of a species is part of its *biotic potential* for stocking an area. Some people become so absorbed in snooping into animals' life histories that they never do get around to trying to manage the animals' affairs. Perhaps these humbler people are the wiser ones. (7, 22, 77)

Family life is still an important part of the ecology of a prairie-dog town. Devil's Tower National Monument, Wyoming.

ENVIRONMENTAL SUPPORT AND ENVIRONMENTAL RESISTANCE

Each of us animals finds the world somewhat kind and somewhat harsh. That is life. Sometimes we wonder how we can have so many blessings yet be exposed to such miseries as winter winds, diseases, and war. To each his desert; to each his land of milk and honey. Good food, cover, and comrades in our habitat give *support*. Bad weather, parasites, predators, and competing members of our own kind create *resistance*. The wildlife manager does most of his managing by helping the environment provide support or by removing that support, depending upon whether he wants a larger or smaller population of a particular kind of wildlife. At the same time he tries to decrease or increase environmental resistance. Of course he may control animal numbers directly. By artificial stocking (introducing) of wildlife he may be able to build up populations; and by hunting, trapping, or poisoning he can reduce their numbers. However, such techniques often involve special licenses as well as special equipment and the knowledge for handling dangerous materials. Most of us can best manage wildlife indirectly by modifying animals' habitat, making it more or less advantageous. *(102, 423)*

HABITAT MANAGEMENT

Our first feeling in wildlife management should be empathy, a sense of personal identity with and caring about a certain kind of animal, be it ant, chickadee, mouse, rabbit, salmon, or whale. Our first thought may be to identify it, so that we have a name to use as a handle in thinking, reading, and talking about it. Then we must be curious about its way of life, so we investigate its life history, which inevitably leads us to consider its habitat, the environment in which it typically lives. If we want to attract chickadees to a window feeder and we learn that they frequent pine woods in winter and nest in dead stubs of birch trees, then we think to make our suet holder out of a birch log and to fasten sprigs of pine to the window ledge. When we learn that chickadees avoid strong wind in winter, we attach the pine boughs to the windward side of the feeder to give a little more shelter. The chickadees will come to us about to the extent that we reach out to them, trying to see the world from their point of view. *(157)*

Variety. Seldom does any single, rather uniform environment satisfy the needs of an animal. Even a barnacle living on a wharf piling, though it may seem content in a static situation, actually has an environment which changes as water currents come bringing new food, and go taking away wastes; and in its younger stages the barnacle floats, up and down and around, in the sea. On land, most animals move around to satisfy their needs. The earthworm comes to the top of the soil at night, especially in wet weather, and drags down leaves for food, leaving his wastes on the surface. The crow leaves his nightly roost in the pines and visits the cornfield for breakfast. Within its territory, an animal has a variety of environments to fill its needs. *(300, 472)*

Creating edges. A most important principle of wildlife management is called the *edge effect:* it recognizes that wildlife is more abundant, in number of species and of individuals, at the edges between environments than in their middles. By living near an edge, an animal can quickly go to whichever environment best fills its needs of the moment. At a wood margin, a bird can fly out into a field and catch grasshoppers; sensing the shadow of a hawk, it can retreat into the protecting cover of the woods; or it can eat breakfast in the cool of the morning in the sunny field and then in the heat of the day pick up a snack for lunch in the shady woods. An edge between three environments can be even richer in wildlife, as where a stream flows across a treeland-herbland edge or where a shrub border (p. 117) separates a meadow from a wood.

Edge is in one sense a linear phenomenon, and the longer the line of edge the greater the wildlife populations. A crooked line between two points is longer than a straight one; so a wildlife manager likes irregular edges, such as crenulated borders between woods and fields, rather than straight edges, which are cheaper for a farmer who has to buy and stretch fencing. And in making a wildlife pond, a sinuous shore is better than a straight one.

Edge, however, is more than linear; it is three-dimensional, because all habitats are cubic rather than just flat as portrayed on a map. A woodlot has not only the edges adjacent to surrounding fields; it also has a top edge against the sky and a bottom edge at the ground. So a bird like the red-eyed vireo, which we may think of as a typical animal of the middle of the woods, in fact spends much of its time at the top edge of the trees, while the ovenbird frequents the bottom edge, nesting and feeding on the woodland floor. And we must realize that the woods has an even lower edge at the tips of its roots, where subterranean woodland creatures live.

So if you wish to increase wildlife, one of your best ways is to create more edges, either by making new environments within existing habitats or by making their boundaries more irregular. Variety is more than the spice of life; it provides the basic bread. This edge principle can improve our own human homes and institutions, particularly prisons, hospitals, homes for the elderly, and schools which too often lack enough variety to serve people's varied needs.

Changing topography. In managing wildlife we do not, as a rule, make changes in the lay of the land, because to do so we must disrupt the environment considerably, destroying much of the vegetative cover in order to move rock or soil; such disturbances may cause more grief than they are worth to the wildlife. However, especially with dry barelands (p. 38), we can sometimes creatively shape the land to benefit wildlife, for instance by blasting or scooping out

On the coastal plain of the Solway Firth, even a tall Scot is well hidden from waterfowl on the merse (salt marsh) by these embankments, which lead to an observation tower built by the Wildfowl Trust. Caerlaverock Nature Reserve, Dumfrieshire, Scotland.

a sheltering hollow or shallow pond, or by piling up a ridge of rock or soil against the wind. And flatlands near water can sometimes be diked to make impoundments for waterfowl, fish, and other aquatic life (p. 183). Land–water alterations are some of the most significant in managing wildlife, a notable exception to the rule about not disturbing the topography. Give attention to creating maximum edge between land and water environments, as well as variety of environments, such as pondings of various depths.

Altering soils.   Soil is heavy and expensive to move, and as with topography its redistribution can be disruptive to vegetation and wildlife. Its fertility, however, can sometimes be improved, a factor important to wildlife because the more vigorous the plant life of an area is, the larger the wildlife populations it can support. Fertilizer applications are seldom used to promote vegetation for wildlife; but in areas where soil tests indicate need, fertilizers can be applied to berry-bearing shrubs, food patches of annual crops, or other plants of special value to wild animals.

Some soils may be deficient in minerals needed for wildlife nutrition. Salt blocks with one or more supplementary minerals, sold by farm suppliers for livestock, can be distributed for wild animals. Consult your game warden first, however; some states have laws regulating salt licks because they have at times been used to bait deer and other game out of season.

In some regions heavy snows make it difficult for birds to get enough gravel to use in their gizzards for grinding the seeds they eat. A little fine gravel or coarse sand scattered on top of the snow may be appreciated. *(208)*

Manipulating microclimates.   Suitable temperatures of air, soil, and water help wildlife; extremes can kill them. In many ways your thoughtfulness about microclimates can aid the animals for which you have concern. Maintaining shade trees along a brook may keep the water cool enough for trout, whereas cutting them would let it warm up too much. Removing a few trees to form a semicircular clearing on the south side of a woodlot can make a warm pocket much sought by birds in cold weather. By feeding there, they will distribute the seeds of their favorite berry-bearing shrubs, which will grow to make warmer protective cover. Facing a nesting box away from prevalent storm winds can mean survival for nestlings. Watch-

Conical sand traps made by ant-lions, also called doodlebugs, are often found around foundations, where their holes are sheltered from rain. The penny indicates the size of the traps. "Crabgrass Hill," Springfield, Massachusetts.

ing wildlife in bad weather can give you other suggestions of how to make favorable conditions for them. (See Chapter 10, *Air Management.*)

Providing cover. *Cover,* is a very important concept; it includes both *escape cover,* which helps an animal avoid capture by predators, and *microclimatic cover,* which helps it get away from excessive heat, cold, wind, rain, snow, or other inclement weather. Often protective cover serves both functions. Sometimes topography and soil provide the cover in which animals hide and take refuge; examples include the rocky dens of porcupines or the loamy holes of gophers. Most often the cover is provided by vegetation, the trees, shrubs, vines, and herbs of an animal's habitat. Your most effective attempts in wildlife management will usually involve managing vegetation, so consult Chapters 3-5 and Chapter 14. Occasionally artificial structures such as nesting boxes and feeders supply extra cover, making the difference between presence and absence of a species in your area—for example, elevated nests in salt marshes for rails, wood duck boxes in marshes, and bluebird boxes in apple orchards where all hollow branches have been pruned away. *(249)*

Protecting vegetative cover.   Except where prescribed burning is used to stimulate growth of certain plants like bear oak and blueberries, all possible precautions should be taken to safeguard wildlife habitats from wildfire. Removing all plants to expose mineral soil in making linear fuelbreaks may at first appear to be lessening cover, but if its long-term effect is to prevent burns, denser vegetation will usually result; also, linear fuelbreaks create beneficial edges.

Sometimes it is necessary to erect fencing to exclude cattle, deer, or other animals while establishing new cover in barren areas. The exclosures of Britain are notable examples. Food plants introduced into vegetated areas may also need protective fencing, sometimes around individual plants. Well-established vegetation also may need to be protected by a reduction of the number of animals allowed to feed upon it.

Thicketing.   Making woody vegetative cover thicker in patches is called *thicketing*. Cutting out older stems permits sunlight to penetrate to the ground, allowing new energy to reach plants which have languished in shade. In many species (p. 419), new sprouts will come up from the cut stumps, and seedlings will spring up in intervening spaces. A big problem in environmental management is convincing people that trees should be cut for such purposes. Making openings in a forest can rejuvenate it and tremendously stimulate its production of wildlife. Of course you should study the woods carefully to decide just which trees to cut. Make sure you always know the species and that there are plenty of others of the same kind and in the same age class (p. 149); and do not fell a tree while animals are using it to raise young, except for small forms such as insects whose populations are usually vast enough to survive minor tragedies. One good method of thicketing is to cut a tree trunk part way through, enough to bend it over so its top rests on the ground; then trim off just the tips of some of the major branches and the top to stimulate suckering. A dense tangle can be made by piling brush against the trunk and planting vines around it.

Thicken shrubs by clipping off many tips of branches and by removing older stems basally here and there (p. 439). Annual or semiannual shearing (p.443) helps provide both cover and food for browsers close to the ground. In exposed sites, shear with attention to wind direction. A well-sheared hedge of yew or arborvitae, or even an isolated bush well trimmed, can so deflect cold wind that the interior of the bush will be several degrees warmer than the outside air, with the difference in chill factor significant to a roosting bird.

Establishing new vegetative cover. In large open areas, planting new trees and/or shrubs can help wildlife which is ill-adapted to exposed places. Often wild birds fail to come to a window feeder across a stretch of lawn or field unless a row of woody plants provides cover. A *wing planting* extending outward from a corner of the house toward treelands or shrublands may create a come-on adequate to lure them to the window; or a hedge may be run all the way out to natural cover to make a *wildlife pathway.* In large open areas such as prairies and plains, shelterbelts and windbreaks make the difference between presence and absence of many animals. Also, planting shrubs in irregular patches in draws and on protected sides of knolls will be even more effective than the rectangular windbreak plantings typical of the plains (p. 121). The increase in wildlife may well be worth the sacrifice of a little agricultural growing space.

Providing dead trees for cover. For many animals, cover is a home in a dead tree or hollow log. Do not make the frequent mistake of "improving" treelands by removing all dead trees and leaving all live ones. At least some large dead trees should be left as *den trees.* Where they are not already present, some can be made by killing selected trees, by girdling (p. 399) or careful planticiding (p. 400), and leaving them standing. Be sure they are far enough back from trails, roads, parking lots, and other gathering places so that their dead limbs will not create potential hazards over people's heads. As these trees die and progressively tumble down, they provide cover for a multitude of animals, both in their dead snags and in the logs which accumulate on the ground and eventually form new soil to enrich the forest for new trees and more wildlife.

Experimenting with cover. The above are only a few of the ways to help wildlife by creating cover. You will find more in the National Audubon Society's excellent publication, *Wildlife Habitat Improve-*

Never knock down dead stumps without good reason. They are usually full of life—not just the denizens of old woodpecker holes but also a multitude of insects and other invertebrates, as well as fungi actively recycling for new life the dead tissues of the tree. Brookville, Indiana.

ment (472) and in leaflets from the National Wildlife Federation, such as *Brush Shelters for Wildlife.* But do not be restricted by always imitating others. Experiment. Perhaps, rather than protecting all your land from fire, you may wish to try some controlled burning, which can thicken a blackberry patch beautifully from a rabbit's point of view. Do not worry about predators suffering because you have established too much escape cover. The more cover, the greater the prey population (so long as food or some other factor is not limiting), and the better chance that a fox can find dinner at the edge of the cover—at least if you remember to create plenty of edge.

Supplying food. If food is a factor limiting numbers or vitality of desirable wildlife, research their preferred foods, using your own powers of observation and information published in books such as *American Wildlife and Plants (345).* Obviously, for plant-eaters you will try to augment their favorite plants; but for animal-eaters too, you will have to increase the plants, in this case those upon which their prey feed. To assist a fox, for instance, do not try to raise rabbits; create thickets interspersed with succulent nibbles such as clover and grass. The rabbits will raise themselves under such conditions and feed the fox for you.

Much information on wildlife food plants is available in books such as the one mentioned above *(345).* Also you can get help from nurserymen, soil conservationists, agricultural extensionists, and officers of Audubon, garden, and sportsmen's clubs.

Planting may not be necessary if food plants are already abundant, although they may need help in order to be productive. This is true of fruiting shrubs in humid regions where trees grow up through their protecting shade and then reduce the vitality of the shrubs by dominating them so they do not flower or fruit. *Release cutting* (p. 410) by felling or girdling some trees lets light in again on the shrubs. Leave some trees to create variety and an irregular top edge to the vegetation. In herblands, shrubs may need to be weeded to give release from choking grasses. *(109)*

Feeding stations. Supplying food artificially draws wildlife to places where people can more readily see them, providing both enjoyment and education—a good first step in wildlife management. However, animals—and of course birds are animals, the ones most often fed—soon become more or less dependent on human handouts. Supply food faithfully throughout seasons when natural foods are in short supply, so the animals do not get caught short. Also, avoid over-concentrations of wildlife, boosting populations to the level where they are more subject to disease or they damage their natural habitat and thus reduce its carrying capacity so that they starve later. While larger animals may become partially tame, they remain partially wild and therefore potentially dangerous. Because a cuddly-looking raccoon will eat out of your hand does not mean that in an instant of fright or hunger he will not bite or claw the hand which feeds him. If you feed wildlife, try to go beyond the initial satisfactions. Take the second step of studying and protecting the animals in their more natural environments where you do not feed them. Also get others to join you in defending wildlife against artificialities of human self-centeredness.

Making feeders for birds, mammals, insects, and other kinds of wildlife is a worthy occupation for young and old, something they can do together. If you have mastered suet-holders and seed-dispensers, even those which thwart squirrels or turn with the wind so they always provide a sheltering microclimate, try to set out sugar-water vials for hummingbirds among flowers particularly sought by them. Enjoy the wonderful experience of having a partially tame hummer alight on your finger as you hold the sweet-filled vial. The impact of air from the wings is more noticeable than the weight on your finger. *(157)*

Providing water.   Most animals need to drink, though some get enough water from their food. In dry areas without adequate surface water, the greatest assistance you can give wildlife is often supplying water. Most of our cities and many of our suburbs are deserts because we have paved so much land and buried our streams in pipes, to the great detriment of wild things. The trend must be reversed. Whenever possible save streams from being culverted in the name of economy, for the gain is almost always only for the few who profit by filling in floodplains and building houses which make the city crowded, arid, and poorly adjusted to its watershed.

Birdbaths and small *wildlife pools* (p. 205) can to some extent compensate for the loss of natural watering places. Pedestal birdbaths give protection from cats and other terrestrial predators. Excavated shallow pools lined with concrete, well-packed clay, or plastic are enjoyed by more kinds of wildlife, though they are more subject to predation. The occasional unwary or sluggish animal picked off by a predator may well be a weak one which the population can spare. The pool will be most appreciated if set at the edge of an open space bordering shrubbery or woods. If cats are a recurrent hazard, some protection can be given by a low fence of green- or black-painted chicken wire in the shrubbery behind the pool. A cat will then have to approach more visibly from the open side and small birds will escape back through the wire into the shrubbery.

Birds are attracted to water in motion, so if possible arrange a little fountain of fine spray. Where pipes, hoses, or water pressure are inadequate, hang a jug or prop up a barrel as a reservoir above the birdbath or pool, with a rubber or plastic tube siphoning out water. Regulate the flow to a slow drip by means of an adjustable clamp or a twig jammed in the lower end to almost stop the flow. Even two or three drops a minute will make ripples which make the water more attractive, drawing birds which would not otherwise visit. The larger the storage vessel, the less often it will need refilling.

Where water pipes run outdoors to sillcocks, drinking fountains, athletic fields, or irrigated gardens, install an *extra faucet* which can be adjusted to provide a slight drip into a watering basin for wildlife, independent of the shuttings-off and turnings-on of the main valve. Barren schoolgrounds and college campuses particularly can benefit from such an arrangement, and so can parks. A young person will grow in wildlife wisdom from taking responsibility for adjusting the faucet and periodically cleaning the birdbath beneath; or an older person may delight in helping oversee such a project.

Windowsill watering troughs can be appreciated by city birds. Be sure they are securely fastened and kept clean. Birdbaths on flat roofs or adjusted to sloping roofs can also be a foreward step in trying to use these desert areas to bring more wildlife back into the city. One or more potted plants, including shrubs and small trees in tubs, can help make a *rooftop sanctuary*. Even if pigeons and house sparrows should spurn it—which they will not—interesting insects will be attracted.

Water for wildlife in wilder areas is important too. Many animals

Just a little help for wildlife is usually better than trying to control it with a heavy hand. Here a tropical coconut shell adds a little something for bird life in a tangly corner of John Lavendar's middle-latitude garden. Burley, Hampshire, England.

are directly dependent on ponds, streams, lakes, and wetlands, so see Chapters 6, 7, and 8 for ideas on managing aquatic habitats.

Watering places and feeding stations make good sites for hides for observation and photography (p. 185).

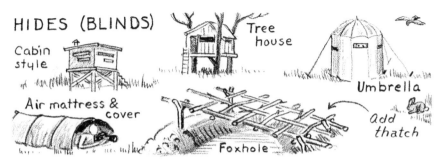

HIDES (BLINDS)

Cabin style

Tree house

Umbrella

Air mattress & cover

Add thatch

Foxhole

ALTERING PREDATION

Old-fashioned predator control is seldom necessary. We have already upset too many predator-prey balances by ill-advised shooting and poisoning campaigns urged by self-interest groups and bolstered by government bounties paid for dead animals or pieces thereof. An occasional individual animal who develops a habit of preying on domestic animals may need to be removed by a game official or conscience-guided farmer or rancher; and sometimes a feral cat (one gone wild), possibly dumped in the suburbs by a city resident, may have to be live-trapped and taken to the humane society if it becomes addicted to catching birds around the feeders at a nature center.

In some cases the destruction of large predators by man has led to a population upsurge of prey with a large biotic potential (p. 456). Overpopulation of deer, often reported in texts and periodicals on wildlife, may require carefully supervised hunting to prevent overbrowsing of their environment. Such reduction needs popular understanding of the biological laws involved, not just pseudoethical criticism based on the idea that hunting is wrong. It may be equally "wrong" to let animals starve because their populations have not been kept within limits, large predators having been eliminated. The challenge is for man to find his place amid all other animals while causing minimal disruption. We have a lot to learn; but we already have far more knowledge than we are applying. *(168, 475)*

REDUCING COMPETITION

Often many species can inhabit the same environment yet compete remarkably little with each other because each species puts different demands on its environment. Each has an *ecological niche*, a special way of making a living, with its own kind of hiding place, its own times of day or night for being active, and its own foods. Of course there may be considerable *inter*specific competition, for instance when catbirds and robins both scramble for juneberries, their first fresh fruit of the new season. But *intra*specific competition, between individuals of the same species, may be much more severe, because requirements are essentially the same. Such competition becomes severe only when the population is too great for the carrying capacity of the area, as when too many deer "yard up" in sheltering woods in winter and consume so much of the browse that the smallest deer starve because they cannot reach up to the remaining food twigs. Nature has her own ways, seemingly harsh, of thus reducing competition for those who survive. Sometimes man, hoping he is wise, steps in to reduce populations by hunting before the misery of starvation can set in. A first thought may be to supply more food, an apparently humane gesture. But that may prove to be working against nature rather than with it, causing a population increase so that during the next winter the deer will make even greater inroads on the food supply and perhaps cause longer-lasting damage to their environment. It seems wiser to make an early reduction in the number of breeding individuals to prevent overpopulation. Perhaps with wild animals as with humans, the greatest hope is for man to learn methods of chemical control of conception and to use that knowledge according to biological laws of environmental sharing yet to be ethically worked out. Once modern man took steps to remove large predators, he inevitably took upon himself the responsibility of helping nature manage the numbers of their prey. (*12, 168, 361, 475*)

HARVESTING WILD ANIMALS

Instant breakfasts notwithstanding, man does not live on synthetics. Everything we use comes from nature. Whether we like the idea or not, we are consumers, and that means destroyers. Vegetarians know that the seeds they eat include embryonic plants sacrificed to provide a human with life. Organic evolution fortunately has worked out reproductive processes which provide necessary surpluses of organisms which other organisms may use. Nature overplants, assuming that all will not live. Similarly with animals, nature overconceives, for all will not survive. But for a species to persist, there must always be an adequate supply of breeding animals, the *breeding stock*, to raise more young.

When man needs or feels he needs to kill animals, he is acting out the inherited behavior of an omnivorous animal, one which eats both plants and animals. Whether he really needs these days to consciously kill animals is a question to be decided by each individual using his own values. If we eat meat and wear real leather, we are willing to kill animals, even our fellow mammals who we believe have higher levels of consciousness than the so-called lower animals. If we are sensitive at all to the feelings of other animals—and you probably are if you are reading this book—we must be concerned about two things.

First, we must be sure that our killing never reduces the breeding stock of an area to a level where the population cannot sustain itself. We are recognizing a biological law of survival. Second, we must use hunting techniques which minimize suffering. That is not a law of nature; it is a human law developed by the big-brained primate who has the mentality to empathize not only with a singing bird but also with an injured squirrel.

How many animals we can harvest should be determined only after careful study of the carrying capacity of their habitat, their life histories, the environmental resistances to which they are subjected, and our own needs. Their fate should not depend solely on our skill as marksmen. We can prove our manliness better by photographing wildlife, and if necessary shooting at inanimate targets, trying conscientiously to fit into nature harmoniously rather than to dominate it. Indications to date are that man knows too little about his environment and about his own biological self. The animal species he most needs to learn to control is his own. *(153, 319)*

(See also *39, 61, 72, 85, 91, 112, 174, 180, 195, 215, 482, 511, 551*.)

When you let the light in, be subtle, thoughtful, and humble.

Postscript

Reverence for nature comes from seeking to understand it. Nature is both beautiful and terrible. Human nature also is a bit that way. In working with nature, we try to bring out the best that we see in it, eagerly pursuing the beautiful and minimizing what may seem ugly. In so doing we must feel and we must think, and so we come to understand ourselves better. While writing this book I have come to believe that there is no need to try to change human nature; rather we must work harder to bring out the best in it. In our more godlike moments, we know that we are only a very small part of nature and that we must work with nature humbly.

Bibliography

The purpose of this bibliography is to help you along the road to greater knowledge of how to work with nature. This list, despite its fascinating diversity, is necessarily incomplete; but each book is in some special way illuminating. For instance, *517, Twenhofel's Principles of Sedimentation*, can throw light on the ancient rocks deep in the shadows of the Grand Canyon, while *518*, Udall's *1976: Agenda for Tomorrow*, can—if we read it and act on it—brighten our future for long after 1976.

1. Abbey, Edward. *Desert Solitaire*. New York: Ballantine, 1970.
2. Abraham, Herbert, *Asphalts and Allied Substances: Their Occurrence, Uses in the Arts, and Methods of Testing*. 6th ed. Princeton, N.J.: Van Nostrand, 1960.
3. Abrams, L. *Illustrated Flora of the Pacific States*. Stanford, Calif.: Stanford University Press, 1960.
4. Abrams, George F., and Jerome Wyckoff. *Landforms*. New York: Golden Press, 1971.
5. Adriance, Guy Webb, and Fred R. Brison. *Propagation of Horticultural Plants*. New York and London: McGraw-Hill, 1939.
6. Agnew, Rea. *Profitable Private Campground Construction and Operation*. New York: Rajo Publications, 1965.
7. Allee, Warder Clyde. *The Social Life of Animals*. Rev. ed. Boston: Beacon Press, 1958.
8. Allen, Durward. *The Life of Prairie and Plains*. New York: McGraw-Hill, 1967.
9. Allen, Edward. *Stone Shelters*. Cambridge, Mass.: M.I.T. Press, 1969.
10. Allen, James Spencer, and Alvin C. Lopinot. *Small Lakes and Ponds: Their Construction and Care*. Springfield: Illinois Division of Fisheries, 1968.
11. Allhands, James Llwellyn. *Tools of the Earth Mover, Yesterday and Today*. Huntsville, Texas: Sam Houston College Press, 1951.

12. Allison, Anthony. *Population Control*. Harmondsworth, Eng.: Penguin Books, 1970.
13. American Association for the Advancement of Science. *Air Conservation*. Washington, D.C.: AAAS Publication #80, 1965.
14. American Camping Association. *Conservation of the Camp Site*. Martinsville, Ind.: 1960.
15. American Right of Way Association. *An Analysis of Right of Way Educational Needs*. Los Angeles: 1964.
16. Amos, William H. *The Life of the Pond*. New York: McGraw-Hill, 1967.
17. Angier, Bradford. *How to Build Your Home in the Woods*. New York: Sheridan House, 1952.
18. Archer, Sellers G. *Soil Conservation*. Norman: University of Oklahoma Press, 1953.
19. Archer, Sellers G., and Clarence E. Bunch. *The American Grass Book: A Manual of Pasture and Range Practices*. Norman: University of Oklahoma Press, 1953.
20. Armco Drainage Products Association. *Handbook of Culvert and Drainage Practice*. Middletown, Ohio: 1948.
21. Armstrong, Christopher F. *Soil Mechanics in Road Construction*. London: E. Arnold, 1950.
22. Armstrong, E. A. *Bird Display and Behavior*. Gloucester, Mass.: Peter Smith, 1965.
23. Arnold, Lionel Kenneth, and Richard E. Walker. *Wood Preservation*. Ames: Iowa State College of Agriculture and Mechanical Arts, 1953.
24. Artz, Robert M., and Hubert Bermont, eds. *Guide to New Approaches in Financing Parks and Recreation*. Washington, D.C.: Acropolis Books, 1970.
25. Arvill, Robert. *Man and Environment: Crisis and the Strategy of Choice*. Harmondsworth, Eng.: Penguin Books, 1967.
26. Asphalt Institute. *Soils Manual for Design of Asphalt Pavement Structures*. College Park, Maryland: 1961.
27. Aukerman, Robert. *Classifying Water Bodies*. Washington, D.C.: National Water Commission, Technical Information Service, 1972.
28. Ayres, Quincy Claude, and Daniels Scoates. *Land Drainage and Reclamation*. 2nd ed. New York and London: McGraw-Hill, 1939.
29. Baer, Firmon. *Earth: The Stuff of Life*. Norman: University of Oklahoma Press, 1962.
30. Bagnold, Ralph Alger. *The Physics of Blown Sand and Desert Dunes*. London: Methuen, 1965.
31. Bailey, Liberty Hyde. *The Nursery Manual: A Complete Guide to the Multiplication of Plants*. New York: Macmillan, 1938.
32. Baker, Samm Sinclair. *Gardening Do's and Don'ts: How to Grow Your Lawn and Gardens Best to Prevent Trouble Before It Happens*. New York: Funk & Wagnalls, 1970.
33. Bale, Robert O. *Conservation for Camp and Classroom*. Minneapolis: Burgess Publishing Company, 1962.
34. Balfour, E. B. *The Living Soil*. New York: Devin-Adair, 1950.
35. Ballard, Ernesta Drinker. *The Art of Training Plants*. New York: Harper, 1962.

36. Bardach, John. *Downstream: A Natural History of the River.* New York: Harper & Row, 1964.

37. Barnard, Colin, ed. *Grasses and Grasslands.* London: Macmillan; New York: St. Martin's Press, 1964.

38. Bascom, Willard. *Waves and Beaches: The Dynamics of the Ocean's Surface.* Garden City, N.Y.: Doubleday, 1964.

39. Bates, Marston. *Animal Worlds.* New York: Random House, 1963.

40. Bauer, Anthony Matthew. *A Guide to Site Development and Rehabilitation of Pits and Quarries.* Toronto: Ontario Department of Mines, 1970.

41. Bauer, Edward Ezra. *Highway Materials.* 2nd ed. New York and London: McGraw-Hill, 1932.

42. Bawden, H. *Making a Shrub Garden.* London: Faber & Faber, 1966.

43. Beard, Daniel Carter. *Shelters, Shacks, and Shanties.* New York: Scribner's, 1937.

44. Beaumont, Arthur B. *Garden Soils: Their Conservation and Use.* New York: Orange Judd Publishing Company, 1948.

45. Beddall, John Leslie. *Hedges for Farm and Garden.* London: Faber & Faber, 1950.

46. Beecher, William J. *Nesting Birds and the Vegetation Substrate.* Chicago: Chicago Ornithological Society, 1942.

47. Benarde, Melvin A. *Our Precarious Habitat.* New York: W. W. Norton, 1970.

48. Bennett, George William. *Management of Lakes and Ponds.* New York: Van Nostrand Reinhold, 1971.

49. Bennett, Hugh H. *Soil Conservation.* New York: McGraw-Hill, 1939.

50. Bennett, Thomas. *The 20th Century Track: All-Weather Resilient Surfacing for Track and Field.* Madison: University of Wisconsin Press, 1963.

51. Benton, Allen H., and E. E. Werner. *Field Biology and Ecology.* 2nd ed. New York: McGraw-Hill, 1966.

52. Berger, Kermit C. *Introductory Soils.* New York: Macmillan, 1965.

53. Berland, Theodore. *The Fight For Quiet.* Englewood Cliffs, N.J.: Prentice-Hall, 1970.

54. Berrisford, Judith Mary. *The Very Small Garden: Unlimited Ideas For Limited Space.* London: Faber & Faber, 1968.

55. Berry, Wendell. *The Long-Legged House.* New York: Ballantine, 1971.

56. Beston, Henry. *The Outermost House: A Year of Life on the Great Beach of Cape Cod.* New York: Rinehart, 1949.

57. Beveridge, W. I. B. *The Art of Scientific Investigation.* 3rd ed. New York: W. W. Norton, 1957.

58. Billings, W. D. *Plants, Man, and the Ecosystem.* Belmont, Calif.: Wadsworth, 1970.

59. Blackshaw, Alan. *Mountaineering: From Hill Walking to Alpine Climbing.* Harmondsworth, Eng.: Penguin Books, 1968.

60. Blake, Peter. *God's Own Junkyard: The Planned Deterioration of America's Landscape.* New York: Holt, Rinehart & Winston, 1964.

61. Blond, Georges. *The Great Migrations.* Trans. Frances Frenaye. New York: Macmillan, 1956.

62. Blumenstock, David I. *The Ocean of Air.* New Brunswick, N.J.: Rutgers University Press, 1959.

63. Borgstrom, Georg. *Too Many*. New York: Macmillan, 1969.
64. Boughey, Arthur S. *Fundamental Ecology*. Scranton, Pa.: Intext, 1971.
65. ———. *Man and the Environment: An Introduction to Human Ecology and Evolution*. New York: Macmillan, 1971.
66. Boyce, John Shaw. *Forest Pathology*. 3rd ed. New York: McGraw-Hill, 1961.
67. Brainerd, John W. *Nature Study for Conservation: A Handbook for Environmental Education*. New York: Macmillan, 1971.
68. Brasnett, Norman Vincent. *Planned Management of Forests*. London: Allen & Unwin, 1953.
69. Braun, E. L. *Deciduous Forests of Eastern North America*. Riverside, N.J.: Hafner, 1967.
70. Braun, Walter A. *Planning a Playground*. St. Louis, Missouri: Fred Medart Manufacturing Company, n.d.
71. Breetveld, Jim. *Treasure of the Timberlands*. New York: Scholastic Magazines, in cooperation with Weyerhaeuser Company, 1967.
72. Breland, Osmond Philip. *Animal Friends and Foes*. New York: Harper, 1957.
73. Briggs, Peter. *Water: The Vital Essence*. New York: Harper & Row, 1967.
74. Brimer, John B. *Homeowners' Complete Outdoor Building Book*. New York: Harper & Row, 1971.
75. Britton, Max Edwin. *Vegetation of the Arctic Tundra*. 2nd ed. Corvallis: Oregon State University Press, 1966.
76. Britton, N. L., and A. Brown. *An Illustrated Flora of the Northeastern United States and Canada*. New York: Dover, 1913.
77. Broadhurst, P. L. *The Science of Animal Behavior*. Baltimore: Penguin Books, 1963.
78. Brockman, Christian Frank. *Recreational Use of Wild Lands*. New York McGraw-Hill, 1959.
79. Brown, Carol Barrier. *The Control of Reservoir Silting*. Washington, D.C.: U.S. Government Printing Office, 1943.
80. Brown, George Willard. *Desert Biology*. New York: Academic Press, 1968.
81. Brown, Harrison. *The Challenge of Man's Future*. New York: Viking, 1954.
82. Brown, Vinson. *The Amateur Naturalist's Handbook*. Boston: Little, Brown, 1948.
83. ———. *Reading the Woods: Seeing More in Nature's Familiar Faces*. Harrisburg, Pa.: Stackpole Books, 1969.
84. Brown, Vinson, and Ernest Braun. *Exploring Pacific Coast Tide Pools*. Healdsburg, Calif.: Naturegraph Books, 1966.
85. Buchsbaum, Ralph Morris. *Animals Without Backbones: An Introduction to the Invertebrates*. Chicago: University of Chicago Press, 1967.
86. Buchsbaum, Ralph, and Mildred Buchsbaum. *Basic Ecology*. Pacific Grove, Calif.: Boxwood Press, 1957.
87. Buck, Margaret Waring. *In Ponds and Streams*. New York: Abingdon Press, 1955.
88. Buckman, Harry O., and Nyle C. Brady. *The Nature and Properties of Soils*. New York: Macmillan, 1969.
89. Bue, Conrad D. *Flood Information for Flood-Plain Planning*. Washington, D.C.: U.S. Government Printing Office, 1967.

90. Burges, N. A., and F. Raw, eds. *Soil Biology*. London: Academic Press, 1967.
91. Burton, Maurice. *Animal Courtship*. London: Hutchinson, 1953.
92. Bush-Brown, James, and Louise Bush-Brown. *America's Garden Book*. New York: Charles Scribner's Sons, 1965.
93. Bush-Brown, James. *Shrubs and Trees for the Home Landscape*. Philadelphia: Chilton Books, 1963.
94. Butler, George Daniel. *Introduction to Community Recreation*. 4th ed. New York: McGraw-Hill, 1967.
95. ———. *Pioneers in Public Recreation*. Minneapolis: Burgess Publishing Company, 1965.
96. ———. *Recreation Areas: Their Design and Equipment*. New York: Doubleday, 1957.
97. ———. *Standards for Municipal Recreation Areas*. Rev. ed. New York: National Recreation Association, 1962.
98. Cadbury, B. Bartram. *Fresh and Salt Water*. Mankato, Minn.: Creative Educational Society, Inc., n.d.
99. Cadwallader, Laura Hanes, and Sarah Ada Rice. *Principles of Indexing and Filing*. 3rd ed. Baltimore: H. M. Rowe Company, 1951.
100. Cain, Stanley A. *Foundations of Plant Geography*. Riverside, N.J.: Hafner, 1971.
101. Cain, Stanley A., and G. M. de Oliveira Castro. *Manual of Vegetation Analysis*. New York: Harper, 1959.
102. Calhoun, John B., and James U. Casby. *Calculation of Home Range and Density of Small Mammals*. Washington, D.C.: U.S. Department of Health, Education, and Welfare, 1958.
103. California Division of Highways. *Bank and Shore Protection in California Highway Practice*. Sacramento: 1960.
104. Campbell, F. B. *Hydraulic Design of Rock Riprap*. Vicksburg, Miss.: U.S. Army Engineer Waterways Experiment Station, 1966.
105. Campbell, Ian. *A Practical Guide to the Law of Footpaths*. London: Commons, Open Spaces and Footpaths Preservation Society, 1969.
106. Carhart, Arthur B. *Timber in Your Life*. Philadelphia: Lippincott, 1955.
107. Carhart, Arthus H. *Water or Your Life*. Philadelphia: Lippincott, 1951.
108. Carr, Donald Eaton. *The Deadly Feast of Life*. Garden City, N.Y.: Doubleday, 1971.
109. ———. *Death of Sweet Waters*. New York: Norton, 1966.
110. Carson, Rachel. *Edge of the Sea*. Boston: Houghton Mifflin, 1955.
111. Carrighar, Sally. *A Day at Teton Marsh*. New York: Knopf, 1947.
112. Carthy, John Dennis. *Animal Navigation: How Animals Find Their Way About*. New York: Scribner, 1957.
113. Cedergren, Harry R. *Seepage, Drainage and Flow Nets*. New York: Wiley, 1967.
114. Chapman, Herman Haupt. *Forest Management*. Bristol, Conn.: Hildreth Press, 1960.
115. Chorley, Richard J., ed. *Water, Earth, and Man: A Synthesis of Hydrology, Geomorphology, and Socio-economic Geography*. London: Methuen, 1969.
116. Clancy, Edward P. *The Tides*. Garden City, N.Y.: Doubleday, 1968.
117. Clarke, George. *Elements of Ecology*. New York: Wiley, 1965.
118. Clausse, Roger, and Leopold Facy. *The Clouds*. New York: Grove Press, 1961.

119. Clawson, Marion. *Methods of Measuring the Demand for the Value of Outdoor Recreation.* Washington, D.C.: Resources for the Future, 1959.

120. Clement, E. S. *Adventures in Ecology: Half a Million Miles from Mud to Macadam.* Riverside, N.J.: Hafner, 1960.

121. Clement, Roland, and Ian Nesbet. *The Suburban Forest: Trees and Insects in the Human Environment.* Lincoln: Massachusetts Audubon Society, 1972.

122. Cloud, Katharine Mallet Provost. *Evergreen and Flowering Shrubs for Your Home.* New York: Greenberg, 1957.

123. Coats, Alice Margaret. *Garden Shrubs and Their Histories.* New York: Dutton, 1965.

124. Cocannouer, Joseph A. *Weeds: Guardians of the Soil.* New York: Devin-Adair, 1950.

125. Coker, Robert Ervin. *Streams, Lakes and Ponds.* New York: Harper & Row, 1968.

126. Collings, Gilbert Hooper. *Commercial Fertilizers: Their Sources and Use.* New York: McGraw-Hill, 1955.

127. Collins, Henry Hill. *Complete Guide to American Wildlife.* New York: Harper, 1959.

128. Collins, Stephen. *Forest and Woodland.* Mankato, Minn.: Creative Educational Society, Inc., 1956.

129. Colman, Edward A. *Vegetation and Watershed Management.* New York: Ronald Press, 1953.

130. Committee on Environmental Quality of the Federal Council for Science and Technology. *Noise—Sound Without Value.* Washington, D.C.: Office of Science and Technology, 1968.

131. Conard, Henry S. *How to Know the Mosses and Liverworts.* Dubuque, Iowa: William C. Brown Company, 1959.

132. Cook, James Gordon. *The World of Water.* New York: Dial Press, 1957.

133. Coon, Nelson. *Fragrance and Fragrant Plants for House and Garden.* Grandview, Mo.: Diversity Books, 1967.

134. ———. *Using Wayside Plants.* New York: Hearthside Press, 1969.

135. Cooper, Turner, *Practical Land Drainage.* London: L. Hill. 1965.

136. Cooper, William S. *Coastal Sand Dunes of Oregon and Washington.* New York: Geological Society of America, 1958.

137. Cornarchia, Harold J., and John E. Nixon. *Playground Facilities for Small Elementary Schools.* Stanford, Calif.: Stanford University Press, 1955.

138. Correvon, Henry. *Rock Garden and Alpine Plants.* New York: Macmillan, 1930.

139. Costello, David F. *The Prairie World: Plants and Animals of the Grassland Sea.* New York: Crowell, 1969.

140. Cowan, Charles S. *The Enemy is Fire.* Seattle: Superior, 1961.

141. Craighead, John J.; Frank C. Craighead; and Ray J. Davis. *A Field Guide to Rocky Mountain Wildflowers.* Boston: Houghton Mifflin, 1963.

142. Crane, Howard Hamp. *Gardening on Clay.* London: W. H. & L. Collingridge, 1963.

143. Cromie, William J. *The Living World of the Sea.* Englewood Cliffs, N.J.: Prentice-Hall, 1968.

144. Cronquist, A., et al. *Intermountain Flora.* Riverside, N.J.: Hafner, 1972.

145. Cullen, Allan H. *Rivers in Harness: The Story of Dams*. Philadelphia: Chilton Books, 1962.
146. Dade County, Florida, Planning Department. *Methods Manual: Land Use Study for Metropolitan Dade County, Florida*. Miami: 1961.
147. Dambach, Charles Arthur. *A Study of the Ecology and Economic Value of Crop Field Borders*. Columbus: Ohio State University Press, 1948.
148. Dana, Samuel Trask. *Problem Analysis Research in Forest Management*. Washington, D.C.: U.S. Department of Agriculture Forest Service, 1957.
149. Darling, F. F., and J. P. Milton, eds. *Future Environments of North America*. Garden City, N.Y.: Natural History Press, 1966.
150. Dasmann, Raymond F. *Wildlife Biology*. New York: Wiley, 1964.
151. ———. *A Different Kind of Country*, New York: Macmillan, 1968.
152. ———. *Environmental Conservation*. 3rd ed. New York: Wiley, 1971.
153. Davies, Brian. *Savage Luxury: The Slaughter of the Baby Seals*. New York: Taplinger, 1971.
154. Davies, Delwyn G. *Fresh Water: The Precious Resource*. Garden City, N.Y.: Natural History Press, 1969.
155. Davis, James Elwood. *Windbreaks for Illinois Farmsteads*. 3rd ed. Urbana: University of Illinois Press, 1949.
156. Davis, Kenneth Pickett. *Forest Management*. New York: McGraw-Hill, 1966.
157. Davison, Verne E. *Attracting Birds: From Prairies to the Atlantic*. New York: Crowell, 1967.
158. Dawson, E. Yale. *How to Know the Seaweeds*. Dubuque, Iowa: William C. Brown, 1956.
159. De Bell, Garrett. *The Environmental Handbook*. New York: Ballantine, 1970.
160. Debenham, Frank. *Map Making*. London: Blackie, 1956.
161. Deer, William Alexander; R. A. Howie; and J. Zussman. *An Introduction to the Rock-Forming Minerals*. London: Longmans, 1966.
162. Dellow, E. L. *Methods of Science: An Introduction to Measuring and Testing For Laymen and Students*. New York: Universe Books, 1970.
163. *Desert Gardening*. Menlo Park, California: Lane Magazine and Book Company, n.d. (Sunset Books).
164. Detwyler, Thomas R. *Man's Impact on Environment*. New York: McGraw-Hill, 1971.
165. Dittmer, Howard James. *Lawn Problems of the Southwest*. Albuquerque: University of New Mexico Press, 1950.
166. Douglass, Robert W. *Forest Recreation*. Oxford, N.Y.: Pergamon Press, 1969.
167. Dyson, James L. *The World of Ice*. New York: Knopf, 1962.
168. Eadie, William Robert. *Animal Control in Field, Farm, and Forest*. New York: Macmillan, 1954.
169. Eckel, Edwin Clarence. *Building Stones and Clays: Their Origins, Characters, and Examination*. New York: Wiley, 1912.
170. Edlin, Herbert Lesson. *Woodland Crafts in Britain*. London and New York: B. T. Batsford, 1949.
171. Egler, Frank Edwin. *Vegetation Management for Rights-of-Way and Roadsides*. Washington, D.C.: Smithsonian Institution Annual Report, 1953.
172. Ehrenfeld, David. *Conserving Life on Earth*. New York: Oxford University Press, 1972.

173. Ehrlich, Paul R., and Anne H. Ehrlich. *Population, Resources, Environment: Issues in Human Ecology.* San Francisco: Freeman, 1972.

174. Elton, Charles Sutherland. *Animal Ecology.* London: Muthuen, 1968.

175. Errington, Paul L. *Muskrats and Marsh Management.* Harrisburg, Pa.: Stackpole, 1961.

176. Esmiol, Elbert E. *Rock as Upstream Slope Protection for Earth Dams.* Denver: U.S. Department of the Interior, Bureau of Reclamation, 1967.

177. Esser, Aristide H. *Behavior and Environment: The Use of Space by Animals and Man.* New York: Plenum, 1971.

178. Evans, I. O. *The Observers' Book of Geology.* London: Frederick Warne, 1971.

179. ———. *The Observers' Book of Sea and Shore.* London: Frederick Warne, 1962.

180. Evans, William F. *Communication in the Animal World.* New York: Crowell, 1968.

181. Eward, William R. *Environment for Man: The Next Fifty Years.* Bloomington: Indiana University Press, 1967.

182. Fairbrother, Nan. *New Lives, New Landscapes: Planning for the 21st Century.* New York: Knopf, 1970.

183. Fairchild, David. *The World Grows Round My Door.* New York: Scribner's, 1947.

184. Faltermayer, Edmund K. *Redoing America: A Nationwide Report on How We Can Make our Cities and Suburbs Livable.* New York: Harper & Row, 1968.

185. Farb, Peter. *The Face of North America: The Natural History of a Continent.* New York: Harper & Row, 1963.

186. ———. *Living Earth.* New York: Harper, 1959.

187. Farb, Peter, and the editors of *Life. The Forest.* New York: Time, Inc., 1961.

188. Fassett, Norman Carter. *A Manual of Aquatic Plants.* New York: McGraw-Hill, 1940.

189. Faust, Joan Lee. *Around the Garden, Week by Week: A Guide to Garden Planning for Every Season.* New York: Appleton-Century, 1966.

190. Fenton, Carrol Lane, and Mildred Adams Fenton. *The Rock Book.* Garden City, N.Y.: Doubleday, 1946.

191. Fernald, Merritt Lyndon. *Gray's Manual of Botany.* 8th ed. New York: American Book Company, 1950.

192. Fernald, Merritt Lyndon, and Alfred Charles Kinsey. *Edible Wild Plants of Eastern North America.* New York: Harper, 1958.

193. Fields, Curtis P. *The Forgotten Art of Building a Stone Wall.* Dublin, N.H.: Yankee, 1971.

194. Findlay, Walter P. K. *The Preservation of Timber.* London: A. & C. Black, 1962.

195. Fingerman, Milton. *Animal Diversity.* New York: Holt, Rinehart & Winston, 1969.

196. Fisher, James; Noel Simon; and Jack Vincent. *Wildlife In Danger.* New York: Viking Press, 1969.

197. Flawn, Peter Tyrell. *Environmental Geology: Conserving, Land-Use Planning, and Resource Management.* New York: Harper & Row, 1970.

198. Forbes, Reginald Dunderdale, ed. *Forestry Handbook.* New York: Ronald Press, 1955.

199. Forbes, Reginald O. *Woodlands for Profit and Pleasure.* Washington, D.C.: American Forestry Association, 1971.

200. Forman, Jonathan. *Water and Man: A Study in Ecology.* Columbus, Ohio: Friends of the Earth, 1950.

201. Foster, Edgar Eugene. *Rainfall and Runoff.* New York: Macmillan, 1948.

202. Foster, H. Lincoln. *Rock Gardening.* Boston: Houghton Mifflin, 1968.

203. Free, Montague. *Plant Propagation in Pictures.* New York: American Garden Guild, 1957.

204. Freeman, William Marshall. *Rights of Way.* 4th ed. by J. F. Garner. London: Solicitors' Law Stationery Society, 1958.

205. Friedlander, Cecil Paul. *Heathland Ecology.* London: Heinemann, 1960.

206. Frome, Michael. *The Varmints: Our Unwanted Wildlife.* New York: Coward-McCann, 1969.

207. Fryer, J. D., and S. A. Evans, eds. *Weed Control Handbook.* Oxford, Eng.: Blackwell Scientific Publications, 1968.

208. Gabrielson, Ira Noel. *Wildlife Conservation.* 2nd ed. New York: Macmillan, 1959.

209. Garner, Robert John. *The Grafter's Handbook*, 3rd ed. London: Faber, 1967; New York: Oxford University Press, 1968.

210. Garvey, Gerald. *Energy, Ecology, Economy: A Framework for Environmental Policy.* New York: Norton, 1972.

211. Geiger, Rudolf. *The Climate Near the Ground.* Cambridge, Mass. Harvard University Press, 1965.

212. George Washington University. *Shoreline Recreation Resources of the United States.* Washington, D.C.: U.S. Government Printing Office, 1962.

213. Gibbons, Euell. *Stalking the Wild Asparagus.* New York: McKay, 1962.

214. ———. *Stalking the Healthful Herbs.* New York: McKay, 1966.

215. Gilbert, Bil. *How Animals Communicate.* New York: Pantheon Books, 1966.

216. Gleason, Henry Allan. *The New Britton and Brown Illustrated Flora of the Northeastern United States and Adjacent Canada.* New York: New York Botanical Garden, 1963.

217. Goethe, Charles Matthias. *The Elfin Forest: A Glimpse of California's Chaparral.* Sacramento, Calif: Keystone, 1953.

218. Gooch, R. B. *Selection and Layout of Land for Playing Fields and Playgrounds.* London: National Playing Fields Association, 1956.

219. Graham, Edward Harrison, and William R. Van Dersal. *Water for America: The Story of Water Conservation.* New York: Oxford University Press, 1956.

220. Greenhood, David. *Mapping.* Chicago: University of Chicago Press, 1964.

221. Gresswell, Ronald Kay. *The Physical Geography of Beaches and Coastlines.* London: Hulton Educational Publications, 1957.

222. Grimm, William Carey. *Recognizing Native Shrubs.* Harrisburg, Pa.: Stackpole, 1966.

223. Grosier, Mary M. *Street-Space-for-People.* New York: Council on the Environment, 1972.

224. Grossman, Mary Louise; S. Grossman; and J. H. Hamlet. *Our Vanishing Wilderness.* New York: Grosset & Dunlap, 1969.

225. Guggenheimer, Elinor Coleman. *Planning for Parks and Recreation Needs in Urban Areas.* New York: Twayne Publishers, 1969.

226. Gustafson, Axel Ferdinand. *Land for the Family*. New York: McGraw-Hill, 1948.

227. Hagen, Robert Mower. *Successful Irrigation: Planning, Development, Management*. Rome: Food and Agriculture Organization of the United Nations, 1968.

228. Hall, Jay V. *Artificially Nourished and Constructed Beaches*. Washington, D.C.: Beach Erosion Board, U.S. Army Corps of Engineers, 1952.

229. Hall, L. C. *Bibliography of Freshwater Wetlands Ecology and Management*. Madison: Wisconsin Department of Natural Resources Report 35, 1968.

230. Handler, Philip. *Biology and the Future of Man*. New York: Oxford University Press, 1970.

231. Hanes, J. Carter, and Charles H. Connors, eds. *Landscape Design and Its Relation to the Modern Highway*. New Brunswick, N.J.: Rutgers University College of Engineering, 1953.

232. Hanna, Frank Willard, and Robert C. Kennedy. *The Design of Dams*. 2nd ed. New York and London: McGraw-Hill, 1938.

233. Haring, Elda. *The Complete Book of Growing Plants from Seed*. New York: Hawthorn Books, 1969.

234. Harlow, William M. *Trees of the United States and Canada: Their Woodcraft and Wildlife Uses*. New York: Whittlesey House, 1942.

235. Harris, Ben Charles. *Eat the Weeds*. Barre, Mass.: Barre Publishers, 1971.

236. Harris, Cyril M., ed. *Handbook of Noise Control*. New York: McGraw-Hill, 1957.

237. Harris, Robert. *Canals and Their Architecture*. London: H. Evelyn, 1969.

238. Harrison, Sydney Gerald. *Garden Shrubs and Trees*. London: Eyre & Spottiswoode, 1960.

239. Hart, Robert Adrian de Jauralde. *The Inviolable Hills: The Ecology, Conservation and Regeneration of the British Uplands*. London: Stuart & Watkins in conjunction with The Soil Association, 1968.

240. Harte, John, and Robert H. Socolow. *Patient Earth*. New York: Holt, Rinehart and Winston, 1971.

241. Hartley, Dorothy. *Water in England*. London: Macdonald, 1964.

242. Hartmann, Hudson Thomas, and Dale E. Kester. *Plant Propagation: Principles and Practices*. 2nd ed. Englewood Cliffs, N.J.: Prentice-Hall, 1968.

243. Hausmann, Leon A. *Beginner's Guide to Fresh-Water Life*. New York: Putnam, 1950.

244. ———. *Beginner's Guide to Seashore Life*. New York: Putnam, 1949.

245. Haworth-Booth, Michael. *Effective Flowering Shrubs*. New York: Crowell, 1951.

246. Hay, John. *The Sandy Shore*. Riverside, Conn.: The Chatham Press, 1969.

247. Hay, John, and Peter Farb. *The Atlantic Shore: Human and Natural History from Long Island to Labrador*. New York: Harper & Row, 1966.

248. Hayes, William A. *Guide for Wind Erosion Control in the Northeastern States*. Upper Darby, Pa.: U.S. Soil Conservation Service, 1966.

249. Headstrom, Birger Richard. *A Complete Field Guide to Nests in the United States*. New York: I. Washburn, 1970.

250. Hennes, Robert Graham. *Analysis and Control of Landslides*. Seattle: University of Washington Press, 1936.

251. Hess, La Rena. *How to Paint with Natural Earths and Sands.* Healdsburg, Calif.: Naturegraph, 1968.

252. Hesse, Richard, et al. *Ecological Animal Geography.* 2nd ed. New York: Wiley, 1961.

253. Hiley, Wilfred Edward. *Woodland Management.* 2nd ed. London: Faber, 1967.

254. Hinks, Arthur Robert. *Maps and Surveys.* Cambridge, Eng.: Cambridge University Press, 1942.

255. Hitchcock, A. S. *Manual of the Grasses of the United States.* New York: Dover, 1950.

256. Hofmann, Melita. *A Trip to the Pond: An Adventure in Nature.* Garden City, N.Y.: Doubleday, 1966.

257. Hottes, Alfred Carl. *The Book of Shrubs.* New York: De La Mare, 1958.

258. Hotchkiss, Niel. *Common Marsh, Underwater, and Floating-Leaved Plants of the United States and Canada.* New York: Dover, 1972.

259. Hoult, David P., ed. *Oil on the Sea.* New York: Plenum, 1969.

260. Hoyt, William G., and Walter B. Langbein. *Floods.* Princeton, N.J.: Princeton University Press, 1955.

261. Hubbard, Alice Harvey. *This Land of Ours: Community and Conservation Projects for Citizens.* New York: Macmillan, 1960.

262. Hudson, Roy L. *Pruning Handbook.* Menlo Park, Calif.: Lane Books, 1969.

263. Huffaker, C. B. ed. *Biological Control.* New York: Plenum, 1971.

264. Huggard, Eric Richard, and T. H. Owen. *Forest Tools and Instruments.* London: A. & C. Black, 1960.

265. Hulbert, A. B. *Soil: Its Influences on the History of the United States.* New Haven: Yale University Press; London: Oxford University Press, 1930.

266. Hull, Seabrook, *The Bountiful Sea.* Englewood Cliffs, N.J.: Prentice-Hall, 1964.

267. Humphrey, Robert R. *Range Ecology.* New York: Ronald Press, 1962.

268. Hunt, Cynthia A., and Robert M. Garrels. *Water: The Web of Life.* New York: Norton, 1972.

269. Hunt, George McMonies, and George A. Garratt. *Wood Preservation.* New York: McGraw-Hill, 1967.

270. Hyams, Edward S. *Ornamental Shrubs for Temperate Zone Gardens.* South Brunswick, N.J.: Barnes, 1965.

271. Hylander, Clarence J. *Sea and Shore.* New York: Macmillan, 1950.

272. Hynes, H. B. N. *The Biology of Polluted Waters.* Liverpool, Eng.: University of Liverpool Press, 1966.

273. Ingle, J. C. *The Movement of Beach Sand.* Brussels: Elsevir, 1966.

274. International Cut Stone Contractors' and Quarrymen's Association. *A Catalog of Building Stones.* Indianapolis: 1954.

275. Israelsen, Orson Winwo, and Vaughn E. Hansen. *Irrigation Principles and Practices.* 3rd ed. New York: Wiley, 1962.

276. Jackson, John Brinckerhoff. *American Space: The Centennial Years.* New York: Norton, 1972.

277. Jackson, Richard M., and Frank Raw. *Life in the Soil.* New York: St. Martin's Press, 1966.

278. Jacques, H. E. *How to Know the Weeds.* Dubuque, Iowa: William C. Brown, n.d.

279. Jaeger, Edmund C. *The North American Deserts*. Stanford, Calif.: Stanford University Press, 1957.
280. Jaeger, John Conrad, and N. G. W. Cook. *Fundamentals of Rock Mechanics*. London: Methuen, 1969.
281. Jensen, David Richard. *Selecting Land Use for Sand and Gravel Sites*. Silver Spring, Md.: National Sand and Gravel Association, 1967.
282. Johnsgard, Paul A. *Waterfowl: Their Biology and Natural History*. Lincoln: University of Nebraska Press, 1968.
283. Johnson, Huey D., ed. *No Deposit—No Return*. Reading, Mass. Addison-Wesley, 1970.
284. Johnson, Leonard H. *Foundation Planting*. New York: De La Mare, 1927.
285. Johnson, Peter L. *Wetlands Preservation*. New York: Open Space Institute, 1969.
286. Johnston, David Robert; A. J. Grayson; and R. T. Bradley. *Forest Planning*. London: Faber, 1967.
287. Kazmann, Raphael G. *Modern Hydrology*. New York: Harper & Row, 1965.
288. Keeler, Harriet. *Our Northern Shrubs and How to Identify Them*. Dover reprint, 1969.
289. Kellogg, Charles E. *Our Garden Soils*. New York: Macmillan, 1952.
290. ———. *The Soils That Support Us*. New York: Macmillan, 1941.
291. Kendall, R. *Land Drainage*. London: Faber & Faber, 1950.
292. Kendeigh, S. Charles. *Animal Ecology*. Englewood Cliffs, N.J.: Prentice Hall, 1961.
293. Kenfield, W. G. *The Wild Gardener in the Wild Landscape*. New York: Hafner, 1966.
294. Kerbec, Matthew J. *Noise and Hearing*. Arlington, Va.: Output Systems Corp., 1972.
295. Ketchum, Robert II. *The Secret Life of the Forest*. New York: McGraw-Hill, 1970.
296. King, Cuchlaine Audrey Muriel. *Beaches and Coasts*. London: E. Arnold, 1960.
297. King, Thomas, *Water: Miracle of Nature*. New York: Macmillan, 1955.
298. Kittredge, Joseph. *Forest Influences: The Effects of Woody Vegetation on Climate, Water, and Soil, With Applications to the Conservation of Water and the Control of Floods and Erosion*. New York: McGraw-Hill, 1948.
299. Kiellestrom, Bjorn. *Be Expert With Map and Compass*. La Porte, Ind.: American Orienteering Service, n.d.
300. Klopfer, Peter H. *Habitats and Territories*. New York: Basic Books, 1969.
301. Klots, Alexander B., and Elsie Klots. *The Desert*. Mankato, Minn.: Creative Education Society, Inc., n.d.
302. Klots, Elsie B. *The New Field Book of Freshwater Life*. New York: Putnam, 1966.
303. Kneese, Allen V. *The Economics of Regional Water Quality Management*. Baltimore: Johns Hopkins University Press, 1964.
304. Knight, Rex Owen. *The Plant in Relation to Water*. New York: Dover, 1965.
305. Kotter, David Herman. *Landscape Design Criteria for Ski Slope Development*. Urbana: University of Illinois Press, 1967.

306. Kraus, E. H., and C. B. Slawson. *Gems and Gem Materials*. New York: McGraw-Hill, 1947.
307. Kraus, E. H.; W. F. Hunt; and L. S. Ramsdell. *Mineralogy*. New York: McGraw-Hill, 1951.
308. Krutch, Joseph Wood. *The Desert Year*. New York: Sloane, 1952.
309. Küchler, A. W. *Vegetation Mapping*. New York: Ronald Press, 1967.
310. Kuenen, P. H. *Realms of Water*. New York: Wiley, 1955.
311. Kuhns, William. *Environmental Man*. New York: Harper & Row, 1969.
312. LaChapelle, Edward R. *Field Guide to Snow Crystals*. Seattle: University of Washington Press, 1969.
313. Lamson, M. D. *Garden Housekeeping*. New York: Oxford, 1951.
314. Landscape Research Group. *Symposium: Methods of Landscape Analysis*. London: 3 May 1967.
315. Langefors, Ulf and B. Kihlstrom. *The Modern Technique of Rock Blasting*. 2nd ed. New York: Wiley, 1967.
316. Lapage, Geoffrey. *Art and the Scientist*. Baltimore, Md.: Williams and Wilkins, 1961.
317. Larson, Joseph S. *Managing Woodland and Wildlife Habitat In and Near Cities*. Amherst: University of Massachusetts Press, 1971.
318. Ledlie, John A., ed. *Handbook of Trail Campcraft*. New York: Association Press, 1954.
319. Leeds, Anthony, and Andrew P. Vayda, eds. *Man, Culture, and Animals: The Role of Animals in Human Ecological Adjustments*. Washington, D.C.: American Association for the Advancement of Science, 1965.
320. Leopold, Luna Bergere. *The Flood Control Controversy: Big Dams, Little Dams, and Land Management*. New York: Ronald Press, 1954.
321. Lester, Reginald M. *The Observer's Book of Weather*. London: Frederick Warne, 1955.
322. Le Sueur, Arthur D. C. *Hedges, Shelterbelts, and Screens*. London: Country Life, 1951.
323. Li, Hui-lin. *The Origin and Cultivation of Shade and Ornamental Trees*. Philadelphia: University of Pennsylvania Press, 1963.
324. Linde, A. F. *Techniques for Wetland Management*. Wisconsin Natural Resources Research Report #45, 1969.
325. Linton, David. *Photographing Nature*. Garden City, N.Y.: Doubleday, 1964.
326. Little, Charles E. *Challenge of the Land*. New York: Open Space Action Institute, 1968.
327. Longenecker, George William, *Summer Camp Site Development: The Ecological Base in Site Selection, Planning, and Design*. Urbana: University of Illinois Press, 1962.
328. Lotkowski, W. M. *The Soil*. Chicago: Educational Methods, Inc., 1966.
329. Louisiana Forestry Commission. *The Unwanted Tree: Its Control and Removal*. Baton Rouge, La.: 1965.
330. Low, Julian W. *Geological Field Methods*. New York: Harper, 1957.
331. Luce, William P. *Family Camping: A Self-Instruction Guide to Camp Skills and Sites*. New York: Collier Books, 1965.
332. Lunt, Dudley C. *Thousand Acre Marsh*. New York: Macmillan, 1959.

333. Maas, Arthur. *Muddy Waters; The Army Engineers and The Nation's Rivers.* Cambridge, Mass.: Harvard University Press, 1951.

334. Marsh, George P. *Man and Nature.* London: Sampson, Low and Son, 1864.

335. McCormick, Jack. *The Life of the Forest.* New York: McGraw-Hill, 1966.

336. McDivitt, James F. *Minerals and Man: An Exploration of the World of Minerals and Its Effect on the World We Live In.* Baltimore: Johns Hopkins University Press, 1965.

337. McGinnies, William; Bram J. Goldman; and Patricia Paylore, eds. *Deserts of the World.* Tucson: University of Arizona Press, 1968.

338. McGuinness, C. L. *The Role of Ground Water in the National Water Situation.* Washington, D.C.: U.S. Geological Survey Water Supply paper 1800, 1963.

339. McHarg, Ian L. *Design With Nature.* Garden City, N.Y.: Doubleday, 1969.

340. Magill, Paul L.; Francis R. Holden; and Charles Ackley. *Air Pollution Handbook.* New York: McGraw-Hill, 1968.

341. Maher, Ramona. *Shifting Sands: The Story of Sand Dunes.* New York: John Day, 1968.

342. Malin, James Claude. *The Grassland of North America: Prolegomena to Its History.* Lawrence, Kan.: 1961.

343. Manning, Harvey. *Mountaineering: The Freedom of the Hills.* Seattle: The Mountaineers, 1960.

344. Manton, Basil George Grenville. *The Road and the Vehicle.* London: Arnold, 1953.

345. Martin, Alexander C.; Herbert S. Zim; and Arnold L. Nelson. *American Wildlife and Plants: A Guide to Wildlife Food Habits.* New York: McGraw-Hill, 1951.

346. Martz, Clyde O. *Rights Incident to Possession of Land.* Boston: Little, Brown, 1954.

347. Marx, Wesley. *The Frail Ocean.* New York: Ballantine, 1967.

348. Masters, Charles O. *Pond Life: A Field Guide to the Inhabitants of Temporary Ponds.* Jersey City, N.J.: T. F. H. Publishers, distributed by Crown Publishers, 1968.

349. Matthews, William H.; William H. Kellogg; and G. D. Robinson, eds. *Man's Impact on Climate.* Cambridge, Mass. M. I. T. Press, 1972.

350. Mavis, Frederic Theodore. *The Hydraulics of Culverts.* State College: Pennsylvania State College, 1943.

351. Mayer, Harold M., and Clyde F. Kohn, eds. *Readings in Urban Geography.* Chicago: University of Chicago Press, 1959.

352. Meethan, A. R. *Atmospheric Pollution.* New York: Macmillan, 1964.

353. Meikle, Robert Desmond. *British Trees and Shrubs.* London: Eyre & Spottiswoode, 1958.

354. Meinecke, Conrad. *Your Cabin in the Woods.* Buffalo, New York: Foster & Stewart, 1945.

355. Mendenhall, Ruth, and John Mendenhall. *Introduction to Rock and Mountain Climbing.* Harrisburg, Pa.: Stackpole Books, 1969.

356. Menninger, Edwin A. *Seaside Plants of the World.* New York: Hearthside Press, 1964.

357. Merrill, Anthony French. *The Golf Course Guide.* New York: Crowell, 1950.

358. Merrill, George Perkins. *Stones for Building and Decoration.* 3rd ed. New York: Wiley, 1910.

359. Meyer, Hans Arthur. *Forest Management.* 2nd ed. New York: Ronald Press, 1961.

360. Middle Georgia Area Planning Commission. *Reclamation of Pits, Mines and Quarries.* Macon: 1969.

361. Milne, Lorus Johnson, and Margery Milne. *The Balance of Nature.* New York: Knopf, 1960.

362. ———. *The Mountains.* New York: Time, Inc., 1962.

363. Miner, Roy Waldo. *Field Book of Seashore Life.* New York: Putnam, 1950.

364. Minikin, Robert. *Coast Erosion and Protection: Studies in Causes and Remedies.* London: Chapman & Hall, 1952.

365. ———. *Winds, Waves, and Maritime Structures: Studies in Harbour Making and in the Protection of Coasts.* 2nd ed. rev. London: Griffin, 1963.

366. Money, David Charles. *Climate, Soils, and Vegetation.* London: University Tutorial Press, 1965.

367. Monkhouse, Francis John, and Henry Robert Wilkinson. *Maps and Diagrams: Their Compilation and Construction.* 2nd ed. London: Methuen; New York: Dutton, 1963.

368. Moore, Wildred George. *The Temperate Grasslands.* London: Hutchinson Education, 1966.

369. Morgan, Ann Haven. *Field Book of Ponds and Streams.* New York: Putnam, 1930.

370. Morisawa, Marie E. *Streams: Their Dynamics and Morphology.* New York: McGraw-Hill, 1968.

371. Morse, Harriet. *Gardening in the Shade.* Rev. ed. New York: Scribner, 1962.

372. Mutch, William Edward Scott. *Public Recreation in National Forests: A Factual Survey.* London: Her Majesty's Stationery Office, 1968.

373. Nash, Roderick. *Wilderness and the American Mind.* New Haven, Conn.: Yale University Press, 1967.

374. ———. *The American Environment: Readings in the History of Conservation.* Reading, Mass.: Addison-Wesley, 1968.

375. Nathans, Allan A. *Maintenance for Camps and Other Outdoor Recreation Facilities.* New York: Association Press, 1967.

376. National Academy of Sciences. *Eutrophication: Causes, Consequences, Correctives.* Washington, D.C.: 1969.

377. ———. *Weed Control.* Washington, D.C.: 1968.

378. ———. *Vertebrate Pests: Problems and Controls.* Washington, D.C.: 1970.

379. National Golf Foundation. *Planning and Building the Golf Course.* Chicago, Illinois: n.d.

380. National Park Service. *A Report on Our Vanishing Shoreline.* Washington, D.C.: U.S. Government Printing Office, 1955.

381. National Playing Fields Association. *Sports Ground Construction Specifications for Playing Facilities.* London: National Playing Fields Association and the Sports Turf Research Institute, 1965.

382. National Tuberculosis and Respiratory Disease Association. *Air Pollution Primer.* New York: 1969.

383. Neal, E. G. *Woodland Ecology.* 2nd ed. Cambridge, Mass.: Harvard University Press, 1965.

384. Needham, J. G. and J. T. Lloyd. *Life of Inland Waters.* Ithaca, N.Y.: Comstock, 1937.

385. Needham, Paul Robert. *Trout Streams.* Ithaca, N.Y.: Comstock, 1938.

386. Nichols, Donald R. and Catherine C. Campbell, eds. *Environmental Planning and Geology.* Washington, D.C.: U.S. Government Printing Office, 1969.

387. Nichols, Herbert Lounds. *Moving the Earth: The Workbook of Excavation.* Greenwich, Conn.: North Castle Books, 1962.

388. Nicholson, Max. *The Environmental Revolution: A Guide for the New Masters of the World.* New York: McGraw-Hill, 1970.

389. Niering, William A. *The Life of the Marsh.* New York: McGraw-Hill, 1966.

390. ———. *Nature in the Metropolis: Conservation in the Tri-State New York Metropolitan Region.* New York: Regional Plan Association, 1960.

391. Obert, Leonard, and Wilbur I. Duvall. *Rock Mechanics and the Design of Structures in Rock.* New York: Wiley, 1967.

392. Odum, Eugene P. *Fundamentals of Ecology.* Philadelphia: Saunders, 1971.

393. O'Flaherty, Coleman A. *Highways: A Textbook of Highway Engineering.* London: Edward Arnold, 1967.

394. Ogburn, Charlton Jr. *The Winter Beach.* New York: William Morrow, 1966.

395. O'Kane, Walter C. *The Intimate Desert.* Tucson: University of Arizona Press, 1969.

396. Olgyay, Victor. *Design with Climate: Bioclimatic Approach to Architectural Regionalism.* Princeton, N.J.: Princeton University Press, 1963.

397. Omaston, F. C. *Management of Forests.* Riverside, N.J.: Hafner, 1968.

398. Open Space Action Committee. *Stewardship: The Land, the Landowner, the Metropolis.* New York: 1965.

399. Orr, Robert Thomas. *Animals in Migration.* New York: Macmillan, 1970.

400. Osborn, Herbert. *Meadow and Pasture Insects.* Columbus, Ohio: The Educators' Press, 1939.

401. Otto, Blanc, and Towle Otto. *Biological Investigations.* New York: Holt, Rinehart & Winston, 1960.

402. Overman, Michael. *Water: Solutions to a Problem of Supply and Demand.* Garden City, N.Y.: Doubleday, 1969.

403. Ovington, J. D. *Woodlands.* London: English University Press, 1965.

404. Owen, Oliver S. *Natural Resource Conservation: An Ecological Approach.* New York: Macmillan, 1971.

405. Palmer, Ephraim Laurence. *Field Book of Natural History.* New York: Whittlesey House, 1949.

406. Panshin, Alexis John. *Forest Products: Their Sources, Production, and Utilization.* 2nd ed. New York: McGraw-Hill, 1962.

407. Parcher, Emily Seaber. *Shady Gardens: How To Plan and Grow Them.* Englewood Cliffs, N.J.: Prentice-Hall, 1955.

408. Parking and Highway Improvement Contractors Association. *Parking Design Manual.* Los Angeles: Education Fund, Parking and Highway Improvement Contractors Association, 1968.

409. Pearl, Richard M. *Gems, Minerals, Crystals, and Ores.* New York: Western, 1963.
410. Pearsall, William Harold. *Mountains and Moorlands.* London: Collins, 1950.
411. Penman, Howard Latimer. *Vegetation and Hydrology.* Farnham Royal, Eng.: Commonwealth Agricultural Bureaux, 1963.
412. Petrides, George A. *A Field Guide to Trees and Shrubs.* Boston: Houghton Mifflin, 1958.
413. Petry, Loren C. *Beachcomber's Botany.* Chatham, Mass.: Chatham Conservation Foundation, 1968.
414. Pettijohn F. J. *Sedimentary Rocks.* New York: Harper & Row, 1957.
415. Phillips, C. E. *How to Know the Weeds.* Newark: University of Delaware Agricultural Experiment Station, 1956.
416. Phillips, Edwin Allen. *Methods of Vegetation Study.* New York: Holt, 1959.
417. Pile, Dolette. *Methods of Analysing Original Vegetation Cover Using Early Land Survey Records.* Hamilton, Ont.: McMaster University, 1969.
418. Pirages, Dennis, ed. *Seeing Beyond: Personal, Social, and Political Alternatives.* Reading, Mass.: Addison-Wesley, 1971.
419. Pirrault, Pierre. *On the Origin of Springs.* Trans. Aurele LaRogue. New York: Hafner, 1967.
420. Platt, Rutherford. *A Pocket Guide to Trees.* New York: Washington Square Press, 1960.
421. ———. *The Great American Forest.* New York: P & H Sales Company, 1965.
422. Pohl, Richard W. *How To Know the Grasses.* 2nd ed. Dubuque, Iowa: William C. Brown, 1968.
423. Portmann, Adolf. *Animal Camouflage.* Trans. A. J. Pomerans. Ann Arbor: University of Michigan Press, 1959.
424. Pough, Frederick H. *A Field Guide to Rocks and Minerals.* Boston: Houghton Mifflin, 1953.
425. Powell, Melchoir Daniel; William C. Winter; and William B. Bodwitch. *Community Action Guidebook for Soil Erosion and Sediment Control.* Washington, D.C.: National Association of Counties Research Foundation, 1970.
426. Power, R. A. *Know Your Weeds.* Nebraska: Department of Agriculture and Inspection, Division of Noxious Weeds, n.d.
427. Prescott, Gerald Webber. *How to Know the Aquatic Plants.* Dubuque, Iowa: William C. Brown, 1969.
428. Preston, John Frederick. *Developing Farm Woodlands.* New York: McGraw-Hill, 1954.
429. Preston, Richard J. *North American Trees.* Ames: Iowa State University Press, 1961.
430. *Proceedings of the Marsh and Estuary Management Symposium.* Baton Rouge: Louisiana State University Press, 1968.
431. Quick, Lelande. *The Book of Agates and Other Quartz Gems.* Philadelphia: Chilton Books, 1963.
432. Quinn, Alonzo DeF. *Design and Construction of Ports and Marine Structures.* New York: McGraw-Hill, 1961.
433. Ransom, Jay Ellis. *A Range Guide to Mines and Minerals.* New York: Harper & Row, 1964.

434. Rebuffat, Gaston. *On Ice and Snow and Rock.* New York: Oxford University Press, 1971.

435. Reich, Charles. *The Greening of America: The Coming of a New Consciousness and the Rebirth of the Future.* New York: Random House, 1970.

436. Reid, George K. *Ecology of Inland Waters and Estuaries.* New York: Van Nostrand and Reinhold, 1961.

437. ———. *Pond Life: A Guide to Common Plants and Animals of North American Ponds and Lakes.* New York: Golden Press, 1967.

438. Reid, Giorgina. *How to Hold Up a Bank: A New Way to Control Shore Erosion.* New York: A. S. Barnes, 1969.

439. Ress, Etta Schneider. *Field and Meadow.* Mankato, Minn.: Creative Educational Society, Inc., 1967.

440. Rickett, Harold William. *Botany for Gardeners.* New York: Macmillan, 1957.

441. Ricketts, E. F., and Jack Calvin. *Between Pacific Tides.* 4th ed. Stanford, Calif.: Stanford University Press, 1968.

442. Riess, Elizabeth M. *The Garden of Chaparral: Plants of the Lower Rio Grande Valley.* New York: Vantage Press, 1958.

443. Robbins, Wilfred William, and Alden S. Crafts. *Weed Control: A Textbook and Manual.* New York: McGraw-Hill, 1962.

444. Rodale, Jerome. *Pay Dirt: Farming and Gardening with Composts.* New York: Devin-Adair, 1945.

445. ———. *Stone Mulching in the Garden.*, Pa.: Emmaus, Pa.: Rodale Press, 1949.

446. Rodale, Robert, ed. *The Basic Book of Organic Gardening.* New York: Ballantine, 1971.

447. Rodgers, Andrew Denny. *Bernhard Eduard Fernow: A Story of North American Forestry.* New York: Hafner, 1951.

448. Roueche, Berton. *What's Left: Reports on a Diminishing America.* Boston: Little, Brown, 1968.

449. Roxon, Lillian. *Rock Encyclopedia.* New York: Grosset & Dunlap, 1969.

450. Russell, Sir Edward John. *Soil Conditions and Plant Growth.* 9th ed. by E. Walter Russell. London: Longmans, 1961.

451. Rutsam, Calvin. *The Wilderness Cabin.* New York and London: Collier-Macmillan, 1972.

452. Rydberg, Per Axel. *Flora of the Prairies and Plains of Central North America.* New York: The New York Botanical Garden, 1932.

453. Salisbury, Sir Edward James. *Downs and Dunes: Their Plant Life and Environment.* London: G. Bell, 1952.

454. Salomon, Julian Harris. *Camp Site Development.* New York: Girl Scouts of the United States of America, 1959.

455. Sargent, Charles Sprague. *Manual of the Trees of North America.* New York: Dover, 1922.

456. *Saskatoon Wetlands Seminar.* Canadian Wildlife Service Report Series #6. Ottawa, 1969.

457. Schaller, Friedrich. *Soil Animals.* Ann Arbor: University of Michigan Press, 1968.

458. Schenk, George Walden. *How to Plan, Establish and Maintain Rock Gardens.* Menlo Park, Calif.: Lane Books, 1964.

459. Shepard, Paul. *Man in the Landscape.* New York: Ballantine, 1967.

460. Schery, Robert W. *The Lawn Book.* New York: Macmillan, 1961.

461. Schmidt-Nielsen, Knut Stortebecker. *Desert Animals: Physiological Problems of Heat and Water.* Oxford, Eng.: Clarendon Press, 1964.

462. Searle, Alfred Broadhead. *An Introduction to British Clays, Shales, and Sands.* London: C. Griffin and Company, 1912.

463. Sears, Paul B. *Deserts on the March.* Norman: University of Oklahoma Press, 1935.

464. ———. *Lands Beyond the Forest.* Englewood Cliffs, N.J.: Prentice-Hall, 1969.

465. Semple, Arthur Truman. *Grassland Improvement.* Cleveland, Ohio: Chemical Rubber Company Press, 1970.

466. Seton, Ernest Thompson, *The Arctic Prairies.* New York: International University Press, 1943 (orig. publ. 1912).

467. Seymour, Whitney North, comp. *Small Urban Spaces: The Philosophy, Design, Sociology, and Politics of Vest-Pocket Parks and Other Small Urban Open Spaces.* New York: New York University Press, 1969.

468. Shanklin, John F. *Forest Conservation.* U.S. Department of the Interior. Washington, D.C.: U.S. Government Printing Office, 1963.

469. Sharpe, Charles Farquharson Stewart. *Landslides and Related Phenomena: A Study of Mass-Movements of Soil and Rock.* New York: Columbia University Press, 1938.

470. Shaw, Samuel P., and C. Gordon Fredine. *Wetlands of the United States.* Washington, D.C.: U.S. Government Printing Office, 1956.

471. Shirley, Hardy Lomax. *Forest Ownership for Pleasure and Profit.* Syracuse, N.Y.: Syracuse University Press, 1967.

472. Shomon, Joseph J.; Byron L. Ashbaugh; and Con D. Tolman. *Wildlife Habitat Improvement.* New York: Nature Centers Division, National Audubon Society, 1966.

473. Shomon, J. *Open Land for Urban America.* New York: National Audubon Society, 1972.

474. Sinkankas, John. *Mineralogy for Amateurs.* Princeton, N.J.: Van Nostrand, 1964.

475. Slobodkin, Lawrence B. *Growth and Regulation of Animal Populations.* New York: Holt, Rinehart & Winston, 1961.

476. Small, John Kunkel. *Manual of the Southeastern Flora.* Chapel Hill, N.C.: University of North Carolina Press, 1953.

477. Smith, David Martin. *The Practice of Sylviculture.* 7th ed. New York: Wiley, 1962.

478. Smith, Frank E. *The Politics of Conservation.* New York: Random House, 1966.

479. Smith, Howard G. *Hunting Big Game in City Parks.* New York: Abingdon, 1969.

480. Smith, Percy White. *The Planning, Construction and Maintenance of Playing Fields.* London: Oxford University Press, 1950.

481. Smith, Robert Leo. *The Ecology of Man: An Ecosystem Approach.* New York: Harper & Row, 1972.

482. Smythe, Reginald Harrison. *Animal Habits: The Things Animals Do.* Springfield, Ill.: Thomas, 1962.

483. Snow, William Brewster. *The Highway and the Landscape.* New Brunswick, N.J.: Rutgers University Press, 1959.

484. Society of American Foresters—Committee on Forest Types. *Forest Cover Types of North America.* Washington, D.C.: 1954.

485. Soil Conservation Society of America. *Creative Conservation for Life and Living.* Ankeny, Iowa: 1968.

486. ———. *Soil and America's Future.* Ankeny, Iowa: 1967.

487. ———. *Water and America's Future.* Ankeny, Iowa: 1966.

488. Southward, A. J. *Life on the Sea-Shore.* Cambridge, Mass.: Harvard University Press, 1965.

489. Sparrow, Kenneth Christopher. *Surveying and Mapping Simplified: A Book of Suggestions for Those Who Adventure with Maps.* 2nd ed. Glasgow: Brown, Son & Ferguson, 1950.

490. Spock, L. E. *Guide to the Study of Rocks.* New York: Harper & Row, 1962.

491. Spurr, Stephen Hopkins. *Forest Inventory.* New York: Ronald Press, 1952.

492. ———. *Forest Ecology.* New York: Ronald Press, 1964.

493. Stallings, James Henry. *Soil: Use and Improvement.* Englewood Cliffs, N.J.: Prentice-Hall, 1957.

494. Staten, Hi W. *Grasses and Grassland Farming.* New York: Devin-Adair, 1952.

495. Steffek, Edwin F. *The Pruning Manual.* Rev. ed. New York: Van Nostrand Reinhold, 1969.

496. Stix, Hugh, and Marguerite Stix. *The Shell: 500 Million Years of Inspired Design.* New York: Ballantine, 1972.

497. Stockard, James G. *Designing Neighborhood Commons.* Washington, D.C.: Washington Center for Metropolitan Studies, 1964.

498. Stone, Doris. *Projects: Botany.* New York: Washington Square Press, 1964.

499. Storer, Tracy I., and Robert L. Usinger. *Sierra Nevada Natural History.* Berkeley: University of California Press, 1971.

500. Stout, Ruth. *Gardening Without Work.* New York: Devin-Adair, 1961.

501. ———. *How to Have a Green Thumb Without an Aching Back: A New Method of Mulch Gardening.* New York: Exposition Press, 1955.

502. Strohm, John L. *The Golden Guide to Lawns, Trees, and Shrubs.* New York: The Golden Press, 1961.

503. SCEP. *Man's Impact on the Global Environment. Study of Critical Environmental Problems.* Cambridge, Mass.: M. I. T. Press, 1970.

504. SMIC. *Study of Man's Impact on Climate: Inadvertent Climate Modification.* Cambridge, Mass.: M. I. T. Press, 1972.

505. Sutcliffe, James Frederick. *Plants and Water.* New York: St. Martin's Press, 1968.

506. Sweet, Muriel. *Common Edible and Useful Plants of the West.* Healdsburg, Calif.: Naturegraph Books, 1962.

507. Taylor, Joshua C. *Learning to Look: A Handbook for the Visual Arts.* Chicago: University of Chicago Press, 1957.

508. Teal, J. and M. *Life and Death of the Salt Marsh.* Boston: Little, Brown, 1969.

509. Thomas, Harold E. *Conservation of Ground Water.* New York: McGraw-Hill, 1951.

510. Thomas, William L., ed. *Man's Role in Changing the Face of the Earth.* Chicago: University of Chicago Press, 1956.

511. Tinbergen, Nikolaas, and the editors of *Life*. *Animal Behavior*. New York: Time, Inc., 1965.

512. Tomanek, G. W. *Pasture and Range Plants*. Bartlesville, Okla.: Phillips Petroleum Co., 1963.

513. Trefethen, Joseph B. *Wildlife Management and Conservation*. Indianapolis, Ind.: Heath, 1964.

514. Treshow, Michael. *Whatever Happened to Fresh Air?* Salt Lake City, Utah: University of Utah Press, 1970.

515. Tunis, John Roberts. *Lawn Games*. New York: A. S. Barnes, 1943.

516. Tunnard, Christopher, and Boris Pushkarev. *Man-Made America, Chaos or Control: An Inquiry into Selected Problems of Design in the Urbanized Landscape*. New Haven: Yale University Press, 1963.

517. Twenhofel, W. H. *Principles of Sedimentation*. New York: McGraw-Hill, 1950.

518. Udall, Stewart L. *1976: Agenda for Tomorrow*. New York: Avon Books, 1968.

519. ———. *The Quiet Crisis*. New York: Avon Books, 1963.

520. U.S. Army Corps of Engineers. *Design of Breakwaters and Jetties*. Washington, D.C.: U.S. Government Printing Office, 1963.

521. ———. *Navigation Locks: Engineering and Design*. Washington, D.C.: U.S. Government Printing Office, 1959.

522. ———. *Routing of Floods Through River Channels: Engineering and Design*. Washington, D.C.: U.S. Government Printing Office, 1960.

523. U.S. Bureau of Reclamation. *Design of Small Dams*. Washington, D.C.: U.S. Government Printing Office, 1960.

524. U.S. Department of Agriculture. *Climate and Man*. Washington, D.C.: U.S. Government Printing Office, 1941.

525. ———. *Collection and Preservation of Insects*. Washington, D.C.: U.S. Government Printing Office, 1948.

526. ———. *Common Weeds of the United States*. New York: Dover, 1970.

527. ———. *Farmers' Bulletin 2046: Farm Drainage*. Washington, D.C.: U.S. Government Printing Office,

528. ———. U.S. Forest Service. *Forest Recreation Research; Bibliography of Forest Service Outdoor Recreation Publications, 1942 through 1966*. Washington, D.C.: U.S. Government Printing Office, 1967.

529. ———. *Grass*. Washington, D.C.: U.S. Government Printing Office, 1948.

530. ———. *How to Control a Gully*. Farmers' Bulletin 2171. Washington, D.C.: U.S. Government Printing Office, 1961.

531. ———. *Soil*. Washington, D.C.: U.S. Government Printing Office, 1957.

532. ———. *Soils and Men*. Washington, D.C.: U.S. Government Printing Office, 1938.

533. ———. *Standard Map Symbols*. Washington, D.C.: U.S. Government Printing Office, 1965.

534. ———. *Water*. Washington, D.C.: U.S. Government Printing Office, 1955.

535. U.S. Department of Commerce, Bureau of Public Roads. *Parking Guide for Cities*. Washington, D.C.: U.S. Government Printing Office, 1956.

536. ———. *Design of Roadside Drainage Channels*. Washington, D.C.: U.S. Government Printing Office, 1965.

537. U.S. Department of the Interior, National Park Service. *Man and Nature in the City*. Washington, D.C.: U.S. Government Printing Office, 1969.

538. U.S. Department of the Interior. *Surface Mining and our Environment.* Washington, D.C.: U.S. Government Printing Office, 1967.

539. U.S. Government. *Aerial Photo Interpretation in Classifying and Mapping Soils.* Washington, D.C.: U.S. Government Printing Office, 1968.

540. ——. *Biological Associated Problems in Freshwater Environments.* Washington, D.C.: U.S. Government Printing Office, 1967.

541. ——. *Forester's Guide to Aerial Photo Interpretation.* Washington, D.C.: U.S. Government Printing Office, 1966.

542. ——. *Know Your Soils.* Available at district offices of U.S.D.A. Soil Conservation Service, 1967.

543. ——. *Records Management Handbook: Subject Filing.* Washington, D.C.: U.S. Government Printing Office, 1966.

544. ——. *Soil Survey Laboratory Methods and Procedures for Collecting Soil Samples.* Washington, D.C.: U.S. Government Printing Office, 1967.

545. U.S. White House Conference. *Beauty for America.* Washington, D.C.: U.S. Government Printing Office, 1965.

546. Usinger, Robert L. *The Life of Rivers and Streams.* New York: McGraw-Hill, 1967.

547. Vanders, Iris, and Paul F. Kerr. *Mineral Recognition.* New York: Wiley, 1967.

548. Van Dersal, William Richard. *The Land Renewed: The Story of Soil Conservation.* New York: H. Z. Walck, 1968.

549. ——. *Ornamental American Shrubs.* New York and London: Oxford University Press, 1942.

550. Van Melle, Peter Jacobus. *Shrubs and Trees for the Small Place.* Rev. ed. New York: American Garden Guild, 1955.

551. Vernberg, F. John, and Winona B. Vernberg. *The Animal and the Environment.* New York: Holt, Rinehart & Winston, 1970.

552. Vollmer Associates. *Parking for Recreation.* Wheeling, W.V., 1965.

553. Vosburgh, John. *Living With Your Land: A Guide to Conservation for the City's Fringe.* Bloomfield Hills, Mich.: Cranbrook Institute of Science, 1968.

554. Wagar, J. Alan. *The Carrying Capacity of Wild Lands for Recreation.* Washington, D.C.: Society of American Foresters, 1964.

555. Wagener, Albert M., and Harlan R. Arthur. *Hand Tools.* New York: Van Nostrand, 1943.

556. Wagner, Philip. *The Human Use of the Earth.* New York: Macmillan, 1960.

557. Wagner, Richard H. *Environment and Man.* New York: Norton, 1971.

558. Walton, William Clarence. *The World of Water.* New York: Taplinger, 1970.

559. Ward, Henry B., and George C. Whipple. *Fresh Water Biology.* New York: Wiley, 1959.

560. Warring, Ronald H., comp. *200 Ingenious Gardening Gadgets.* London: Postlib Publications, 1954.

561. Watts, May Theilgard. *Reading the Landscape.* New York: Macmillan, 1957.

562. Weaver, John Ernest. *North American Prairie.* Lincoln, Neb.: Johnsen Publishing Co., 1954.

563. ——. *Grasslands of the Great Plains: Their Nature and Use.* Lincoln, Neb.: Johnsen Publishing Co., 1956.

564. ——. *Prairie Plants and Their Environment.* Lincoln: Neb.: University of Nebraska Press, 1968.

565. Welch, Paul S. *Limnology.* New York: McGraw-Hill, 1952.
566. Wells, James S. *Plant Propagation Practices.* New York: Macmillan, 1955.
567. Western Industries, Inc. *How to Lay Out a Parking Lot.* Chicago: 1961.
568. Whittaker, Robert H. *Communities and Ecosystems.* New York: Macmillan, 1970.
569. White, Gilbert F. *Strategies of American Water Management.* Ann Arbor: University of Michigan Press, 1969.
570. Whyte, William H. *Securing Open Space for Urban America.* Washington, D.C.: Urban Land Institute, 1959.
571. Wilde, S. A. *Forest Soils: Their Properties and Relation to Silviculture.* New York: Ronald Press, 1958.
572. Wilder, Louise Beebe. *The Fragrant Path: A Book About Sweet Scented Flowers and Leaves.* New York: Macmillan, 1932.
573. Wingo, Lowdon Jr., ed. *Cities and Space: The Future of Urban Land Use.* Baltimore: Johns Hopkins University Press, 1963.
574. Wolman, Abel. *Water, Health and Society.* Bloomington: Indiana University Press, 1969.
575. Wood, Frances. *Animals in Danger: The Story of Vanishing American Wildlife.* New York: Dodd, Mead, 1968.
576. Worrall, William Ernest. *Clays: Their Nature, Origin and General Properties.* New York: Transatlantic Arts, 1968.
577. Wright, H. E., Jr. *Arctic and Alpine Environments.* Bloomington: University of Indiana Press, 1968.
578. Wright, J. E. B. *Rock Climbing in Britain.* London: Kaye, 1964.
579. Wyckoff, James. *Rock, Time and Landforms.* New York: Harper & Row, 1966.
580. Wyman, Donald. *Ground Cover Plants.* New York: Macmillan, 1956.
581. ———. *Hedges, Screens and Windbreaks: Their Use, Selection and Care.* New York: McGraw-Hill, 1938.
582. Wynne-Edwards, Vero Copner. *Animal Dispersion in Relation to Social Behavior.* New York: Hafner, 1962.
583. Youngman, Wilbur H., and Charles E. Randall. *Growing Your Trees.* Washington, D.C.: The American Forestry Association, 1967.
584. Zim, Herbert S. *Rocks and How They Were Formed.* New York: Golden Press, 1961.
585. Zim, Herbert S., and Paul R. Shaffer. *Rocks and Minerals.* New York: Western, 1957.
586. Zim, Herbert S., and Lester Ingle. *Seashores.* New York: Golden Press, 1955.
587. Zim, Herbert S., and Alexander C. Martin. *Trees.* New York: Western, 1956.
588. Zimmerschied, Gerd. *Natural Stone as an Element in Design.* Berlin: Interbuch, 1961.
589. Zion, Robert L. *Trees for Architecture and the Landscape.* New York: Reinhold, 1968.

Index

Plants are indexed by common name, mostly following *Standardized Plant Names*, with a technical name in parentheses.